INVENTING AMERICA

INVENTING AMERICA

Twenty-six of the Best Articles from American Heritage of Invention & Technology

Sponsored by

 General Motors.

TABLE OF CONTENTS

INTRODUCTION

When we published the very first issue of *Invention & Technology*, in the summer of 1985, we knew people would wonder why. So we started the issue with a statement explaining our conviction that the history of technology was as exciting and vital a subject as we could imagine: "For both good and bad, the modern *is* the technological in almost every arena of life. As invention supplants invention, as one change leads to a thousand more changes in an unceasing cycle, we struggle to keep up, to be aware of what's happening. We are told that, at whatever cost, we must stay 'at the cutting edge' of the latest technological devices and fashions.

"By design, *American Heritage of Invention & Technology* will not compete with the many periodicals that bring us news of the cutting edge. On the contrary, we intend to look behind the edge to the nature of the blade itself: its heft, strength, and resiliency—all those qualities that support the cutting edge and cannot be separated from it. Our province, in short, is the whole of the history of invention and technology and the people, machines, and ideas in our past that have brought us to our present degree of mastery."

In the years since, we have run articles on all sorts of people and events that have shaped the world we live in; we've covered inventors from the most famous, like Thomas Edison, to the virtually unknown, like Jan Matzeliger, a slave's son who rose to transform an industry before the nineteenth century was out. We've written about the most straightforward success stories, like the breakthroughs by the young Charles Hall and his sister that made aluminum a part of everyone's life, and about the most abject failures, like the reckless planning and building of the Quebec Bridge over the St. Lawrence River, which ended in 1907 in deadly disaster. Most of the stories have fallen between those extremes—they have turned out to be tales of essential humanity, of ambitious, flawed people struggling to make their place in the world or to change the world and neither entirely succeeding nor failing, yet leaving their imprint as shapers of some aspect of our own lives. Such is the tale of Charles Goodyear, whose obsession with the possibilities of rubber gave us vulcanization and landed him in debtor's prison, or of Edwin Armstrong, who invented FM radio but spent the years before his suicide embroiled in lawsuits over his patents, or of Thomas A. Watson, who after helping Alexander Graham Bell invent the telephone went on to become among other things a failed farmer, the head of the biggest shipyard in the nation, a respected paleontologist, a prospector in Alaska, and a touring Shakespearean player.

The very breadth of our subject has made difficult the selection of articles for this anthology. On the one hand, we've wanted simply to put in our favorite pieces of writing, such as Elting Morison's appreciation of his Victorian engineer great-uncle, and the most visually arresting articles, such as Erik Ronnberg's examination of a detailed 1852 painting of New York Harbor, revealing the many varieties of ships and boats and what they all did. On the other hand, we have hoped to compile from all these pieces a fair overview of American technological history. In that, we realize, we could not possibly succeed. The subject is too big for twenty-six articles—which is one reason a magazine about it can go on and on with surprises in every issue. Somewhat to our dismay, we find this volume contains only one article on railroads, one on aviation, one on communications technology, one on military technology—and none on the automotive industry. Still, we believe the book we've assembled manages to convey a sense of the wonder and texture and scope of the American inventive experience over the past two hundred years. If you find that this volume isn't enough, we hope you will turn to the magazine itself.

A great many people have worked over the years to make *Invention & Technology* and this book possible, among them Byron Dobell and Richard Snow, who have helped guide the magazine from its start; Emma Cobb, Curt Wohleber, and Frederic Schwarz, who assigned and edited many of the articles; Sabra Moore, Catherine Calhoun, Jane Colihan, and Laura Allen, who gathered the wonderful illustrative materials; Beth Whitaker, Theodore Kalomirakis, and Peter Morance, who have designed the magazine; Carol Smillie, who has copy-edited it all and shepherded it through from the start; Barbara Strauch, who made all the articles into a book; and our sponsor, General Motors, which has generously underwritten *Invention & Technology* from the beginning.

Frederick Allen
Editor

THE IMPROBABLE SUCCESS OF JOHN FITCH

by C. M. Harris

He ran a whole season of scheduled steamboat service on the Delaware in 1790 — seventeen years before Robert Fulton's famous first trip

On April 16, 1790, a tall, odd-looking man and his long boat without sails performed the impossible on the Philadelphia waterfront. After many trials and a variety of errors, John Fitch and the *Experiment*, propelled only by the force of a steam engine, ran out into the Delaware River against a strong northeast wind and got up sufficient speed to easily outdistance several unfriendly challengers. Fast sailboats and strongly rowed oar boats all fell astern, and for once the jeers and sarcastic hoots of the rivermen could not be heard.

A trial on a measured course and the accounts of eyewitnesses established that the steamboat made, on average, between six and eight miles per hour during the summer of 1790. That was a speed that promised early commercial success for Fitch's company of investors, for it rivaled the speeds of the stagecoaches that carried passengers and freight along the banks of the Delaware. And the achievement hinted at much more: nothing less than the opening up of the interior of the North American continent.

Throughout the summer and early fall of 1790, Fitch's steamboat made regular runs along the Delaware, as far north as Trenton, New Jersey, and as far south as Wilmington and Christiana, Delaware. Its schedule was printed in the Philadelphia newspaper, and the runs were completed with only minor mechanical mishaps that were easily repaired. It was a novel pleasure indeed, as one passenger related, to proceed on water against the wind in a straight line. Fitch, he observed, was "one of the most ingenious creatures alive, and will certainly make his fortune." Yet Fitch did not. In fact, Robert Fulton's trip up the Hudson seventeen years later is still widely believed to be the first successful trial of a steamboat.

John Fitch was born in 1743, on a farm near Hartford, Connecticut, to a life, as he later remembered it, of hardship and cruelty, punctuated by the death of his mother when he was four, hard labor in the fields without formal schooling, and a dominating Calvinist father. He ran away to sea at seventeen, but he didn't take to a sailor's life. He twice apprenticed himself to clockmakers but was kept by his jealous masters to "trifleing, pottering brass work." Still, the skill of his hands eventually enabled him to set up as a brass founder, promising a comfortable life as a small-town artisan. These prospects attracted one Lucy Roberts, whom he married and later described as "in no ways ugly, but somewhat delicate in her make . . . inclined to an old maid." She could not cope with his restlessness and quickly became something of a shrew, given to frequent tantrums. So in January 1769 Fitch left her and their son, "having no fixed place in my mind where to wander . . . bare of money, not having more than seven or eight dollars with me." Making his way eventually to Trenton, New Jersey, he took employment with a silversmith; he soon set himself up in that trade and made a success of it. The American Revolution brought another life, first as an officer in the mi-

A woodcut portrait of Fitch.

litia and then as a supplier to the Continental Army, which yielded him four thousand dollars in paper money. This capital Fitch took to the Ohio country, intending to speculate in land warrants in the hope of making a killing. Captured by Indians, he somehow survived several dramatic brushes with grisly deaths. Eventually he was delivered up to the British, then released and transported back to the East Coast. At the conclusion of the war, he went west to survey his claims, but by the spring of 1785 he was back east again, in Bucks County, Pennsylvania.

During April of that year, having hired out his horse, Fitch was walking along a road, pained by rheumatism in his knees, when he saw a fancy horse and carriage go by. He was struck by the idea of what it would be like to have a fine carriage without the upkeep of the horse, and this set him to thinking about a steam carriage, though he quickly seized on the idea of a steamboat. He later wrote, "I did not know that there was a Steam Engine on Earth when I proposed to gain a force by Steam." From an encyclopedia he learned of Newcomen's and other British atmospheric steam engines, used primarily to operate pumps in mines. Had he been in England he might have been able to obtain one of James Watt's new engines and thereby been permitted to concentrate on the boat itself; but like most Americans, he knew nothing of this, so he proceeded to work up drawings of an engine similar to Newcomen's. He made a model boat, to one side of which he attached an endless chain with pad-

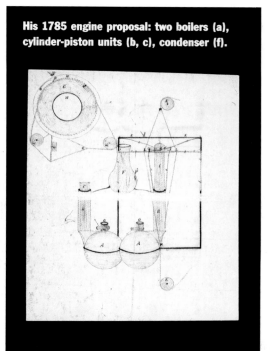

His 1785 engine proposal: two boilers (a), cylinder-piston units (b, c), condenser (f).

dles; then he excitedly explained his plans to a few men of learning and influence. With their encouragement he petitioned the Continental Congress on August 29, 1785, hoping for the chance to demonstrate his ideas and gain support for the undertaking. The petition was not even reported out of committee. The papers accompanying it were returned three days later, and during the same session a law was passed that nullified most of Fitch's Ohio land claims. He resolved "to prove to the world by actual experiment" that the committee that had ignored his petition was made up of "blockheads." That goad stands as the only contribution the American government made to the development of the first successful steamboat.

Without capital of his own, Fitch needed to raise money, either from state governments or from wealthy men willing to speculate on his prospects. Public finance during this pre-Constitution period was chaotic, and owing to a postwar de-

pression, money was hard to come by. It is helpful in measuring these conditions to recall the historian Henry Adams's jarring reminder to his own age: "The entire banking means of the United States in 1800 would not have answered the stock-jobbing purposes of one great operator on Wall Street in 1875. The nominal capital of all the banks, including the Bank of the United States, fell short of $29 million."

Fitch raised some funds for his steamboat from the sales of a map he drew of the Northwest Territory, an improvement on two existing maps based on his firsthand knowledge and surveys of the region, which he engraved on a sheet of copper and printed on a press of his own making. This new, reliable chart of the western regions of the new nation helped him gain a hearing with a few prominent public officials—most notably Gov. Patrick Henry of Virginia—but he met with little success in such company.

John Fitch was an unlettered, rapid-fire talker, an intense, insecure man confident only in his vision, with a decided class chip on his shoulder and what he himself judged to be an unpleasing appearance. His natural disposition, he wrote later, was to be "when in easy circumstances, Modest to excess, and [able to] put up with almost any indignities . . . but when in wretchedness: haughty, imperious, insolent to my superiors, tending to petulance." Full of his dream and plans, he was not careful to steer them clear of touchy political issues.

Fitch extolled the potential of the steamboat for opening up the great inland regions of the country by way of the Mississippi and Ohio rivers, an argument that certainly troubled many Eastern interests and probably George Washington, who envisioned inland commerce flowing by means of canals down the Potomac River. In addition, Fitch's machinery was too complicated to take hold of the prevailing scientific thinking of the late eighteenth century. Benjamin Franklin, for example, was enamored of the idea that a vessel might be propelled by employment of what he called a "fire engine" to work a pump that would take in water at the bow and force it through an aperture in the stern. Fitch's steamboat, by contrast, relied on too many moving parts and promised to be expensive to maintain.

Against great odds, Fitch devoted much of 1786 to the promotion of his scheme, which was risky also because he was broadcasting his ideas. One of his best prospects as a backer asked for time to consider the proposal, then claimed much of it for himself. Then, in March 1786, Fitch ob-

I did not know that there was a Steam Engine on Earth when I proposed to gain a force by Steam." Fitch found the information in an encyclopedia.

tained an exclusive monopoly for constructing boats propelled by the force of steam in the state of New Jersey, and he used this to advantage in other states, eventually gaining monopolies from the legislatures of Pennsylvania, New York, Delaware, and Virginia. He translated these paper rights into a company of fifteen small backers, who put up a total of three hundred dollars, enabling him to begin work on the steamboat. This was, it would seem, the only path open to him, but quite fatefully it allied him for the most part with small merchants, tavern- and shopkeepers, and a few gentlemen of property in Philadelphia. Franklin did not subscribe but tried to give five or six dollars to his shabby caller, who obviously needed the money but resented the idea of a handout and refused it. Fitch wished he had treated Franklin "with the indignity which he merited, and stomped the paltry ore under my feet," he later wrote.

With working capital at last, however small, Fitch found a friend and an able assistant in Henry Voigt, a German-born watchmaker and skilled mechanic, and the two men commenced to experiment, using a skiff to try out various methods and devices for translating the force of an engine. These included the side-mounted endless chain with paddles and a "screw of paddles," both devices apparently maneuvered by cranks. Without benefit of Watt's work, they in effect reinvented the steam engine by trial and error, a very considerable task. They had certainly by this time developed their own double-acting engine (one that admits steam alternately to each end of the cylinder), if not yet a separate condenser.

Fitch's 1785 map of the Northwest Territory, printed and engraved by himself.

One day in July 1786, after suffering one of many failures and the "scoffs and snears" of onlookers, Fitch repaired to a tavern, where he consumed great quantities of "West-India produce." The next day, somewhat worse for the effects of the rum, he went to bed early but was too upset to sleep. Then, as he wrote in his autobiography, something like a vision came to him, and he visualized a boat with oarlike paddles on both sides, rowed mechanically by the action of cranks, as if by an invisible crew. This method of action was tried in 1787 before members of the Constitutional Convention, and the results, despite the feeble power of the engine, proved that the steamboat was more than a dream. It continued to make short runs that year, sustained no disasters, and was improved by experiments on the engine, which, according to a published description, was

"placed in about two thirds of the boat." This was the first steamboat to move with any consistency in waters anywhere.

At this point Fitch surely expected his labors and anxieties to be somewhat eased. Instead he found his claim to the invention seriously challenged and was forced to divert much of his attention and energy to the defense of his state monopoly rights. His rival was James Rumsey (see "'The Most Original,'" by Edwin T. Layton, Jr., *Invention & Technology*, Spring 1987). Rumsey, like Fitch, was an artisan by training, living on the edge of poverty. But unlike Fitch, he possessed good looks, natural charm, and the manners of a confident gentleman, a species he had studied at close range as the owner of an inn in the Virginia resort town of Bath, on the Potomac. Just being a Virginian counted a good deal, we may be sure, with Washington and Jefferson.

James Rumsey's great opportunity came when General Washington slept at his inn, an occasion Rumsey used to describe to the great man his invention of a mechanical boat that could ascend the most rapid of streams. Here was something to feed the general's dreams of the Potomac as a highway of inland commerce. Rumsey's pole boat, or stream-boat, as he called it, was a catamaran with a small paddle wheel between the two hulls. The flow of water turned the paddles, which in turn caused poles to touch bottom and push the boat upstream against the current. The utility of the contraption was limited; but Washington was greatly interested and impressed by Rumsey, and he hired him in July 1785 as chief engineer of the Potowmack Company, formed for the purposes of constructing a canal and rendering the Potomac River navigable. At this time Rumsey was certainly thinking of steamboats, but unlike Fitch, who openly confessed his inadequacies as an engineer and his failed experiments, he was secretive and purposely vague. Beginning in 1788, Rumsey claimed, and offered accounts of eyewitnesses to prove, that he had conceived the idea of a steamboat earlier than had Fitch, although much of his evidence would not hold up. At any rate the real issue in determining priority in the invention, until the United States passed its first patent law in April 1790, was who had first made his ideas public. That clearly was Fitch.

In terms of actual achievement, Rumsey's only real success came in December 1787, when a boat of his design

Fitch tried out this oar-driven steamboat before members of the Constitutional Convention in Philadelphia in 1787 (not, as indicated above, 1786).

made two successful trials on the Potomac—on one of these occasions, he claimed, making four miles an hour. His boat was considerably lighter than Fitch's, was designed on the propulsion principle favored by Franklin, and employed a single-acting engine and a pipe boiler. This boiler, a two-layer grille of pipe coils, is considered by some the forerunner of the tubular boiler. (Voigt claimed priority with an identical design.) As a component of Rumsey's engine, however, it continually leaked and burned out.

R umsey made the most of his two successful trials and his knowledge of Franklin's ideas on propulsion. He went to Philadelphia the following spring, published pamphlets claiming he was the true inventor of the steamboat, and quickly formed a company of wealthy and influential backers who styled themselves the Rumseian Society. Before the end of the year he had been elected a member of the American Philosophical Society and was on his way to England in quest of patent rights, with the very best letters of introduction. Franklin, who held an interest in the Rumseian Society, advised his English friends that Rumsey, not Fitch, held priority in the steamboat invention. Dr. Benjamin Rush wrote that Rumsey possessed "a very uncommon mechanical genius" and "modesty equal to his talents," also indicating that his plan, it was suspected, "had been copied with a few trifling variations," by Fitch.

In Europe Rumsey continued his social successes, impressing Jefferson, then the minister to France, as "the most original and greatest mechanical genius I have ever seen." But he failed to forge an alliance between his society of backers and Mathew Boulton and his partner James Watt, and he died suddenly of a stroke in London in December 1792. The documentary evidence suggests that the boat he was experimenting with on the Thames had failed to demonstrate sufficient promise to encourage his backers to continue.

The challenge of the Rumseian Society brought out the

natural timidity of Fitch's company, whose tightness with funds forced him to live "by inches" and often in rags, with creditors at his heels. They were willing to make contributions when they had evidence of success, but they seem to have expected Fitch to be put up like his boat in winter. When they reached the limit of their resources and faith, however, Fitch was able to expand the company by bringing in new shareholders, one of whom, joining in 1788, was Dr. William Thornton.

Thornton bought four, or 10 percent, of the company's shares (at £42 Pennsylvania currency each) and soon became its leading shareholder and director, but he also contributed much more than money. Born on a sugar plantation on Tortola, in the British Virgin Islands, he had been educated at the medical school of the University of Edinburgh and traveled through Britain and Europe before emigrating to the United States in 1786. An artist, naturalist, and inventor himself, he was the only person associated with Fitch's company ever to have seen a steam engine, and he quickly injected new enthusiasm into Fitch's backers and put forward his own ideas for improvements. Though a gentleman, and excitable himself, he was able to befriend Fitch and gain his confidence while generating more support among the shareholders.

Between 1787 and 1790 Fitch and Voigt openly experimented with various methods of steam propulsion on the Delaware. They tried out Voigt's pipe boiler in July 1788 before discarding it. They changed the proportions of their new boat from forty-five by twelve feet to sixty by eight feet (the proportions later employed by Fulton). They replaced the side-mounted oars with three broad paddles that resembled snow shovels, attached at the stern to separate cranks. The French journalist and politician Jacques Brissot de Warville, present at a trial of the new machinery, wrote that Thornton informed him the new paddles made twenty-six strokes per minute, with a promise of sixty. Brissot added that Thornton "was the object of much derision

H

is talk of opening Western rivers troubled many Eastern interests, and his ideas about machinery were too complicated to take hold at the time.

about this steamboat" and that he was "tired of these gibes."

The problem for Fitch and his company was to achieve and sustain greater speed, and a new eighteen-inch cylinder and a variety of condensers (including one of Thornton's design) were experimented with before they hit on the proper components and good working proportions. On April 16, 1790, a new trial was made, and in Fitch's words: "Altho the Wind blew very fresh at Northeast, we reigned Lord high admirals of the Delaware, and no Boat on the River could hold way with us, but all fell a-stern, altho several Sail Boats, which were very light, and heavy sails, that brought their Gunwails well down to the Water, came to try us. We also passed many Boats with Oars. . . . Th[u]s has been effected by little Johney Fitch and Harry Voigt, one of the Greatest and most useful arts that was ever introduced into the World."

Thornton later related that soon a mile was laid off on Front Street in Philadelphia, with flagmen at each end. When the tide was motionless, the vessel started down the course and was clocked at eight miles per hour.

With business in mind, Thornton designed a handsome cabin, but Fitch thought it too high, and likely to slow the boat. "If it must be elegant," he quipped, "make it low and line it with gold." Thornton prevailed. Although he and Fitch occasionally had serious quarrels over such matters, all were resolved amicably. The steamboat began to make trips on a regular schedule, covering during the summer of 1790 more than two thousand total miles, but without profit. Stagecoaches were still faster and cheaper and no doubt seemed safer. Attempts to entice new passengers with lower fares—and sausages with beer, rum, and port in the cabin—had little effect.

Thornton contributed more to the design of the steamboat of 1790 than an elegant cabin. As he later wrote to Robert Fulton, it went "only from 2½ to 3½ miles per hour till I put in a boiler of about 6 feet long by about 4 feet wide of which I was the inventor, and the same boat with some small alterations then went 8 miles an hour through dead water . . . and 80 miles in a day." It is significant to note than in 1811, four years after his own successful trial on the Hudson River, Fulton offered to pay $150,000 if Thornton

could demonstrate that a steamboat could make six miles an hour in still water.

Perhaps overlooking the steamboat's failure to pay for its costs, Thornton left Philadelphia with his young bride in October 1790 and spent the next two years on Tortola. His correspondence with Fitch and others provides insight into the failure and collapse of the company, which followed quickly after its promising public success.

A devastating blow, particularly to Fitch, was the decision of the new board of patent commissioners to award identical patents, under the same date of issue, to both Fitch and Rumsey, even though their claims overlapped and conflicted. This left it to lawyers and courts to resolve the substantive question of who held priority in the invention. Fitch was clearly broken in spirit by this decision and by its effect on his company. In the spring of 1791 he began to apply for various government surveying jobs. Still, he had bold plans to take a boat to New Orleans and demonstrate its usefulness on the Mississippi to Spanish officials there. Thornton wrote in June urging that this be done before the fall and advised Fitch to salvage the question of patent rights by applying for patents on the boiler ("the very first ever made with copper in that way"), "the roch [i.e., ratchet] wheels as applied to the steam engine," and the "double pump." Patents, he emphasized, "are so easily got that by taking out privileges for the necessary parts you exclude your enemies and will put them to the greatest difficulties." In response to Fitch's complaints that he had to walk the streets in "wretchedness and rags," Thornton instructed: "Request the Company in my Name to get you new Cloaths as you would not (though much of an Indian) look very respectable with a bare Tail, and bare-skin Epaulettes."

Fitch's idea for a steamboat driven by bellows is the subject of this four-page memo.

Throughout 1791 and 1792 Thornton received gloomy news of delays and failures with the new boat, the *Perseverance (II)*. The company had sold off the *Experiment*, the steamboat of 1790, for parts, and, in an attempt to save money and simplify, had installed a wooden boiler with lead pipes on the new boat. Fitch and Voigt became embroiled in a controversy over who had the rights to a horse- or cattle-powered boat, which both thought might be used to commercial ad-

Like most "breakthrough" inventions, the steamboat was the product of many minds. Fitch was the visionary forerunner who proved it feasible.

vantage without the difficulties involved with steam propulsion. A fragment of one of Thornton's letters written on Tortola sums up his view of the situation: "I lament exceedingly the Fate of the Steam-boat, but mean to expend no more Money upon it. If I had been present the foolish Schemes they pursued of *Wooden Boilers & such Trash* would never have taken place. The Horse Boat . . . is only another *Whim*, for whenever Water is rough although the Horses are tied in Vessels they are dangerous by running back always to leeward, and a Boat could never be worked by Horses but in dead Calms. *T'is a Scheme that will never answer!* The Steam-boat if properly constructed would have been very productive, but [Richard] Stockton [the leading member of the company in Thornton's absence] has ruined the whole Scheme. They had better not have begun it than to have done it badly because it not only *does nothing* but ruins the public Faith, so as to prevent any Subscriptions from being made in our Favour on the Western Waters, and on the Mississippi."

Thornton returned to Philadelphia in October 1792 but did not attempt to revive the company, perhaps because he had been diverted by other projects, such as his drawings for the United States Capitol, which won the premium in the design competition for that building the next year. But he remained Fitch's champion and occasional provider, and he carefully organized and preserved his letters and papers, clearly intending them to document Fitch's place in history. In 1802 Thornton joined the State Department to superintend the Patent Office. From that position, which he held until his death in 1828, he fought the claims and monopolies of Robert Fulton and his powerful partner, Robert R. Livingston, defending Fitch, "a poor ignorant, but worthy and ingenious man," as "the true inventor of the steam boat."

And what of John Fitch? In 1793 he went to France and England in hopes of claiming patent rights and of building and operating boats there. Thornton gave him some excellent letters of introduction and advised him in using them: "Do not fight the Algerines, Johnny. . . . You know what I mean. Regulate your genius." Fitch's company had obtained a patent from King Louis XVI for protection of the steamboat invention in 1791, but the turbulence of the French Revolution, in

which Fitch found himself upon his arrival in France, prevented him from gaining any advantage from it. Penniless again, he had to endure a ghastly passage to America belowdecks and work off its cost once he had landed in Boston. Still, he managed to compose and have printed a navigation chart by which the course of a ship could be determined without the use of geometry or logarithms.

Fitch returned to silversmithing for a time, but by 1797 he was in Kentucky, having written his autobiography and "Steamboat History" and deposited the manuscripts at the Library Company of Philadelphia, where they remain today. In Kentucky he bargained away the rights to his remaining land claims with a tavernkeeper in exchange for his board and a pint of whiskey a day, soon increased to two pints. Fully aware of what he was doing, he drank himself to death (possibly accelerating it with doses of opium), a thoroughly broken man.

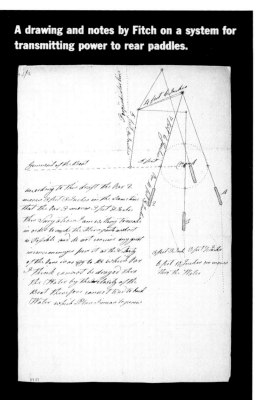

A drawing and notes by Fitch on a system for transmitting power to rear paddles.

The saga of John Fitch and his steamboat owes much to luck and personalities, but it also has ingredients with broader significance. Fitch struggled against the predictable resistance of human beings to innovation—as well as against the difficult technical aspects of steam navigation, which had proved insurmountable even in industrially advanced England. Geographic and economic factors urged the invention of the steamboat to the extent that they penetrated the mind of the times; the American interior, with its valuable commerce, was inaccessible by roads and upland rivers and streams. However, while access to the inland promised great wealth, it was still by no means certain whether the western regions of the country would be developed as new states within the Union. Spain's presence in the Mississippi Valley seemed an immovable obstacle.

The general lack of capital in the United States made the organization of companies of subscribers necessary for major speculative undertakings like Fitch's. The partners he enlisted to gain capital, like those in many similar companies, took risks by small steps, voting outlays in small increments, forcing the promoter to return repeatedly for necessary funds. Individual shareholders did not have to go along with the majority and only forfeited their shares by refusing to do so, an easy way out of anything considered a likely loss. From the point of view of the small merchants who made up the ma-

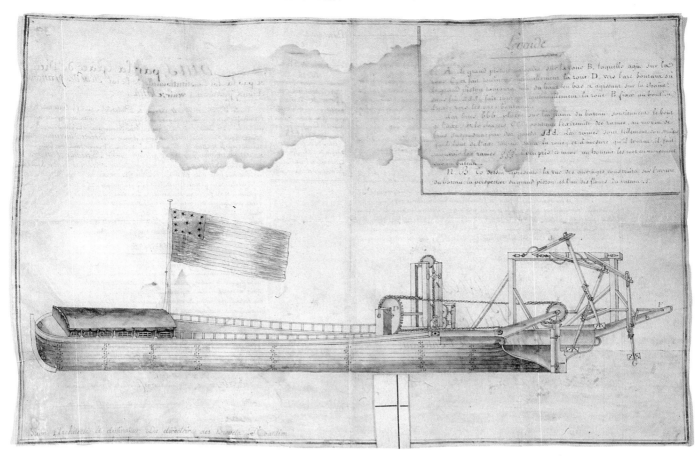

Fitch's 1791 patent from Louis XVI includes a drawing of his successful 1790 boat *Experiment*, which was propelled by paddles at the stern.

jority of the company, Fitch's steamboat was a financial loss even when the machinery worked properly. Contributing to the timidity of small investors was the weak protection given to intellectual property by the new federal patent system.

There was one way Fitch might have turned a quick profit. Had he been less serious and advertised rides on his mechanical curiosity as an amusement, he might have barnstormed coastal cities and towns to gain working capital, as the balloonists of his time had begun to do. But this was not in his nature. Real financial and commercial success with steamboats required a polished, confident promoter like Rumsey, together with one or a very few powerful, adventurous, and wealthy backers.

Such a man, quickly sketched, was Robert Fulton, whose trial on the Hudson, twenty years after Fitch's demonstration before the Constitutional Convention, has too often been described as the first successful steamboat experiment. Fulton shamelessly borrowed ideas from others (including Fitch) and cleverly allied himself with a reliable source of capital (his partner, Robert R. Livingston). He was able thereby to improve on the ideas of others and to launch an extensive enterprise. The heroic proportions given him after his death in 1815, which by the end of the nineteenth century approached the mythic, exaggerated his role in the development of the steamboat and diminished the parts played by others.

As the bicentennial of Fitch's success of 1790 approaches, in a time of greater understanding of entrepreneurship and the challenges of new technologies, we can more accurately measure the contributions of the unlikely, peripatetic artisan from Connecticut. Against great social as well as physical resistance, John Fitch put the idea of steam navigation into workable form and practice; and while his bulky engine and ungainly vessel defied conventional logic and academic theory, they worked. John Fitch and company thereby changed the popular as well as the inventive mind of the early Republic, creating the climate that would be receptive to the sleeker, better-engineered steamboats that Fulton and his rivals would soon put on all the navigable rivers in the country.

Like most "breakthrough" inventions, the steamboat was the product of many minds and many hands. While Fulton and those who followed him refined and developed it as a vehicle of commerce and transportation, Fitch was the visionary forerunner who demonstrated the feasibility of the idea. This role seems especially crucial in the process of invention whenever conventional thinking about the constraints of space and time must be overcome. The steamboat, the most important invention in the early national period of American history, had seemed a logical thing to men of science for many years before the improbable Fitch naively set to work. It was not born of sophisticated conceptual thinking and advanced design; these came later as refinements. It was not the brainchild of genius but the result of trial and error. It was coaxed into the world by the lure of wealth and glory, to be sure, but it was delivered by the handiwork, resourcefulness, and determination of skilled artisans. ★

C. M. Harris is the editor of *The Papers of William Thornton*, to be published by the University Press of Virginia.

NATIONAL MUSEUM OF AMERICAN HISTORY, SMITHSONIAN INSTITUTION. PHOTOGRAPH BY WALTER SMALLING.

17

Goodyear's 1851 London Exhibition medal.

The inventor's French Legion of Honor badge.

A laborer demonstrates the elastic properties of uncured rubber, South America, 1905.

CRAZY ABOUT

Among Goodyear's personal possessions were (above) a watch with a diamond-studded rubber fob and (right) a copy of his book on vulcanization covered in hand-carved rubber depicting the harvesting of latex.

An ornate folding rubber fan that belonged to Goodyear.

RUBBER

by Robert Friedel

Charles Goodyear
was known as
a monomaniac.
Here's why.

His rubber paperweight.

"There is probably no other inert substance, the properties of which excite in the human mind, when first called to examine it, an equal amount of curiosity, surprise, and admiration. Who can examine, and reflect upon this property of gum-elastic, without adoring the wisdom of the Creator?"

One might expect such hyperbole from the man who wrote that, Charles Goodyear, for his enthusiasm for rubber was boundless and famous. Even his admirers would quote the description offered by a more skeptical observer: "If you meet a man who has on an india rubber cap, stock, coat, vest and shoes, with an india rubber money purse, *without a cent of money in it*, that is he."

It is easy to make fun of the much-mocked inventor, but consider the object of his passion. Rubber is a fascinating substance, quite unlike anything else we regularly encounter. There are few substances capable of assuming so many forms, textures, and functions, from a child's balloon to a bowling ball, from shoe heels to rubber bands, from pocket combs to electric plugs, from galoshes to tires. And consider the properties that make these uses possible. Rubber is waterproof, tough, moldable, electrically resistant, and, above all, elastic. Despite the emergence of synthetic rubbers, natural rubber is still very important today—especially for tire treads, because it resists heat well. The springy, stretchy, pliable sub-

Charles Goodyear in the 1840s or '50s.

stance evokes its own special adjective—"rubbery." Small wonder, then, that Charles Goodyear did not suffer his enthusiasm without company; the object of his attentions, the very center of his life, had been a source of wonder and curiosity for almost a century before Goodyear made his legendary stove-top discovery of vulcanization in 1839 and put down his reflections on rubber in the 1850s.

As early as the sixteenth century, Spanish explorers in South and Central America reported watching Indians play games with balls that bounced with the slightest effort. In seventeenth-century Mexico, Juan de Torquemada observed Indians making waterproof shoes, headgear, and clothing with some kind of vegetable gum. Beginning in 1735 C. M. de La Condamine, a member of France's Royal Academy of Sciences, spent almost ten years in the mountains and jungles of Peru and Brazil. Upon his return he published an account of his group's travels that included observations of the Omaguas, an Amazonian tribe that "make a very queer use of this resin; they make bottles of it shaped like a pear and they attach a wooden portion to it; by pressing, the liquid contained in the bottle is expelled through the wooden part; the bottles become real syringes."

De La Condamine described other applications of the material and reported that the Peruvian Indians called it *caoutchouc* (still the French word for rubber); so striking was its use for syringes that the Portuguese dubbed the rubber plant the syringe tree (*pao xiringa*). In a memoir to the Academy of Sciences in 1752, de La Condamine also passed on the observations of the French engineer C. F. Fresneau, who had encountered caoutchouc while exploring French Guiana. Fresneau made the first observations of the extraction of rubber and Indian techniques for manufacturing it. An avid experimenter himself, he was able to make balls and bracelets and a pair of rubber boots. He also tried to find a means for keeping rubber in solution. Since latex was only workable freshly tapped from the rubber tree, the problem of finding a solvent that would make the material usable (or at least spreadable) long after extraction assumed great importance to the Europeans.

Within a few years small amounts of rubber made their way to Europe for the first time, generally in the form of "bottles"—probably the same syringes de La Condamine found so striking. The material was little more than a curiosity, its only real practical application being the one that the English chemist Joseph Priestley described in 1770, when he remarked that a small cube of caoutchouc was handy for rubbing out pencil marks—hence the English term, used in no other language, "rubber." Chemists continued trying to find appropriate solvents, attaining only partial success with common ones like ether and turpentine. The belief took hold that a rubber solution that could be spread on other materials would provide the ideal waterproofing. The potential for such a substance was illustrated nicely in 1785, when J. A. C. Charles and Jean Robert ascended over Paris in a hydrogen-filled balloon of rubber-coated silk. Only five years later the first patents were issued in England for waterproofing solutions made of rubber.

It might seem that the beginning of the nineteenth century would see rubber becoming a useful and widely admired material. But with existing solvents the material never seemed to dry, leaving a sticky, gummy surface that was unpleasant and impractical. It was still not possible to ship the material from South America and later form it into shapes. The only application that really advanced beyond erasers was the use of strings cut from the imported bottles and wound around thread to make elastic webbing, which began to find its way into suspenders. The perfect waterproofing compound still eluded experimenters, and the vision of making rubber into complete shapes like boots or balls seemed remote indeed.

To many men before Goodyear, however, rubber's drawbacks were not inherent defects but challenges to human ingenuity. As chemical science expanded in the first decades of the nineteenth century, experiments on rubber solvents went on, but with few advances. Patents continued to be issued for waterproofing solutions, varnishes, and even inflatable beds and cushions and other applications. But little commercial success was in sight until the material could be more easily worked and made less tacky.

The first breakthrough turned out to be not chemical but mechanical. In the 1820s Thomas Hancock, in England, began experimenting with ways to make use of rubber scraps. As Hancock later admitted, he had much experience with machinery, "but of chemical knowledge I had almost none." Since no solvent was satisfactory, waste bits of rubber cut from the bottle shapes supplied by the Indians were useless. But Hancock observed that fresh-cut pieces of rubber were stickier than older ones and that quickly cutting pieces of rubber produced heat. He therefore built a machine that chewed up the rubber scraps—a giant "masticator." The machine generated enormous quantities of heat and solid blocks of workable rubber. The qualities of the finished rubber did not differ from that supplied by the Indians, but from the blocks of it rubber sheets, tubes, and other shapes could be readily produced. In 1825 Hancock joined with a Scottish rubber pioneer, Charles Macintosh, who was mixing waste naphtha from coal-gas plants with rubber and sandwiching it between double layers of cloth—making "mackintoshes" and a whole host of other waterproof goods. Building on the work of Hancock and Macintosh, the British quickly became the world's leaders in rubber manufacture.

In the United States enterprising sea captains began taking on small loads of crude rubber goods, largely boots and shoes, in their South American cargoes in the mid-1820s. By 1830 stores in Boston were regularly advertising rubber footwear and even occasionally rubber balls. By the middle of the decade there was talk of a "rubber boom." The first and largest of several factories that opened was that of the Roxbury India Rubber Company, set up just outside Boston. There processes similar to those used by Hancock and Macintosh were used to make masses of rubber that could be applied with solvents to cloth. When the architect and engineer Robert Mills visited the Roxbury factory in 1833 or '34, he described a dazzling array of new products. In addition to the shoes and boots (still the mainstay of rubber manufacturing), there were rubber-coated jackets, pants, vests, aprons, caps, and capes, inflatable pillows, life preservers, fire hose, and flexible rubber pipe.

The rubber boom of the 1830s was a vigorous one. Factories appeared in other Boston suburbs and in New York, Pennsylvania, and New Jersey. Imports of the raw material

CULVER PICTURES

Men cut V-shaped grooves to drain latex from a rubber tree.

from Brazil increased tenfold between 1828 and 1834, and novel products caught the attention of both the commercial world and a curious public. Air mattresses were devised, promising safety for the seaborne and comfort for the sick (King George IV was said to have died on one). Portable bathtubs, waterproof mailbags, and rubber toys also appeared. Machinists attempted to use rubberized cloth for belting, and rubber "springs" were tried on carriages.

The great boom came to a crashing end. The immediate cause for the failure of most of the rubber companies was the Panic of 1837, which put hundreds of fledgling industrial enterprises under in a matter of months. But the rubber manufacturers were particularly vulnerable; it had become apparent that their product still had serious deficiencies. In

the reputation of rubber itself suffered mightly. As early as August 1837 a New York journalist wrote: "The failure of the gum to answer the purposes anticipated, and the almost entire abandonment of the manufacture, has become a subject of general notoriety, without the cause of such failure being generally known." After enumerating the problems with rubber, the reporter pointed to a hopeful sign: "Mr. G.'s entire success in overcoming these objections, as well as adding such variety and beauty to his fabrics, had been the result of three years' constant experiments; and the new uses to which this material becomes applicable, such as maps, charts, carpeting, &c., follow in consequence. We understand Mr. G. is one of the firm of Goodyear & Sons, hardware merchants and manufacturers." Goodyear & Sons was

The material had long been both unpleasant and impractical.

Native youths in sixteenth-century Florida play with balls made from a natural elastic vegetable gum.

Goodyear reenacts his 1839 discovery of vulcanization, when a rubber sample he dropped onto a hot stove charred but did not melt.

1836 the Roxbury Company, for example, had to take back thirty thousand dollars' worth of sold goods—capes, life preservers, shoes, and wagon covers that trickled back into the shop as smelly, sticky, shapeless lumps of rubber and cloth. The warm North American summers took a toll on rubber goods that the British makers rarely had to deal with; rubber's tendency to soften and even run in hot weather was not arrested by any of the manufacturing practices of the day. The use of solvents like turpentine or naphtha made things even worse, and it was soon discovered that extreme cold could make rubber so hard and brittle that it would crack with the slighest use. Finally, over time it was observed that simple exposure to air and light would cause rubber goods to decompose, turning into flakes or dust. An old rubber band—dried, sticky, and cracking—is perhaps the closest the modern observer can find to something resembling this early rubber, for all the products of the boom itself have long since turned to dust.

Not only were fortunes lost in the great rubber bust, but

an early victim of the country's financial woes; "Mr. G" was soon to link his destiny finally and inextricably to rubber.

Charles Goodyear had already decided that he was better suited to inventing than to hardware dealing. Born in New Haven, Connecticut, in 1800, he was trained in technical matters by his father, Amasa, whose patent hay fork was one of several innovations in the mundane but important implements of American life. Goodyear's acquaintance with rubber was initially that of a mechanic, as he tried to use it in one or two of his own mechanical contrivances, such as an improved faucet. But in 1834, as he told the story, he purchased an inflatable life preserver and began dabbling with the valve. Upon returning to the rubber merchant with his improvement, he was told there was little call for such things, since the instability of the rubber itself was proving an insurmountable problem. Thereupon Goodyear determined to solve the greater problem—to make rubber into a stable, dependable material.

After the bankruptcy of Goodyear & Sons, Charles set himself up as a blacksmith in Philadelphia, but he soon uprooted his family and began moving around the Northeast, seeking backing for his work on rubber and advice from experienced rubber producers. He was debt-ridden for the rest of his days, but his enthusiasm and sometimes disarming sincerity always managed to find enough greed, hope, or pity to win financial resources for his work. His efforts necessarily brought him to the Boston area, where he visted the Roxbury Company in 1837, shortly before it folded. He also called on the newer and smaller Eagle Rubber Company in Woburn, near Boston. There he met Nathaniel Hayward, the thirty-one-year-old who kept the company going, making shoes and aprons after the other backers panicked. In September 1838 Hayward sold out to Goodyear, whose amazing powers of persuasion were able to find a hopeful lender even in the midst of a depression. Hayward did not give up on rubber; he agreed to work for Goodyear for at least a year and brought to the ever-optimistic tinkerer a seasoning of real rubber-factory experience.

Nathaniel Hayward also brought with him sulfur. The fumes may have assaulted Goodyear's nose the first time he entered the Woburn factory, and Hayward later said that Goodyear was quick to ask him about it. Just why Hayward was using sulfur in rubber is not clear—apparently he discovered empirically that it helped in drying his rubber-coated cloth, especially when the material was set out in the sun. Earlier chemists had referred to the usefulness of sulfur in rubber solvents, so it was not an odd material to try out. In any case, when Charles Goodyear resumed his rubber experiments in Woburn, sulfur was about. And when in the winter of 1839 Goodyear accidentally dropped one of his rubber samples, coated with sulfur and white lead (a common pigment used to stabilize the rubber), onto a hot stove, he knew that the result—a piece of rubber that charred *but did not melt* on the stove—was due to sulfur.

To say, as tradition does, that this discovery of vulcanization was an accident is to fundamentally misunderstand the nature of scientific and technical work. Goodyear never denied that chance had a hand in presenting that combination of rubber, sulfur, and heat on that cold winter day in Woburn. But he also made it clear that only a mind prepared by years of labor and hope and hundreds of observations of how rubber behaved would have seen what he saw on that stove. He quickly tacked up a piece of the treated rubber outside in the New England winter and found out that it retained its pliability and elasticity when cold, and that the effect did not wear off in a few hours or days or weeks. But months and years of experimenting followed, as Goodyear struggled to understand just what he had made and how he could make it consistent and useful. He was so sure that he had seen what few others would be prepared to see that he failed to take out a patent for several years, trusting secrecy to keep his invention his own.

At just the moment when a great technical discovery was at hand, Charles Goodyear's luck ran out. By 1839 the rubber industry in general and Goodyear in particular were in such bad repute among investors that he could get no one to listen to him. Some spectacular failures in products made by the Eagle Rubber Company overshadowed his claim to have made a real breakthrough. Not until 1841 did Goodyear, now in Springfield, Massachusetts, get enough support to pursue the experiments that gave him control over his new process, and only in April of 1842 was he able to manufacture the rubber sheets he wanted. In the meantime he was reduced to begging from anyone who would listen and was imprisoned for debt more than once before finally declaring himself bankrupt. By 1843, however, his fortunes revived and he finally applied for patent protection for his "Improvement in India-Rubber Fabrics." The result, U.S. Patent 3633, became one of the most litigated in history; in its first twelve years at least 150 suits were filed, and legal expenses were estimated to exceed six hundred thousand dollars.

So dire were his circumstances, Goodyear began selling licenses for his new rubber processes as soon as he could. Thanks to his years of difficulty and his reputation, many of the early licenses were broad and cheap. He managed, with the help of friends, to keep some control over the manufacture of shoes, for some time to come still the most important rubber product, but he was free and careless in allowing his invention to be used for other products. Besides, he had long before concluded that he was not a businessman or manufacturer but an inventor, so he committed his time and energy to developing new uses for his "metallic" rubber.

Among Goodyear's careless moves was sending several samples of his product to England in 1842, with the intention of persuading Macintosh & Co. to purchase general rights for a large sum. Macintosh was not interested, but some of the samples made their way into the hands of Thomas Hancock, who had twenty years earlier built the machine to fuse rubber scraps into blocks. Hancock set out to find Goodyear's secret, and by mid-1843 Hancock understood the role of sulfur in the new rubber. This was early enough to thwart Goodyear's belated efforts to take out an English patent, even though it was only later (perhaps after reading Goodyear's applications) that Hancock realized the crucial

An 1849 advertisement for India rubber.

role of heat in the process. Hancock's claimed discovery of the process to which he gave the name *vulcanization* was actually a brilliant piece of chemical detective work, even if it did not qualify as an original invention.

Further carelessness cost Goodyear his patent claims in France as well, although Europeans were ready to acknowledge the importance and usefulness of his discoveries. At the great international exhibitions in London and Paris in the 1850s, the world could see something of Goodyear's full vision—not simply an improved rubber but a truly new material for a fantastic variety of uses. He and his brother Nelson discovered that by extend-

others' debts, but this sounds like special pleading. Others pointed to the extraordinary expenses incurred by his devotion to rubber, especially the great legal costs. (Secretary of State Daniel Webster left Washington in 1852 to plead a case on Goodyear's behalf for a fee of fifteen thousand dollars.) More likely Charles Goodyear simply fell into that category of men, in which not a few notable inventors have belonged, who were never able to calculate the bounds of fiscal responsibility. Suffering with him were his two wives (the first died in 1853) and six children, who had to travel about with him sometimes not knowing where their next bed would be or if they would have to beg some friend to get Charles out of jail. His sons, however, were always faithful to their father and his memory, so love seems not to have been lacking.

Just as a great discovery was at hand, Goodyear's luck ran out.

Peruvian workers set bales of freshly extracted rubber out to dry on the banks of the Ucayali River.

Modern processing: mass-produced latex gloves are wheeled into a gigantic vulcanizer for curing, sometime in the 1960s.

ing the heating and sulfurization of rubber they could produce hard rubber—a substance that Goodyear, borrowing from Hancock's term, dubbed "vulcanite." This took a central place in the display at London's Crystal Palace in 1851, made into everything from combs and walking sticks to desks and walls. And around the Vulcanite Court were applications of Goodyear's true favorite material—his rubber sheet and tissue. Giant rubber rafts and balloons were hung from the ceiling, and large inflated globes, touted as combined navigational aids and life-saving devices, were proudly featured. The spectacle, which cost Goodyear thirty thousand dollars, was one of the few American displays to win a medal at the exhibition. The success, at a comparable cost, was matched in Paris, where, in a scene that encapsulates the poignancy of his life, Goodyear received word of his honors while sitting in a Parisian debtor's prison.

Even Goodyear's apologists readily admitted there was something about money that the man just couldn't handle. Some ascribed it to his faithfulness in paying off his and

When Goodyear died in 1860, he left his widow and six children two hundred thousand dollars in debts.

Goodyear, the man, simply lacked the sense of proportion that guides most people in life. Even a sympathetic nineteenth-century reviewer called him an "India-rubber monomaniac," and perhaps Goodyear himself would not have denied it. He would have preferred putting it differently, simply speaking of his recognition of rubber's possibilities and of his own capacities for discovering them; "beyond this," Goodyear wrote, he "would refer the whole to the great Creator, who directs the operations of mind to the development of the properties of matter, in His own way, at the time when they are specially needed, influencing some mind for every work or calling."　　★

Robert Friedel, associate professor of history at the University of Maryland, is the author of *Zipper: An Exploration in Novelty* (W. W. Norton, 1994) and *Pioneer Plastic: The Making and Selling of Celluloid* (Wisconsin, 1983).

THE GREAT REAPER WAR

by Joseph Gies

Cyrus McCormick won it—his famed Virginia reaper came to dominate America's harvests—but he didn't win by building the first reaper or, initially, the best

Obed Hussey: mild and modest.

Cyrus McCormick: bold, combative.

I t was "curious to see," reported a Yorkshire newspaper in 1851, "two implements of agriculture lying side by side in rivalry, respectively marked, 'McCormick, inventor, Chicago, Illinois,' and 'Hussey, inventor, Baltimore, Maryland'—America competing with America, on English soil."

The British press and public were indeed witnessing a strange spectacle, for British inventors and engineers had long dominated agricultural technology. McCormick and Hussey were on the road with a "great reaper war" that had been raging in the United States for seventeen years. It had begun when Cyrus McCormick discovered that Obed Hussey had beaten him to the Patent Office with a machine designed to cut standing grain. Ever since, both had been claiming priority of invention and struggling for commercial dominance in the new field of mechanical harvesting.

The two inventors presented a study in opposites. The Maine-born, Quaker-reared Hussey had sailed on a Nantucket whaler and wore a black patch over one eye, the result of an accident, but the piratical look was entirely deceiving: He was the mildest of men, kindhearted, fond of children, and self-effacing. The tall, handsome Cyrus McCormick, born in Virginia, was a pioneer Chicagoan, self-confident, bold, and intensely combative.

Hussey's machine had first seen daylight in 1831, when its modest inventor wheeled a model for it (possibly full-scale) out of a room he had borrowed in a farm-implement factory in Baltimore. Sarah Chenoweth, the seven-year-old daughter of the factory owner, watched him in fas-

After the war was won: by 1902 this combined reaper and thresher required a thirty-eight-horse team for power.

cination and remembered him later as "so very gentle in speech and manner that I never knew fear or awe of him." To simulate a wheat field, Hussey had drilled holes in a large board, which Sarah helped him cover with straws. When he pushed his strange-looking contraption across the board, it succeeded in clipping nearly every straw. He retired to his room to conceal tears of joy.

At almost the same time, Cyrus McCormick was creating his reaping machine in the blacksmith shop of his family's twelve-hundred-acre farm, Walnut Grove, in the Shenandoah Valley of Virginia. His father, Robert McCormick, an incurable tinkerer with several inventions to his credit, had struggled with the reaper problem on and off since Cyrus's birth. He was about ready to give up in frustration when Cyrus, then twenty-two, took over, in May of 1831. By July Cyrus had succeeded in cutting a patch of oats standing in a neighbor's field.

Hussey and McCormick were ignorant not only of each other's work but of that of many others. Hussey is said to have replied when a friend first suggested that he try to make a mechanical reaper, "Why, isn't there such a thing?" The earliest known version was recorded by Pliny in Gaul in the first century A.D. Recent attempts had sought both to speed the harvest (to avoid weather catastrophes) and to lighten the burden of labor involved.

The classic long line of crouching men swinging sickles or scythes, followed by stooping women and children gleaning the residue, had changed little since Neolithic times. It meant not only backbreaking toil but, to increasingly businesslike farm entrepreneurs, excessive labor costs. In 1783 Britain's Society for the Encouragement of Arts, Manufactures, and Commerce offered a gold medal for a practical reaper. The idea seemed simple: to use traction, via suitable gearing, to provide power to move some form of cutting mechanism. By 1831 several techniques had been explored, using a revolving reel of blades, as in a hand lawn mower; a rotating knife-edged disk, as in a modern power mower; and mechanical scissors. Robert McCormick had tried using revolving beaters to press the stalks against stationary knives.

Cyrus McCormick and Obed Hussey both chose a toothed sickle bar that moved back and forth horizontally. Hussey's machine was supported on two wheels, McCormick's on a single broad main wheel, whose rotation imparted mo-

tion to the cutter bar. Wire fingers or guards in front of the blade helped hold the brittle stalks upright. McCormick added a large reel, also turned by the main wheel, to press the stalks against the cutter. Since horses propelling the machine would need to walk in the clear, they would have to either push from behind or pull from the side. McCormick first tried the push principle, then switched to offsetting the machine. Hussey's machine was likewise offset, resting on two wheels plus a roller that supported the platform on which the cut grain fell. His design omitted a reel to press the grain up against the cutter, but his cutter, composed of twenty-one lancetlike teeth riveted to a flat iron rod, proved more efficient than McCormick's. Hussey's platform included a small seat, or prop, for the person who would push the cut grain off the platform in bunches to be made up into sheaves. McCormick's raker walked alongside the reaper.

Modest though the differences in the two machines were, Obed Hussey had created a viable reaper while Cyrus McCormick's was still marginal. "I found in practice innumerable difficulties," McCormick confessed. So had others before him. Simple in principle, the reaper was maddening in practice, especially if the grain was wet or drooping. Even experimentation was difficult, restricted by the brevity of the harvest season. Slowly, over the next two years, McCormick effected improvements and adjustments, and in 1833 he succeeded in cutting all the grain at Walnut Grove and that of several neighbors. In early 1834 he was ready to apply for a patent. Then he discovered in *Mechanics Magazine* a picture of Hussey's reaper, patented on the last day of 1833 and already being manufactured in New York and Ohio.

Hussey's precedence did not prevent McCormick from getting a patent—the Patent Office was not yet empowered to refuse one on such grounds—but it did provoke the young McCormick to fire the first salvo of the reaper war. He wrote to the editor of *Mechanics Magazine*: "Dear Sir: Having seen in the April number . . . a cut and description of a reaping machine . . . I would ask the favor of you to inform Mr. Hussey, and the public . . . that the principle, viz., cutting grain by means of a toothed instrument, receiving a rotatory motion from a crank . . . is a part of the principle of my machine, and was invented by me. Consequently, I would warn all persons against . . . an infringement of my right. . . ."

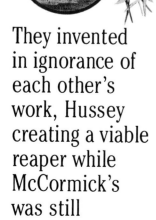

They invented in ignorance of each other's work, Hussey creating a viable reaper while McCormick's was still marginal.

Despite McCormick's truculence, he was not yet ready to back his fighting words with deeds. In 1835 his father made him a present of a five-hundred-acre farm; the next year he got him involved in an iron-manufacturing scheme that terminated in disaster, thanks in part to the Panic of 1837. Cyrus was said to have emerged with "his honor, one slave, a horse and saddle, and $300." He also gained invaluable business experience.

Obed Hussey meanwhile traveled the farm country, often on foot, with a horse to draw his demonstration machine. But business was slow. In the first ten years of his patent, his total sales may have numbered a hundred, not counting piracies (the machine was simple enough for any blacksmith to make, given a few castings). In 1843 McCormick plunged into the marketplace and sold twenty-nine machines. Rival advertising claims quickly led to an exchange of challenges between the two inventors, and a competition was arranged on a farm north of Richmond. Hussey was unable to get the larger of his two models to the rendezvous, and his smaller machine bogged down in wet grain. McCormick's reaper operated successfully and then stalled in turn. That failure did not prevent its inventor from claiming victory. Hussey successfully demonstrated his larger machine a few days later, but the upshot was a lengthy exchange of polemical broadsides in the farm press.

Both inventors licensed a number of manufacturers in New York, Virginia, Ohio, and neighboring wheat-growing states, and the machines competed for honors at numerous local fairs. Hussey's reaper was generally conceded to have the edge in performance, but not by enough to settle the question. Similarly, the priority of invention remained obscure. Misleading advice from the patent commissioner caused Hussey to apply too late for renewal of his patent in 1847; this forced him to petition Congress. McCormick aggressively counterpetitioned against the renewal, but it was granted anyway.

When McCormick's own patent came up the next year, Hussey petitioned against it. The old sailor said he would not have taken the step had McCormick not tried to deny him his own patent rights, and indeed, McCormick was probably guilty of a tactical blunder along with bad sportsmanship. Hussey succeeded in enlisting support among farmers, editors, and licensed reaper manufacturers protesting the McCormick extension, which in the end was denied. The pat-

Field workers cut wheat with preindustrial cradle scythes. The leading edge of each is the blade; the parallel wooden fingers neatly pile the grain.

Hand-cut grain is tied in sheaves to dry for several days; later it will be threshed.

Hussey's reaper, as shown in a catalogue for the 1851 Crystal Palace Exhibition.

McCormick's Virginia Reaper, with its large reel, from the same catalogue.

ent board in effect declared the mechanical reaper too valuable an invention to be monopolized, throwing open the door to any manufacturer who wanted to join the competition. By 1850 there were at least thirty.

The war now reverted to the field, where geography became a major factor. After several years of canvassing the Midwest, Hussey had returned East to find the market there more receptive. As a result he virtually abandoned the West, whither McCormick was at the same moment moving most of his production. This division of the market had a chance but felicitous relationship to the actual merits of the two machines. Eastern grain farmers, having trouble competing with the West, were turning to hay production, and though both machines were advertised as dual-purpose, the Hussey happened to be superior in grass.

On the other hand, it was no longer superior in grain. McCormick had added several technical improvements, beginning with a cutter that resisted clogging better. The job of raking the cut grain off the platform had proved a man-killer in a ten-hour or twelve-hour harvest day; McCormick copied Hussey in moving his raker onto the platform. The reaper's weight had increased and been redistributed; this demanded a completely new design, which in the end included a seat for the driver. The virtually all-new Virginia Reaper, as McCormick christened it, received a patent in 1847. Its defense against the troop of new competitors escalated the reaper war.

McCormick did not allow himself to be distracted from the main battlefield. Studying wheat-farming America with the eye of a Napoleon surveying Italy, he was struck above all by the unmistakable movement of wheat westward. He chose his headquarters accordingly. Chicago in 1848 was as unprepossessing a metropolis as America could exhibit. Its population of seventeen thousand lived and worked in a warren of muddy streets, flimsy hovels, noisome slaughterhouses, and jerry-built factories—and made money hand over fist. Grain and cattle from the huge farms on the prairie flowed in a torrent into the toddling town via the canal that Father Jacques Marquette had envisioned linking the Great Lakes with the Mississippi and via the railroad now booming across the land. Unlimited arable land and cheap transportation promised a new American empire with Chicago as its capital.

McCormick first commissioned a Chicago farm-implement maker to manufacture reapers for the harvest of 1847; he struck a partnership deal with two entrepreneurs in 1848, and the next year the imperious McCormick bought out his partners and plunged ahead alone, having summoned from Virginia his brothers Leander and William to oversee the business. Acquiring a piece of land near the north end of the present Michigan Avenue bridge, he built a factory complex whose powerful steam engine was one of the wonders of Chicago. When most of the factory burned down in 1851, McCormick rebuilt it into what the newspapers hailed as the largest factory of its kind in the world.

The Chicago *Daily Journal* described its operation: "An angry whirr, a dronish hum, a prolonged whistle, a shrill buzz and a panting breath—such is the music of the place. You enter—little wheels of steel attached to horizontal, upright and oblique shafts, are on every hand. . . . Rude pieces of wood [arrive] upon little railways, as if drawn thither by some mysterious attraction. [The lathes] touch them and presto, grooved, scalloped, rounded, on they go. . . . The saw and the cylinder are the genii of the establishment. They work its wonders, and accomplish its drudgery. . . . Below, glistering like a knight in armor, the engine of forty-horse power works . . . silently . . . shafts plunge, cylinders revolve, bellows heave, iron is twisted into screws like wax, and saws dash off at the rate of forty rounds a second."

It was the world's largest reaper factory and probably the most modern factory of any kind. McCormick was thoroughly familiar with Oliver Evans's revolutionary automatic flour mill of 1786—his own father had invented an automatic stopping device for it—and in his Chicago reaper factory he introduced to industrial production a degree of automation that was still startling. The plant's advantages over the smaller, less efficient, more labor-intensive plants of competitors went beyond mere production costs. Its capacity permitted cancellation of all licensing agreements in favor of the manufacture of every McCormick reaper under the same roof, by the same machines, with a consequent gain in uniformity, quality control, and dependability. And it allowed a farmer who broke a reaper part to write to the factory and have it promptly supplied. Replacements did not even need to be stockpiled; they could be quickly fabricated from the casting patterns.

That same year, 1851, the reaper war spread

Rival advertising claims led to competitions. In the first, McCormick's reaper stalled, but he claimed victory anyway.

to foreign soil, mainly Great Britain, which was the country most interested in mechanical harvesting after the United States. Of many British attempts to devise a reaper, the best was that of a Scottish clergyman named Patrick Bell, whose 1828 machine had never performed satisfactorily and had fallen into disuse. Bell's cutter, composed of a series of scissorlike blades, clearly distinguished his machine from both the Hussey and McCormick designs, but not enough to prevent the British press, viewing the American reapers at the Great Crystal Palace Exhibition of 1851, from picturing them as descendants or even plagiarisms of the Bell. Actually neither Hussey nor McCormick had ever seen a Bell machine, a solitary model of which had been imported to the United States in 1835. The myth of Bell's inventive priority was strengthened by the successful resurrection of his reaper with a McCormick cutter replacing the old scissors action, and indeed, Bell still gets credit in some reference works to this day.

The London *Times* scoffed at the Virginia Reaper displayed at the Crystal Palace as "a cross between a flying machine, a wheelbarrow and [a circus] chariot." B. P. Johnson, the sole American member of the exhibition's jury, suggested a field trial of the McCormick and Hussey machines and a British competitor; it was arranged for July 24 at Tiptree Heath, outside London. A heavy downpour soaked the grain. Neither Hussey nor McCormick, both kept in the United States by the demands of the harvest season, was present. Hussey's machine, operated by an inexperienced British hand, clogged because of a poor adjustment of the platform; the British machine could not even get started. But the Virginia Reaper, with an expert on the platform, sailed through the soggy wheat stalks without a stutter, at a speed the jury calculated as twenty acres a day. The crowd cheered it on.

McCormick landed in England in August in time to be present at the final trial, in fair weather, of the rival machines. Hussey had arrived before him but was absent in France, and his reaper once more failed while McCormick's brilliantly succeeded. The Grand Council Medal was awarded to the Virginia Reaper, and the London *Times* now hailed the machine as "the most valuable contribution from abroad . . . that we have yet discovered." The victorious reaper made a journey through the English countryside, everywhere winning adherents and publicity. Hussey, back from France, made a similar tour with his own ma-

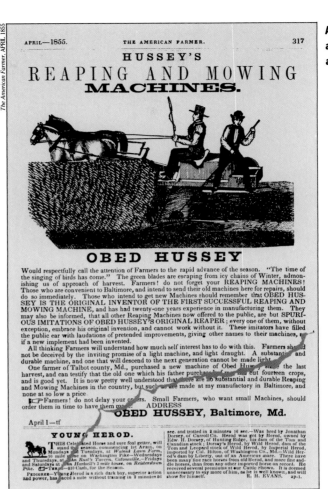

An 1855 advertisement for, and by, Hussey.

A salesman's notice for McCormick reapers, 1850.

chine, which under his guidance also operated effectively. He even managed to turn the tables on McCormick. After McCormick returned to the States, Hussey challenged the British agency caring for the Virginia Reaper to yet another match, and this time the Hussey machine clearly had the advantage. That was the "curious" match reported by the Yorkshire newspaper.

Both manufacturers established sales offices in England and on the Continent (where in 1855 McCormick won a grand medal of honor at the Paris Exhibition), and both rang up sales, but Britain and Europe were not destined to compete with North America as markets. Smaller farms, cheaper labor, and certain technical problems stood in the way. In the long term the very success of the reaper in America and the productivity it spawned helped encourage Europe's farmers to emigrate to these shores.

At home McCormick's competitors ganged up to fight him to a standstill in the courts. John H. Manny of Illinois had the cheek to brag about winning a field competition at Geneva, New York, with a reaper whose main features were copied from McCormick's. McCormick opened fire with his legal corps, headed by William H. Seward, future Secretary of State, but in vain; Manny's defense was ably conducted by Edwin M. Stanton, future Secretary of War, with Abraham Lincoln himself standing by. Lincoln, in fact, may have been the chief winner in the case. His thousand-dollar fee helped underwrite his senatorial campaign against Stephen A. Douglas, which produced the famous debates between the two and spotlighted Lincoln as a presidential candidate.

McCormick appealed to the U.S. Supreme Court, which heard the case in 1858. Having tardily married at age forty-eight, he took as his honeymoon a trip to Washington to attend the hearing, but his presence did not prevent another defeat. The following year brought still another, in a suit initiated against him by Hussey. But the Patent Office, Congress, and Supreme Court notwithstanding, McCormick was winning the reaper war on the battlefield where the grain ripened. He overwhelmed his rivals not merely by the prowess of his Chicago factory but by the genius of his merchandising, which amounted virtually to the invention of modern business methods.

He recruited an army of Midwestern locals as salesmen and commanded them with state agents who received commissions for every reaper sold. The whole force was tracked from headquarters on wall maps kept up-to-date via regular weekly or monthly reports. Some salesmen, like D. L. Burt, of Waterloo, Iowa, described their sales experiences in colorful detail: "I found in the neighborhood . . . quite early in the season one of Manny's agents with a fancifully painted machine cutting the old prairie grass to the no small delight of the witnesses, making sweeping and bold declarations about what his machine could do and how it could beat yours, etc. etc. Well, he had the start of me, I must head him somehow. I began by breaking down on his fancy machine, pointed out every objection that I could see and all that I learned about last year . . . all of which I could prove. [I then said] Now gentlemen I am an old settler, have shared all the hardships of this new country with you, have taken it rough and Smooth . . . have often been imposed on in the way I almost know you would be by purchasing the machine offered you today. I would say to you, try your machine before you [pay] one half or any except the freight. I can offer you one on such terms, warrant it against this machine or any other you can produce, and if after a fair trial . . . any other proves superior and you prefer it to mine, keep [it]. I will take mine back, say not a word, refund the freight, all is right again. No gentlemen this man dare not do this. The Result you have seen. He sold not one. I sold 20."

McCormick's own letters were dictated to a clerk who took them down in the new Pitman shorthand, made a copy for the files, and signed them with a rubber stamp. McCormick's experience as a farmer taught him that his customers could pay for their reapers only after the harvest—that is, after the machine had in effect paid for itself. Therefore, he asked for only $35 down on a price of $125, with the balance due on December 1 and with further credit available. Complaints were given prompt attention. Cyrus and his brothers William and Leander traveled during the harvest to get firsthand information on the competition and other problems. McCormick had been famous since the Crystal Palace triumph, and customers were flattered by his visits.

Advertising, by handbill and periodical, was exploited to the utmost, including its power to corrupt; editors habitually eulogized advertised products in their editorial columns. McCormick bullied and threatened reluctant editors and sometimes bribed them by hiring them as

By 1847 McCormick's machine excelled at cutting wheat. And he wisely followed the movement of wheat westward.

agents. His ads, however, were not limited to puffery. Along with testimonials from satisfied users, who spoke a suspiciously uniform language, the copy provided pictures of the reaper and detailed explanations of its working parts. Salesmen were trained to take pains in demonstrating the machine to make sure the customer knew how to operate and maintain it properly. McCormick hit on the device of printed instructions, pioneering another lasting innovation in mass product marketing.

Customers were instructed in the regular sharpening of the cutter and oiling of moving parts. Raking, even with the aid of the seat, was an acquired skill, and the driver had to know how to avoid stumps and stones. The American farmer was forced to learn a new way of life, which over the next generation turned him from a hand-implement cultivator, little different from his medieval peasant forebear, into a modern farmer-mechanic.

In 1858 Obed Hussey, no longer McCormick's chief competitor, gave up his long, losing struggle and sold his business. In a letter to a friend, the ex-sailor voiced a pathetic protest against fate: "I made no money during the existence of my patent. . . . I would have been better off at the end of fourteen years if I had filled exactly such status as my foreman holds, and got his pay, and would not have had half the hard work. . . . I never experienced half the fatigue in rowing after a whale in the Pacific Ocean. . . . Now I do not believe that there is a reaper in the country . . . at so low a price as mine, and not one on which so little profit is made."

Two years later this talented but ill-starred inventor was riding on a train from Boston to Portland when a little girl asked for a drink of water; the old Quaker descended to the station to get her one and, in reboarding the train as it started up, fell under the wheels and was killed.

By the outbreak of the Civil War the mechanical reaper produced in McCormick's expanding Chicago plant ruled the harvest across the vast Midwest prairie. The reaper's triumph came just in time. For the harvest of 1862, according to *Prairie Farmer*, a total of 33,000 reapers were sold; for 1863, 40,000, and for 1864, some 85,000. By then a grand total of 250,000 reapers had been manufactured. The machines normally lasted "close to ten years," and most of those made since 1854 were still in use. The U.S. commissioner of agriculture asserted that it would have been impossible to harvest the wheat crop of 1862 without

More than forty mowers and reapers made by different manufacturers compete against one another at a state fair in Syracuse, New York, in 1857.

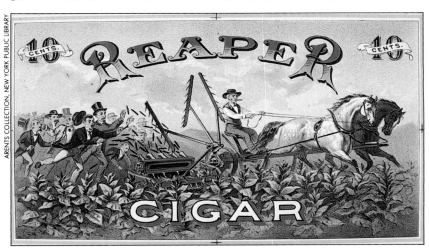
A major improvement on the reaper was the self-binder, which not only cut the grain but then tied it into sheaves such as the two men at the right hold.

A century-old cigar-box label plays on the now familiar image of the reaper.

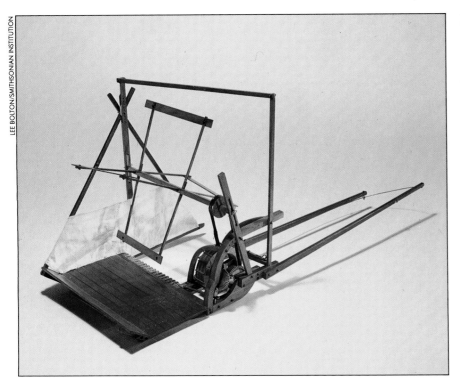

A replica of a lost 1845 McCormick patent model shows it with room for a rakeman—behind the wheel and the gearing and to the side of the big reel—but no seat yet.

McCormick overwhelmed his rivals not merely by the prowess of his Chicago factory but by the genius of his merchandising.

the reapers of the West, for each one released five men for military service. *Scientific American* said that without "horse-racks, mowers and reaping machines, one half the crop would have been left standing in the fields." Secretary of War Stanton, Cyrus McCormick's old courtroom adversary, perceptively declared that "the reaper is to the North what slavery is to the South. . . . Without McCormick's invention I fear the North could not win and the Union would be dismembered."

Stanton's dictum is fraught with irony. The Virginia-born and -bred McCormick was an outspoken enemy of the war and abolition, though he did not allow his sentiments to interfere with business. The vast sales correspondence of the company scarcely mentioned the war, save to regret that the Battle of Gettysburg hurt sales in Maryland and Pennsylvania.

By the war's end McCormick was so dominant that even major innovations by competitors merely aided his business. The self-raker, invented in the 1850s and adopted by McCormick in 1862, did away with the grueling raker task, saving still more labor. The March Harvester, invented by two Illinois farmer brothers, added binding, at first by hand but soon as a fully mechanized final operation of the reaper. McCormick's original binder, using wire, brought com-

plaints that bits of wire were getting into the grain and thence into loaves of bread, as well as into the stomachs of grazing cows. The timely emergence of cheap twine solved that problem. A burgeoning patent war was nipped in the bud by a patent pool, a congenial monopolistic device already pioneered in the sewing-machine industry, by which rival manufacturers shared technological innovations.

The great Chicago fire of 1871 destroyed both McCormick's plant and his house, but it failed to daunt the graying magnate. When Mrs. McCormick hastened back from vacation, she met a sleepless husband with one arm of his coat burned off; he drove her straight to the future site not of their new house but of his new factory.

A rugged individualist, he was also renowned as a pincher of pennies, and expertly terse, he underlined superfluous words in telegrams from his agents and brought them to the senders' attention. When some of his luggage was destroyed in a railroad fire, he sued all the way to the Supreme Court, which ultimately awarded eighteen thousand dollars to his heirs. His dying words in 1884, according to one account, were "Life *is* a battle."

Did Cyrus McCormick invent the reaper? Many people, including Obed Hussey and Cyrus's brother Leander, who quarreled with him and wrote a book ascribing the credit entirely to their father, denied it. Like so many inventions, the reaper had several direct contributors and a host of indirect ones, and when it finally achieved maturity, it distributed its rewards very unevenly. Cyrus McCormick, who got the lion's share, was at least a genuine lion.

In its time the reaper was saluted, above all, for making bread cheap. It was also credited with rescuing farm women from harvest drudgery and with replacing drunken harvest hands. It opened all eyes to the potential of agricultural mechanization and encouraged the continuing farm revolution of the nineteenth and twentieth centuries. Finally, through Cyrus McCormick's innovative production and sales techniques, it helped American business vault to a position of world leadership, with all the train of effects that have followed. ★

Joseph Gies is the author or co-author of some twenty books, including *The Ingenious Yankees* (with Frances Gies) and *Bridges and Men*. He has been the senior editor for technology of the *Encyclopaedia Britannica*.

A Technological Mystery Resolved

The lack of any advanced metallurgy among the Aztecs and Mayas has long been a mystery to students of pre-Columbian civilizations. Why, historians ask, were the great Mexican empires stuck in the Stone Age?

The Spanish crushed the Aztec empire with amazing ease, and the Americans' technological inferiority was undoubtedly partly responsible. The conquistadors had gunpowder and horses; the Aztecs had neither. However, the blades of Aztec swords, made of obsidian, were sharper than steel. They could behead a horse.

Obsidian is a kind of glass formed during volcanic eruptions, and it shares all the basic physical properties of ordinary glass. The fact that the edge of a newly chipped flake is sharper than surgical steel was only discovered in the 1970s, and it has led to the use of obsidian blades in eye surgery, since the evenness of their cut permits much faster healing. The Aztecs called their obsidian-edged sword *macuahuitl.* Usually the swords were lined with ten blades; five on each side. Because obsidian is glass, it naturally fractures into a sharp, even, predictably shaped blade when chipped. Also because it is glass, it is brittle and cannot be resharpened. The blades on a sword undoubtedly had to be replaced after only a few uses; this is the main reason steel eventually supplanted obsidian after the Spanish conquest.

Why didn't the Aztecs fare better against the Spanish with such effective swords? Probably because the swords didn't have tips and were not meant to pierce; they were designed only for slashing. An adept Spanish swordsman could fend off an Indian simply by ducking a swing of the sword and then running the enemy through.

Obsidian was used extensively among pre-Columbian societies throughout North and South America, but it reached its highest development in the hands of the Aztecs. They used the blades for both hunting and warfare. Obsidian provided the projectile points for spears and arrows. Obsidian tools were used to shape the shafts of spears, arrows, and swords. Obsidian knives cut feathers and the cotton thread out of which mantles bestowed on successful warriors were made. The glass was used in butchering and in sacrifice. It was even used to cut a still-born child to pieces before removal from the womb. And the versatility of obsidian made it a prized trade item.

The extreme sharpness of an obsidian blade may help to explain why the

Swords with obsidian blades are used to slash human flesh in a drawing from the sixteenth-century Florentine Codex.

Aztecs were willing to submit to self-sacrifice. They cut their tongues and ears with obsidian blades on ritual occasions, caught the falling blood on the index finger, and flipped the blood in the direction of the sun or moon. Such self-mutilation was formerly believed to have been quite painful, but it is now understood that a fresh obsidian blade has an edge so sharp one barely feels a cut into the flesh.

In fact, the very sharpness of the obsidian blade is probably the primary reason the Aztecs had no metallurgy. To develop a metal that could do the things obsidian already did so exceedingly well would have taken too long. After the conquest, the Spanish adopted obsidian for many of their own tools, including shaving blades. It was not until the late 1700s that steel completely replaced obsidian in Mexican technology.

Another reason the Aztecs didn't look beyond obsidian was its sheer abundance. More than fifty ancient sources of the material have been identified in Mexico and Guatemala, and they are the densest deposits in the world. The Aztecs usually drew obsidian from one mine at a time until the source was exhausted; then they moved on to the next. They surveyed for obsidian and other essential rocks by watching the early morning mists rising from the earth and searching for stones where the mists were densest. If and why this worked is not clear; perhaps the ground was cooler and retained less moisture where there were mineral deposits, and so condensation would be greater.

Obsidian is a semiprecious stone that can be polished, which also contributed to its unchallenged importance. The Aztec aristocracy wore obsidian jewelry; priests and nobles used highly polished obsidian mirrors to divine the future. In their animistic culture, everything, including rocks, had a spirit, and obsidian was especially revered. The principle god influencing life on earth, Tezcatlipoca, had an obsidian mirror in place of one foot. An obsidian knife placed in water in the courtyard of one's home was believed to keep away sorcerers by frightening them with their own reflections. An obsidian blade was tied around the neck of a pregnant woman to prevent her child from being born harelipped.

For the Aztecs obsidian was not only almost ideally suited to all its practical uses, it also had roles in society that transcended the purely practical. It is almost impossible to imagine such a civilization forsaking this magical, useful, and abundant glass in favor of the methodical development of common metals. ∎

Terry Stocker is a research associate in anthropology at the University of West Florida.

A FEW WORDS ABOUT THIS
PICTURE

An 1852 artist's view of New York Harbor
reveals itself to be an invaluable document of the
wood-and-canvas technology of another era

by Erik A. R. Ronnberg, Jr.

New York Harbor, by Fitz Hugh Lane (1804 – 1865):
oil on canvas, thirty-six by sixty inches.

During the first half of the nineteeth century, New York City became the most important mercantile crossroads in North America. Geographically midway between ports in New England and on the Chesapeake Bay, and connected to the interior by the Hudson River and a growing canal system, New York was at the focal point of vital east-west and north-south trade routes. Furthermore, its deep harbor was ringed by land that lent itself to the construction of wharves, shipyards, canal and railroad terminals, and commercial roads and buildings. With this combination of assets, it was inevitable that the country's most important commercial routes would be drawn to this natural concourse.

If the marine artist Fitz Hugh Lane was not concerned with the reasons for New York's commercial preeminence, he was certainly impressed by its results, for his 1852 painting of its harbor is one of his most kinetic works. Renowned in his time for the accuracy and fine detail of his canvases, Lane is today more highly regarded for his pioneering techniques of illuminating his subjects to create moods whose nature and presence seem to transcend their subject matter. With Manhattan's skyline all but hidden by a forest of masts, Lane chose to portray this port by focusing on its harbor traffic, keeping the city behind it at a distance. The painting that resulted is one of the most magnificent and informative views of any harbor in the mid-nineftenth century.

The ships and boats in the painting represent four of the five kinds of waterborne commerce that sustained the city: foreign trade (deep-water voyages to and from Europe, South America, and beyond), coastal trade (the transportation of goods to and from other American ports), river navigation (via the Hudson, Raritan, and East rivers and the Staten Island kills), and harbor navigation (moving vessels, people, and goods to and from city anchorages and wharves). The fifth kind, lost to view, was the extensive barge commerce to and from the canal

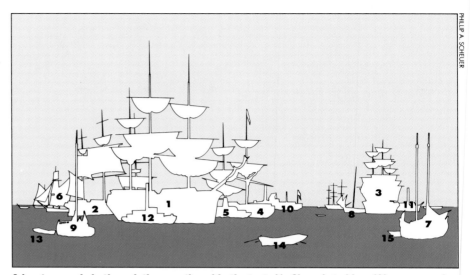

A key to vessels in the painting mentioned in the text: (1, 2) packet ships; (3) ocean carrier; (4) packet brig; (5) side-wheel towboat; (6) hermaphrodite brig; (7, 8) coastal schooners; (9) sloop; (10) sound steamer; (11) deep-water steamship; (12) steam-propeller towboat; (13) yawl boat; (14) Whitehall boat; (15) dory.

terminals across the Hudson, which gave New York access to Philadelphia, the coal-mining regions of eastern Pennsylvania, and barge freight on the Erie and Champlain canals.

The Atlantic Shuttle

Foreign trade was the most glamorous aspect of New York shipping. New York merchants sent their vessels to every significant trading port in the world, leaving only the Baltic, the Levant, India, and Canadian ports to be dominated by Boston, New York's chief rival. Of greatest importance was the "Atlantic shuttle," a regular procession of ships loaded mainly with cotton, tobacco, and flour, bound east to ports like Liverpool, London, and Le Havre, returning with immigrants, textiles, industrial hardware, and fine housewares. The best of these ships were operated by large trading firms called packet lines, which sent their vessels out on regular year-round schedules, regardless of weather. Designed and built in the best American shipyards and manned by capable officers and seamen, the packets set high standards for speed, reliablity, and safety under sail. Beginning in the 1820s, succeeding designs grew steadily larger and finer in hull form; by 1850, ships of a thousand tons and more were common. Two

such ships are prominent in the left middle ground of this view. Their design after three decades of deliberate change was a shrewd and profitable compromise of speed and capacity.

The advancing packet, with a tug alongside, is in all likelihood bound for Europe with a cargo mostly of cotton, this country's leading export at the time. This staple was very light for its bulk; ships loaded only with cotton would ride high in the water, adversely affecting their stability. To make them stiffer, a small but very heavy cargo such as lead or iron pigs might first be placed in the hold for ballast. When this packet reached her European destination, she would likely be loaded with much heavier fare, including seven hundred (more or less) immigrants, who would face the discomforts and dangers of sea travel for five weeks or more in hopes of finding a better life in America. This human cargo was the backbone of the packet trade, the main reason for scheduled voyages, and the last hope for survival of the packet lines after steamships had lured away the mail-carrying contracts and more glamorous cargoes.

Conspicuous by their absence from this scene are clipper ships, which in any year of their heyday were an uncommon sight. There were probably only a few hundred clipper ships ever built, the number depending on how strictly one defines the type and how much one can trust surviving records. If Lane's view of New York includes no such ship, it is likely that none was in sight when he was sketching for the painting.

The simultaneous development of clippers and very large packets in the early 1850s led to a new design that combined characteristics of both, permitting a large, capacious hull with only a moderate sacrifice in the clipper's speed. Many of these ocean carriers were put on the packet runs, where they were admired for their handsome profiles and speed. After the Civil War the shipyards of Maine specialized in this breed, which came to be known as the down easter.

The large ship in the right midground is an early example of this breed, with a graceful bow that combines the fancy headrails of the packet with the hollow lines and flare of the clipper bow. In cross section the hull is very boxlike, with an almost flat bottom and nearly vertical sides. The rigs on these ships were enormous; their lower masts could be three feet or more in diameter, with lower shrouds and topmast backstays nearly four inches thick. The height of the mainmast from deck to flag halyard truck often exceeded 160 feet, and the square sails that hung from the lower and topsail yards were made from canvas nearly one-eighth of an inch thick; one of these sails could weigh well over a ton. For all its mass and power,

The big packets represented a shrewd, profitable compromise of speed and capacity.

a crew of forty could work such a ship, whereas clippers of similar tonnage might require one hundred men.

Sailing the Coasts

Although New York's deep-water trade employed the port's largest ships and has had romanticists and historians under its spell ever since, the more prosaic fleet of coastal vessels actually carried more cargo, connecting New York with virtually every coastal community that had a landing. New York merchants even had their ships plying the West Coast, capitalizing on the gold stampede in California, but also mindful of fish, lumber, and furs. The West Coast was still reserved by our mercantile laws for American ships only, and this protectionism did much to insulate coasting vessels from rapid technological changes.

By mid-century cotton was undisputedly the country's most important export, and New York ships and New York agents were carrying most of it. The cotton was first taken from the plantations in bales to four principal Southern ports: Charleston, Savannah, Mobile, and New Orleans; from there it was sent to New York via the coasting

fleet. At New York the cotton was transferred to large packets and ocean carriers for delivery to Europe. Such a central role for New York in the cotton business might seem illogical and even predatory, but the city's capital, in the form of loans and advances, actually made possible the expansion of cotton production in the South on such a vast scale. Save for Charleston, the Southern ports were poor for the direct-export business, as shifting sandy bottoms and sandbars limited the depths of vessels entering them; the shallow-draft coasters required for that end of the trade were not well suited for the transatlantic trade.

At center in the painting, we see an inbound brig with a side-wheel towboat alongside. At nearly four hundred tons, the brig is about as large as any commonly used in the cotton trade on runs to Savannah, Mobile, and Charleston. The large cabin indicates accommodations for passengers; thus it is a vessel built for coastal packet service, making regular runs south with passengers and supplies and returning with passengers and cotton. The brig rig — with two masts, both square-rigged — was soon to pass out of favor, having reached its practical limits in size. The rig that replaced it was the hermaphrodite brig, a two-master whose foremast was square-rigged but whose mainmast carried the fore-and-aft rig of the schooner. This represented a fifty-fifty compromise between the brig and schooner rigs, but the hulls of hermaphrodite brigs were more like those of the coasting schooners — shallow and

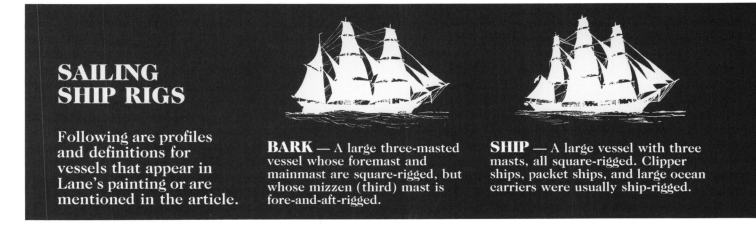

SAILING SHIP RIGS

Following are profiles and definitions for vessels that appear in Lane's painting or are mentioned in the article.

BARK — A large three-masted vessel whose foremast and mainmast are square-rigged, but whose mizzen (third) mast is fore-and-aft-rigged.

SHIP — A large vessel with three masts, all square-rigged. Clipper ships, packet ships, and large ocean carriers were usually ship-rigged.

broad — than the deeper hulls of the brigs.

In the far left background is a typical hermaphrodite brig of the period: a small vessel, less than two hundred tons, her deck loaded with lumber. The lumber trade was a Maine specialty, and most of the vessels working in it also came from there. Their hulls tended to be very boxy and full-ended, with little or no fancy paintwork nor even a figurehead. They were quickly built and plainly fitted for a decade's worth of hard work, then disappeared from the registers, unremembered for having brought millions of board feet of pine and spruce into New York to build hundreds of tenement houses and other rough carpentry. Hermaphrodite brigs were never as common as schooners in the coastal trade, but their larger rigs made them better for the longer passages along the coast, and the square rig gave them an easier motion in heavy seas.

The most common rig in the coasting fleet was the schooner. A number of them have survived to this day and still make a living as summer cruising boats on the Maine coast. In 1850 the two-masted schooner was nearly universal; only a few three-masters, called tern schooners, had yet been built. Schooners fitted for the packet trade often carried square topsails on their foremasts, which steadied their motion in rough seas and gave them an extra push off the wind. The majority of coasting schooners had simple fore-and-aft rigs, which were the handiest for short hauls from one port to the next. Vast stretches of the Atlantic seaboard were still more accessible by sea than by land, even after the coming of the railroads. On the highways of water the coasting schooner was the analogue to the modern motor truck and bus combined, carrying people, mail, and freight to towns and villages that had communicated with the rest of the world this way since their colonial origins.

Lane included two coasting schooners, in the extreme right foreground and the right middle ground. The former is quite small, probably no more than sixty tons, and of a very old model. But for the presence of the large trunk cabin abaft the main mast, she might have passed for a Marblehead schooner, a type of fisherman descended from the colonial fisheries. Her rig is the simplest that still defines a schooner: two masts and three sails, including jib, foresail, and mainsail. The other, much larger schooner, approaching two hundred tons, is rigged with topmasts from which she can set additional jibs as well as the fore- and main topsails. In the decade preceding the Civil War, progressively larger coasting schooners were built until it was realized that the sails set from two masts were too large and difficult for small crews to handle. When a third mast was added, the rig could be made lower, and individual sails smaller and more manageable. The resulting tern schooner did not become common until after 1865.

The sloop — a single-masted fore-and-after — had a complex history in New York waters. Small versions with the simplest rigs were frequently found working from the seaward end of the harbor, but up the Hudson the traffic was dominated by a magnificent class of large sloops whose graceful hulls and enormous sail plans had no parallel elsewhere. Lane shows a solitary coasting sloop in the left foreground, but alas, no Hudson River sloop is to be seen. Like the schooner, this rig had its practical limits in size; the sloop that exceeded ninety tons was a rarity. The large mainsail was a brutish thing to handle, and as crew wages increased, many such vessels were rigged over as schooners to make them easier to handle by a smaller crew.

The Coming of Steam

By 1850, the steamship was well established in the coastal trade and had assumed two basic forms. The older was that of the river steamers built for Robert Fulton, with shallow hulls, flat bottoms, and extensive superstructures. In later designs the superstructures reached even farther, overhanging the sides of the hull and merging with the paddle-wheel housings. The hulls were lightly constructed and very flexible, and the boats were generally confined to runs between New York, Providence, and ports on Long Island Sound. Travel beyond these sheltered waters was as yet risky. One of these sound steamers can be seen in the center background. Very noticeable is its walking-beam engine, which was the

BRIG — A small or medium-size vessel with two masts, both square-rigged.

HERMAPHRODITE BRIG — A two-masted vessel whose foremast is square-rigged and whose mainmast is fore-and-aft-rigged.

SCHOONER — A small to medium-size vessel with two masts, both fore-and-aft-rigged. This was the most common rig in the coastal trade.

cheapest and simplest steam engine suitable for ships and could still function if its parts got out of alignment as a result of the flexing of the hull. At the time of the painting, river steamboats and sound steamers still looked fundamentally alike. Riverboats had open decks around their sterns fitted with guardrails, permitting passengers open-air spaces; the sound steamers were completely enclosed, to shelter their passengers from the less gentle ocean breezes. Both these types remained popular among commuters and travelers well into the twentieth century. Only gradually did the paddle wheel and walking-beam engine yield to the screw propeller and compound engine, and there was always a great reluctance to give up the side-wheeler's distinctive form.

As the steamship ventured farther out into the Atlantic, the weaknesses of the riverboat hull became obvious; hulls for ocean service would have to be stronger, stiffer, and more sea-kindly. The British took an early lead in constructing ocean steamers; American builders were handicapped by unreliable cast- or forged-iron engine parts and the difficulties of building large, rigid hulls in wood. Ever eager to push the wooden steamship to its limits, steamship owners seldom had the patience to allow the technologies of shipbuilding and engine making to catch up with their demands. Not until the mid-1850s were there transatlantic steamers numerous and reliable enough to maintain frequent scheduled crossings.

A coastal schooner was like a modern truck and bus combined, carrying people, mail, freight.

They came too late for Lane's painting.

The operators of coastal steamship lines were more successful in these years. As early as 1846 they were making regular runs from New York to the cotton ports, as well as to the West Indies and Central America. A terminal at the isthmus of Panama allowed westbound passengers to transfer to coastal steamers on the Pacific side, which took them on to California. It was on these routes that the American deep-water steamship was refined and made practical for long ocean passages, and in the far right background of Lane's painting one of them is visible. With her stern hidden from view, one can only assume that she had three masts and that the foremast could carry square sails, which were set from the deck. There is no sign of a walking-beam engine: American steamers built for this service before 1850 were fitted with side-lever engines whose components were mounted very low and contributed much to the stability of the hull. The height of the stack seems exaggerated, but if this were modified, the ship might well pass for either the *Cherokee* or the *Tennessee*, both built in New

York in the late 1840s and employed on the Savannah run.

Harbor Boats and Small Craft

The diversity of New York's harbor craft is well represented in this picture, but by no means comprehensively. Oars, sails, paddle-wheels, and screw propellers moved an amazing variety of hulls, ranging from small rowboats to large towboats, which continuously shuttled about people, goods, and other vessels. Large inbound ships were taken in hand by towboats that moved them to and from wharves. If for any reason a ship had to lie at an anchorage, her cargo could be taken on or off by lighters, small bargelike sailing vessels that engaged solely in transferring goods between vessel and wharf. By 1850 steam-powered ferryboats were transporting thousands of people into Manhattan from Long Island, Staten Island, and the New Jersey shore in a modest prologue to the swarms of commuter traffic of the next century. The ferries bore a strong resemblance to river and sound steamers.

Lane shows two types of towboat, both at work moving large sailing ships. The paddle-wheel towboat in charge of the brig shows plainly its riverboat origins, especially in its primitive crosshead engine, whose use dates back to Fulton's pioneering craft. Mechanically obsolete, these hardy engines nevertheless survived in harbors that offered plentiful coal and very short distances to travel. Much more progressive, and prophetic of the steamship's future, is the tug alongside the packet ship. Of very recent design, it combines the screw propeller with a steam plant using a much later type of engine, probably a one-cylinder vertical or an early two-cylinder engine. The superstructure extends out to the rails, unlike on later tugs, which have open passageways between rails and cabin; excepting this, we see in this boat the basic arrangement that has characterized tugs to this day. In Lane's time American tugboats weren't

MARBLEHEAD SCHOONER—A small schooner of colonial origins, with a full, round bow and a high quarter deck.

TERN SCHOONER, or TERN — A name given to a schooner with three masts when the type first appeared in American shipping.

called such; the early paddle-wheelers were known as towboats. When screw-driven boats appeared, they were called steam propellers. The term *tug-boat* was brought to this country from England, first, probably by 1860, in speech, and much later in print.

While the rowing craft in this painting may seem unimportant, to the artist they were essential elements of contrast in a scene of harbor activity on so gigantic a scale. Lane was as meticulous with small boats as he was with the largest ships, taking care to give hulls their proper forms and proportions; the boats float in proper trim and are rowed with correct oarsmanship. Three very different types of boat are visible in the foreground. At left, the crew of the sloop is approaching in a yawl boat, a type that served as lifeboat and workboat for most sailing coasters and fishermen. Usually twelve to twenty feet long, yawl boats hung from davits when at sea. They were usually full-ended and heavily built; many could be fitted with simple sailing rigs.

In the center foreground is a handsome and large Whitehall boat, so named for New York's Whitehall Street, whose boat shops first produced the type. Finely modeled and easily rowed, they were the preferred means of ferrying individuals or small groups between ship and shore. They varied from fifteen to thirty feet in length (or more for special uses, including racing) and were usually rather narrow. The smaller boats could be rowed by one person; larger examples had up to six oarsmen. The superb lines and han-

One of the two towboats is obsolete; the other is prophetic of the steamboat's future.

dling of these craft endeared them to yachtsmen, so nearly every yacht of respectable size had one or more on the davits. Today they survive as recreational boats, and many rowers enjoy the double pleasure of building as well as owning their own Whitehall boats.

Made fast to the little schooner in the right foreground, with only its stern visible, is a boat very familiar to Lane — a dory. Although we think of dories as piled high in nests on the decks of schooners bound for the fishing banks, they were used in Lane's time almost exclusively for the shore fisheries — lobstering, gill netting, and hand-lining — by men who were too poor to afford anything better. Dories were in fact better suited to be launched from the shore and beached than any other type of boat, but they were the badge of the solitary fisherman who eked out a living the way his forebears had for two centuries.

The Nonphotographic Record

For all the variety of vessels in this picture, many others eluded Lane's critical eye, several of which have already been mentioned. No warships — sail or steam — are in view, nor pilot boats, nor the multitude of specialized craft that were needed to maintain wharves, shipping channels, and loading facilities. In a sense the later photographic record, for all its advantages, could do no better with a single image; there were simply too many ships in too great a variety to include in one view.

In 1850 photography was still handicapped by slow film emulsions and cumbersome equipment, and it was not until the mid-1850s that photographers were able to capture the activity of a waterfront or harbor scene with satisfactory results. For a painter like Fitz Hugh Lane, the problem of "stopping" the activity in a busy harbor was even greater, considering the amount of time required to include so much subject matter in such detail on a canvas five feet wide and three feet high. Lane's large harbor views are the combination of a detailed drawing of the background scenes and a variety of sketches and small paintings of individual vessels, carefully arranged to make a composition that draws the eye easily from one element to another. One startling aspect of Lane's drawing technique is that there is little evidence of the use of mechanical aids for drawing fine lines or establishing proportions. Not even in his ship portraits did he use a straight edge or other device to delineate fine rigging lines. This discipline is probably the result of his rigorous training in lithography.

This view was probably painted in 1852 from sketches and small oils made during Lane's visit to New York in 1850. Seldom has any maritime port of any age had its ships recorded so precisely, in such variety, and with such vitality. ★

Erik A. R. Ronnberg, Jr., is a freelance ship-model maker and consultant on history and has published extensively on technical aspects of historic ships. He is vice-president of the Cape Ann Historical Association, home of the country's largest collection of paintings and drawings by Fitz Hugh Lane.

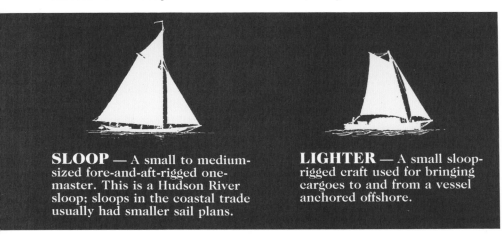

SLOOP — A small to medium-sized fore-and-aft-rigged one-master. This is a Hudson River sloop; sloops in the coastal trade usually had smaller sail plans.

LIGHTER — A small sloop-rigged craft used for bringing cargoes to and from a vessel anchored offshore.

Model Year 1825

The question "Where did it all start?" is always an irresistible, if slippery, one in matters of technology, and the more important and visible an invention, the greater the fascination in finding its origin or earliest use. In the case of the ever visible automobile, the argument can be made that it was an obscure Kentuckian, Dr. Joseph Buchanan, who, in the mid-1820s, built and drove the first in the United States. The case becomes more debatable the closer one looks, but it also becomes more interesting.

Throughout a relatively short life—he was born in 1785 and died in 1829—Buchanan epitomized the frontier intellectual, the jack-of-all-mental-trades, as much by inclination as from necessity. As an undersized, gifted, and combative child, he quickly absorbed all the learning available to him in frontier Kentucky. He qualified as a physician by studying medicine with a local practitioner. In his spare time Buchanan tinkered with a musical instrument that was to produce harmonies of color as well as sound in what he called "the music of light." While in his twenties he served with distinction on the medical faculty of Kentucky's new Transylvania University. He wrote a lengthy treatise on the mind-body problem, *The Philosophy of Human Nature* (1812), a materialist attack on the idea of the soul. In his final years he made his living as an editor, and he gave abuse as freely as he received it, supporting Kentucky's Henry Clay against another frontier hero, Andrew Jackson.

That the doctor has, for all his gifts, slipped into obscurity is perhaps his own fault. He embodied the frontier spirit at its best and worst. Disdaining those who came before him, he was "so fond of originality," a Kentucky historian wrote, "that he would not even condescend to write on any subject on which he had ever read anything."

It is typical of the man that his most solid achievement came from the ruin of a grander project. In the early 1820s Buchanan produced an improved, lightweight "capillary steam engine" and immediately envisioned its use as the means to power a flying machine. Lacking funds, the doctor appealed to his fellow citizens for financial backing. He described a strange and wonderful future, when, weather permitting, "the citizens of Washington may attend dinner parties in Boston, and return home the same evening . . . and our mer-

chants may visit Europe, transact their business and return home in a week." Friendly editors reprinted the appeal. One predicted that "we shall soon see the carriages flying in every direction over our heads with the rapidity of eagles, cleaving the air." Farther east another editor proposed that a few hundred of these "aerial vessels" be armored and sent to the aid of the Greek people, then fighting for their independence from Turkey.

Yet problems both technical and financial soon dragged Buchanan's imagination back to earth. Surrendering the hope of aerial flight, he turned to the construction of a "steam carriage," a wheeled vehicle driven by his lightweight engine. Early in 1825 the scheme met with success. The carriage, on a public trial, performed "beyond the most sanguine expectation of its ingenious inventor." With his engine Buchanan propelled a "waggon" some three or four miles through the streets of Louisville "in the presence of an astonished throng of spectators."

And there the story ends. Decades later the engine and the steam-driven carriage would still be remembered in Kentucky as "among the wonders of the day." Having made his point, though, Buchanan went on to other things; and even the histories that follow American inventors down the same dead-end road of steam propulsion often leave out this early ride.

But if the episode is to be restored to the histories, what should they say about it? It is easy to deny any real connection between the steam carriage and the modern automobile. One can argue that the internal-combustion engine is the car's true ancestor and dismiss all the steam carriages of the nineteenth century—dangerous, unwieldy, and impractical—as extinct fossils in the family tree of inventions.

Rejecting this attitude still does not guarantee pioneer status to the Kentuckian, even in the United States. By 1825, certainly, the invention and building of steam carriages was a common pastime in England. As for the New World, a case can also be made for the priority of the Philadelphia engineer Oliver Evans. In 1805 he built a steam dredge for use on the Schuylkill River, but to prove the point he first had the newly built craft driven, under its own power, through the streets from the workshop to the waterfront. Was it *really* an automobile? Nor is it difficult to suppose that some earlier Yankee mechanic more obscure than Buchanan may have built a working steam carriage and driven it down the road to historical oblivion. So the categories of the record book dissolve, but the inventor himself remains, undamaged, and so does some of the excitement of his audience, who as early as 1825 caught a fleeting if distorted glimpse of the everyday life of the future. ∎

William B. Meyer writes often about environmental history.

THE MASTER

George S. Morison appears hale and confident in an undated photo.

My great-uncle, George S. Morison, one of America's foremost bridge builders, died July 1, 1903, exactly (as he undoubtedly would have said) six years, five months, fourteen days, and six hours before I was born. What follows begins with some incidental intelligence that has nothing to do with his work; these, listed in no order of relative importance, are just some of the things I know about him:

He had, like Zeno, a conviction that time was a solid. If he made an appointment to confer with a person at 3:15 P.M., or as he always put it, at 15:15 hours, that was when they met. Those who arrived earlier waited; those who came at any time after 15:15 never conferred at all.

He read the *Anabasis* in Greek, the *Aeneid* in Latin, and the dime novels of Archibald Clavering Gunter in English.

He had a substitute in the Civil War.

He invariably referred to Mexico as Pjacko.

He thought that people who were good with animals, particularly horses, were popular with their fellows and loose in their morals. When he himself drove a horse, he brought it to a full stop by saying, "Whoa, cow"; and at least once while trying to turn a Concord buggy around, he turned it over in front of White's Machine Shop.

He was rude to waiters.

One Sunday morning he walked out of church after telling the minister, who was explaining to the congregation why he thought silver should be coined at a ratio of 16 to 1, that he should never try to deal with a subject he obviously didn't understand.

Of his neighbor Edward MacDowell, student of Liszt, composer of "To a Wild Rose" and the well-regarded Second Piano Concerto in D Minor, he said he was "a man with whom I had absolutely nothing in common."

A bachelor, he built a house in the years from 1893 to 1897 that had, by one way of counting, fifty-seven rooms, so that he would have a suitable place to eat Thanksgiving dinner and to watch the sun set over Mount Monadnock.

I could go on. Although I do not think that in themselves such items tell very much about the kind of man my great-uncle was, I cite them because, as the world goes, it is remarkable that I know them at all. That such supplementary biographical detritus should survive in such fullness and in such detail into a third, and now, I should say, into a fourth, generation, is remarkable.

There are, to be sure, some contributing circumstances. I spent a considerable part of my youth in the house George Morison built for Thanksgiving dinners and sunsets. Here, beyond those impalpable influences produced by the sense of being on the actual scene, there were more overt reminders of my great-uncle as a first cause. When, for instance, after a storm, moisture leaked through the northwest corner and ate away at the interior plaster, you knew it was because

BUILDER

He was a no-nonsense engineer of bridges in a heroic age

by Elting E. Morison

Morison's 1892 Frisco Bridge, still standing, spans the Mississippi at Memphis. Its 790-foot central truss was at one time the nation's longest.

The peripatetic Morison built this fifty-seven-room house for himself, in Peterborough, New Hampshire, in the 1890s, but stayed in it only about fifty nights during the last six years of his life.

One acquaintance wrote of him: "Force was the striking impression. When he entered a room, power came with him." Another called him "a bulwark."

the novel arrangement of bricks and experimental cement that he had devised had not worked out—a rare exception. Or when, after going to bed, there were strange creaks and murmurs drifting through the halls and up the stairwell, you knew, or hoped you knew, that they were produced not by poltergeists or second-story men but by the contraction of his steel beams in the cooling night air.

But there was more to it than those visible and audible reminders. He was still around. The effect on those who came after was not the attenuated visitation of your run-of-the-mill family ghost; it was a one-on-one encounter with a continuing presence. When he died, his sister lived in that house in a rather grand manner for fourteen years, and then his younger brother, my grandfather, presided in distinctive style for eight more years. They were personages of considerable substance, and I knew them both. But when I came to live there as a boy of fifteen, I found that my great-uncle had set them to one side and was still occupying the place.

Of those who have written about him, one spoke of his ability to enforce a decision taken "with a tenacity and ruthlessness that bore down all opposition. . . ." Another called him "a bulwark." And a third said: "Force was the striking impression. When he entered a room, power came with him." They were all trying to explain the source of his remarkable works—he did in fact put a satisfying dent in oblivion by the things he made. But he bore down on the opposition of time in quite another and less obvious way. That ability to fill a room with power turned out to be sufficient to project the force of his character through three generations of his family.

In March 1902 George S. Morison appeared before the Senate Canal Committee. He explained at length why he believed that the best way to join the waters of the Atlantic and Pacific lay through the Isthmus of Panama. The only real difficulty was posed, he said, by the Culebra Cut. "It is a piece of work that reminds me of what a teacher said to me when I was in Exeter over forty years ago, that if he had five minutes in which to solve a problem he would spend three deciding the best way to do it." Because the Culebra Cut was a big problem, more time would be required. It would take two years to figure out what to do and how to do it.

There were many times when he was put in mind of his old teacher and quoted him on problem solving for the benefit of others. It was, said one associate, "one of the principal rules" of his life. He sought beforehand to take everything into account, analyze the evidence, determine the "best possible solution," and then reach the "inflexible, intractable decision." That, in fact, is the way he decided to become a civil engineer.

It took some time to do so. Born in New Bedford, Massachusetts, in 1842, the son of a Unitarian minister, he was educated, like his father before him, at Phillips Exeter Academy and Harvard College. From there he went South as the government superintendent of plantations on Saint Helena Island. The object was to bring some order out of the chaos produced by the Civil War among the resident whites and freedmen. After a year he returned to enter the Harvard Law School, in 1864, where he won the Bowdoin prize for the best dissertation. In 1866 he joined the great New York law firm of Evarts, Southmayd & Choate.

"Exactly one month later" he confronted the problem of what to do with himself—practice law, study the principles that lay beneath the practice and teach them at some university, or go west as a civil engineer. He set May 1 of the following year, seven months later, as the date to decide the matter. On that day he informed the firm of his intention to leave the law, and five months thereafter he went out to Kansas City, Missouri, to build a bridge with Octave Chanute. I have the distinct impression that he was turned in this direction by some work he did while in the law firm, on the bankruptcy of a small Western railroad. I cannot verify this by the documents now available, but it has the support of a fairly reliable memory, and it suggests a link in the causality he always sought. When he started work "calculating the cubical contents of stone for the masonry piers," the "four years of doubt, vacillation and search" which had "formed the introduction to my life" were ended.

He could not have landed in a better place at a better time with a better man. The Missouri was a wild and willful river often disturbed by heavy floods and destructive ice jams. It constantly filled up old channels and cut out new ones. No serious bridge had ever been built across it, and the received judgment was that if a bridge were built, it could never be maintained. For someone who knew no engineering, it was a great place to begin.

There was also Octave Chanute, who had never built a big bridge before. But he had worked for a dozen years in various capacities constructing small Western railroads, and he had learned a lot on the job. At a time when there was really no other way to learn, Chanute was, at thirty-four, near the top of his class. He was, as all his later career indicates, an "acute and accurate observer," an "inventive engineer," a "truly scientific spirit," and, withal, a man possessing the "Gallic power of clear and forceful expression." When in middle age he turned his attention to "aereal navigation," his experimental glider flights greatly expanded the knowledge of the field. To the success of the Wright brothers he contributed both useful principles and actual designs.

What it meant to start on such a job with such a man was made clear in a journal written in Kansas City on Thanksgiving Day 1867. After laying out his daily work and study schedule from 0800 to 2130 hours "with not more than one evening a week being excepted," Morison went on to plot the move into the future. He was "ambitious, very ambitious." What he had set his sights on was not a financial fortune but "a good and useful life." With that as his purpose he would, when the Kansas City bridge was finished, "cross the Atlantic and devote a year to the study of French and German, and the acquirement of scientific knowledge; it being my wish to make the profession of engineering a truly liberal profession and through it to rise to science and philosophy, raising it with me rather than to prostitute it to mere money making. . . ." Not many of those who at the time were calculating the cubic contents of stones would have put it quite that way, and even now it must appear a very large and liberating definition of the possibilities in the field.

Given such attitudes and such a personal program, it is probably not surprising that he rose rapidly to the position of associate engineer on this first job and that, as soon as the bridge was finished, he went to work on a book that described the solutions to the problems encountered in the building of it. What followed—in a rare departure from his program—was not France and Germany but a six-year internship of steadily increasing responsibility in the design and construction of small, short Western railroads with names like Leavenworth, Lawrence & Galveston or Detroit, Eel River & Illinois. Near the end of this period Chanute called him back to serve as his principal engineer on the Erie Canal.

On May 6, 1875, the bridge at Portageville, New York, said to be the largest wooden trestle in the world, was consumed by fire. Morison was put to work drawing up the design and specifications for an iron structure that would replace it. On May 10, four days later, the first building contract was let, and he assumed the direction of the construction. Eighty-two days after that the bridge was open for rail traffic. It was 818 feet two inches between abutments and it gave him, at age thirty-three, an "international prominence."

For the next seventeen years he devoted most of his time and thought to building railroad bridges in the West. He built these bridges across the Missouri, Mississippi, Ohio, Snake, Columbia, and Willamette rivers. They all had certain common characteristics. Their specifications filled the requirements of the particular situations to a T, and in the building those specifications were satisfied precisely. As at Plattsmouth, Nebraska, where the "total deflection of the main span under the test load of 800,000 pounds was exactly" as previously calculated, so with all the others. They were also on the grand scale. At Memphis, Tennessee, the main span was 790 feet, which made it the longest truss in the country. At Cairo, Illinois, the metalwork was 10,560 feet—two miles—in length, the longest steel bridge in the world. And they were all structures in which the function was obviously made to determine the form, in studied austerity.

It was said that in this period he compiled a record that was "unrivaled in the history of bridge construction." Whatever the truth of this evaluation, it is certain he acquired a reputation that made him sought after for many different kinds of services. He joined the boards of four railroads. For fifteen years he provided Baring Brothers of London with comprehensive analyses of the physical condition, financial structure, and managerial competence of American railroad companies. He played a large part in the study that led to the reconstruction of the Erie Canal. President Cleveland put him on one commission that selected San Pedro as the deepwater port for Los Angeles and on another that started the action that produced, nearly forty years later, the George Washington Bridge across the Hudson.

Then in 1899 he was appointed by President McKinley to the Isthmian Canal Commission. For the next two and a half years he devoted himself to an exhaustive examination of the political difficulties and technical factors, past and present, that were involved in the great enterprise. Twice he went to Europe; once he made a four-month exploration of the isthmus itself; and he attended all the fifty-one meetings of the commission in Washington. In November 1901 the members signed a report that, reflecting a powerful combination of historical, political, and technical pressures, recommended Nicaragua as the site for the canal. Appended to this document was the dissenting opinion of a minority of one. It recommended, with much careful explanation, the choice of the Isthmus of Panama as the preferred site; and it was signed by George S. Morison.

There followed weeks of argument within the commission, debates in Congress, discussion in the press, and earnest consideration in the White House. In January 1902 the commission rendered a supplementary report that unanimously concluded that the "feasible route for an Isthmian Canal to be under the control, management and ownership of the United States is that known as the Panama Route."

In such a tangle of historical, political, international, and technical considerations and in such a concert of dominant personalities, it is hard to determine final causes. David McCullough, who has made the most recent and careful investigation of the situation, concludes as follows: "If one traces back through the chain of events . . . and if it is remembered that Morison . . . made no effort to glorify his contributions, at the time or later, then Morison emerges a bit like the butler at the end of the mystery—as the ever-present, frequently unobtrusive, highly instrumental figure around whom the entire plot turned." It is an image he

NEBRASKA STATE HISTORICAL SOCIETY, LINCOLN

would, beyond much doubt, never have chosen, but it makes a point he would never have made for himself.

Such, briefly, was the nature of his principal works. Before trying to establish a more coherent explanation of the man himself, it may be useful to say something about the man among his fellows. Was his record indeed "unrivaled," should he be called "the leading bridge engineer in America, perhaps in the world," did he deserve the title of Pontifex Maximus bestowed on him at one college commencement? That is a very doubtful kind of exercise that leads to no useful conclusion. What is far more to the point is that he was a

A train crosses the Missouri on Morison's typically unembellished, totally functional Nebraska City Bridge, built in 1888.

His bridges all filled the
requirements of their particular
situations to a T. The function was
obviously made to determine the
form, in studied austerity.

contributing member of a remarkable company, some of whom held his achievements in a good deal higher respect than his person. And what is interesting is not what set the members apart but what they all had and did in common.

There were, of course, some distinguishing temperamental differences. John Roebling played the flute and allowed a caller to be five minutes late before canceling the appointment; Octave Chanute made witty remarks; James Eads interrupted a stunning career for four years because he preferred the "happy environment of his family"; Charles Latrobe liked to go about in society and worked in watercolors; and so on. What really matters is the shared experience of those who practiced civil engineering in the last half of the last century and the effect of that experience on themselves and those around them.

They came up, for the most part, the hard way. Leaving college and, more often, high school, they started out on the ground floor, measuring stone, surveying lines, calculating stresses. They did these things more often than not on a new railroad, which for them, like the Erie Canal for the preceding generation, was the only available institute of technology. Here they learned from men who knew a little more than they did because they had been a little longer on the job. Frequently they followed these instructors into the engineering division of one of the larger, more stable roads in the East. And from there, after a time, they usually struck out on their own as "consulting engineers," which meant they were ready to deal with whatever propositions came to them.

Wherever they went, whatever they did, they found the subject matter was always changing. Larger loads, longer spans, deeper excavations, new materials, novel procedures. In such conditions the name of the game was figuring out sensible new departures from what had been tried and true for centuries. And if the figuring wasn't right, the cost of going wrong could be measured out and the source of difficulty explicitly defined. When, for instance, the bridge Amasa Stone had built at Ashtabula, Ohio, went down one stormy night, it took a train of passengers with it. And after a jury found that the bridge had been an experiment "which ought never to have been tried," Amasa Stone, "as exacting of himself as he had been of many others," took his own life.

Those who started on the ground floor and worked their way through to the top of such a calling were often said to be bold, self-reliant, independent, secure, powerful, daring, resolute, and, sometimes, arrogant and overbearing. At this distance it may be seen that their most continuing collective contribution was not the things they built but their way of going at things. They gave a significant push to the developing new method of solving certain kinds of problems that occur in life.

Over and over they demonstrated that the ingenious solution that worked was reached through accurate observation, exact knowledge of the strength of materials, precise calculation, due respect for the laws and forces of nature, and the resourceful ordering of evidence obtained by the unclouded intelligence. They could be daring when the findings from the hard data—subjected to the logical process—supported the bold conclusion, and they were resolute because, within their scheme of things, they could prove they were right.

Faith might well have its uses, but they had found a surer way to remove a mountain. This method, increasingly refined, has put us wherever it is that we are today.

On this subject he had ideas which in his closing years he put down in a small book. It demonstrates the extent to which he had fulfilled his early intention to rise through his profession to philosophy, and it still speaks to our condition. Our ability to manufacture power in unlimited quantities, begun with Watt and the condenser, had opened up what Morison called a new epoch for mankind. Carried to its logical conclusions, it would in time give men the capacity to create all the essential conditions for their living and to determine their own fate. He foresaw a future when "material developments will come to a gradual pause," when "an immense population will live comfortably and happily, and the qualities which make the good citizen and the contented man will be more in demand than those which make leaders in periods as we are familiar with."

But he also believed that the new epoch, before it reached this possible end, would "destroy many of the conditions which give most interest to the history of the past, and many of the traditions which people hold most dear." Among other things it would "destroy ignorance, as the entire world will be educated, and one of the greatest dangers must come from this very source, when the number of half-educated people is greatest, when the world is full of people who do not know enough to recognize their limitations. . . ."

How do we assemble the bits and pieces of Morison's personality and character in a more intelligible mosaic? If the design is supposed to fulfill a familiar expectation, this is a hard question. Remember that until he built the great brick house, at the age of fifty-five, he had no place to call his own, and during the remaining years of his life his accumulated occupancy of that house came to little more than forty-nine days. Though he had apartments in Chicago and New York, he didn't use them much, and then only for bed and sometimes breakfast. For the most part he stayed in hotels and sleeping cars, and ate in clubs and restaurants. Considered as a social being, he seems a programmed nomad.

There are some family letters, but for the most part they have to do with the arrangement for a proposed visit or the details of some small errand he wished a member to perform. There is also the daily diary he kept throughout his life. In the entries are faithfully reported temperatures, rainfalls, and the number of minutes the train he was riding on was behind schedule.

In such conditions one must respect the dead air spaces, accept the fact that what you see is all you're going to get, and recognize that he planned it that way. If you look back to the journal entry for Thanksgiving Day 1867, you will find his program for a good and useful life. What he did with himself from those first calculations of cubic quantities to his closing consideration of engineering as the source of a new epoch satisfied the terms of that program—not less, not more, but exactly. ∎

Elting E. Morison is Killian Professor of Humanities Emeritus at the Massachusetts Institute of Technology.

Inventing a Life

Thomas A. Watson is remembered mostly as the man who answered the first telephone call. He is known to a few as the actual coinventor of the phone—he worked out the basic idea with Alexander Graham Bell and added major improvements including the bell and the switch hook. But he retired from telephones at twenty-seven and then embarked on a life—or series of lives—so rich and varied that his exploits with Bell might be considered mere preamble. His autobiography, *Exploring Life*, could have been called *Inventing Life*.

He was born in 1854 at his father's livery stable, in Salem, Massachusetts. At sixteen he enrolled in a course in bookkeeping and discovered that it bored him. Then he tried carpentry; it exhausted him. After that he found work at a machine shop in Boston.

This was the shop of Charles Williams, manufacturer of small electrical apparatus, and into this shop in the spring of 1874 walked Alexander Bell, a young professor at Boston University. Bell wanted to create a "harmonic telegraph" that would carry several signals at once. Before long Bell and Watson became a team.

In March 1876 Bell spoke the first intelligible telephoned sentence—the immortal "Mr. Watson, come here, I want you!" Commercial telephone service followed faster than anyone expected, beginning in 1877, and that August Bell went off on honeymoon to England, leaving Watson in charge of both improving the invention and handling all the technical problems that arose with phones everywhere.

In 1881, as the telephone business mushroomed, Watson quit. As he later wrote, "The same desire for a larger life and new experiences that had improved my fortunes by sending me ... into the machine shop, was stronger than ever."

Made wealthy by the telephone, he took a long vacation in Europe. Then,

Watson in costume at Stratford, 1911.

after marrying, he decided to become a farmer—"with the cocksureness of youth fresh from a successful achievement in another line." He was not cut out for it. Two years later he had given up agriculture and begun a machine shop in a suburb of Boston.

He started building engines for small ships and within several years had a flourishing business with thirty employees. In the mid-nineties he decided to radically expand the business, mainly to alleviate the high unemployment in eastern Massachusetts. He started bidding on and winning contracts to build naval destroyers.

Meanwhile, he took up the serious study of the voice, an interest Bell had encouraged. He also, with his wife, took a three-year course in geology and paleontology at MIT. Watson now became a respected enough geologist to have a genus of fossil gastropod named after him.

By 1901 he was running the largest

shipyard in the nation. But shipbuilding was a precarious business. In 1903 he was replaced as president of the company he had founded, which now had four thousand employees.

Nearly bankrupted, he again started over. He went into partnership with a geology professor at MIT to evaluate mines and ore prospects. The two traveled to Alaska and California, but they never found any promising mines.

In 1910, his study of the voice "having superseded all my other occupations," Watson read about the work of Frank R. Benson's Company of Shakespearean Players, in England, and decided to see if he could join. Benson welcomed him. Watson spent that fall living in theatrical digs and playing in crowd scenes. He later wrote that "never before had I felt such a constant freshness, exhilaration and capacity for work and study." The next spring he capped his stage career with speaking parts at Stratford-upon-Avon in celebration of Shakespeare's birthday.

At the end of the season, Watson joined some of the players forming their own company and hit the road again. He wrote plays for them, including adaptations of *A Tale of Two Cities*, *Oliver Twist*, and *Nicholas Nickleby*.

He returned home to Braintree, Massachusetts, in 1912 and settled into a life of giving public readings, producing amateur stage productions, serving as president of the Boston Browning Society, and lecturing, sometimes about geology but most often about the invention of the telephone.

Watson lived until 1934. In his autobiography he wrote, "If I should speak of the purpose that has unified the manifold activities of my life, I would say that it is to be found in the fact that I have been wending my way eagerly to school all my life and am still at it." He was propelled in all his pursuits, he might have added, by the wide-ranging questing spirit of a true inventor. ∎

Total Eclipse of the Sun by the Earth.

The Northern Lights pack valise and move on.

The Moon goes into mourning.

MAY THEY FULFILL THEIR PROMISES—THE NEW YEAR AND THE NEW LIGHT!

New Light on Edison's Light

by Robert Friedel

Digging anew through the voluminous papers of Thomas Edison, scholars are constructing a fresh, more accurate and revealing understanding of his greatest invention

No tale in all the chronicles of American invention would seem to be better known than the story of Thomas Edison's incandescent electric light. The electric light, after all, quickly became the epitome of the bright idea, and its creator was for more than fifty years the living symbol of America's inventive genius. But in truth it is only in recent years that we have begun to piece together the complete story of history's most famous invention.

That the full picture of Edison's work on the electric light in the late 1870s should be obscure is a bit strange, for few inventions before the twentieth century are better documented. The records of the famous laboratory at Menlo Park, New Jersey, were voluminous and have been well preserved over the years. Dozens of laboratory notebooks, hundreds of drawings and sketches, a wealth of letters, patents, and other documents all give testimony to the work and lives of the light's inventors. The importance of the effort to invent a practical electric light was widely evident to contemporary observers, so we have, in addition, an unusual number of journalists' accounts of their trips out to Menlo Park. Finally, the fame that Edison achieved with not only this invention but also dozens of others made him an object of attention and adulation for more than half a century after. Journalists, biographers, popularizers, and other writers besieged Edison with regularity, and accounts of the invention of the electric light were among their most popular works. So how can there be more to be known about such an event?

It is perhaps because there has been *too much* information. The vast numbers of documents, now residing in a large vault at Edison's last laboratory, in West Orange, New Jersey, have so intimidated scholars and other researchers that few

Thomas Edison in 1878, age thirty-one.

have attempted a careful combing of them for evidence. The reports in newspapers were always better sources of color and human interest than of reliable technical information. And the half-century of interviews has resulted in a tale jumbled by romantic recollection and the faulty memories of old men.

From all of this have come two pictures of the electric light's creator. The one that has the larger place in the public mind is of the rough-and-ready inventor whose pursuit of the electric light was a dogged hunt through nature's storehouse, a tireless search through thousands of possible substances for the right filament to make a light bulb work. The second, and very different, image is that of the scientific-laboratory chief, a prototype of the modern research manager, who was guided by a vision of a complete electric light and power system and who left the technical details to a skilled, educated staff. As contradictory as these two pictures are, both of them—or some fuzzy composite of the two—have a firm place in not only the popular mythology but in the history books as well.

The new, clearer picture that we are now piecing together comes from a systematic search through the archives at West Orange. For the first time, scholars are recognizing the great potential of the Edison records for revealing the character of the great technological transformations that made over American society in the last decades of the nineteenth century and the first years of the twentieth. Invention, it turns out, is neither a haphazard tinkering nor is it a mechanical application of scientific knowledge. It is a very human activity, filled with the accomplishments and the failings of most endeavors.

The story of the invention of the electric light is a chronicle of people in the midst of the most exciting creative challenge of their lives, working at a frontier of technology. Edison and his colleagues were participants in an enterprise that was part puzzle-solving, part system-building, and part

The New Year's issue of *Puck* in 1880 heralded the recent arrival of Edison's lamp as an event of truly cosmic significance.

hoopla. When Thomas Edison began to think seriously about the problem of the electric light, he was only thirty-one years old, but already he was the most famous inventor in America. Beginning with an improved stock ticker in 1869, his contributions to telegraphy had made him indispensable to the financiers who controlled the most visible "high technology" of the day. In 1876 he had taken his profits and built in the New Jersey countryside an "invention factory," promising a "minor invention every ten days and a big thing every six months or so." The only thing more astonishing than the young Midwesterner's bravado was his success. Challenged

source of Edison's pleasure was not simply what he saw in Connecticut; it was also what he didn't see. A few weeks later he explained to a newspaper reporter: "I saw the thing had not gone so far but that I had a chance. . . . The intense light had not been subdivided so that it could be brought into private homes." Edison was certain that he could "subdivide the light."

There were known to inventors two ways to derive light from electricity. The first was the electric arc, a blindingly bright spark sustained between two pieces of carbon. This was the form of light made by William Wallace and a host of

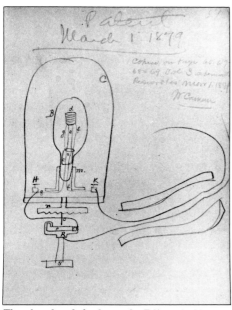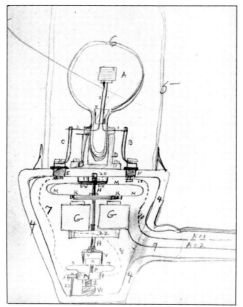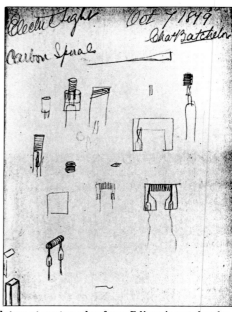

The sketch at left, drawn by Edison in March 1879, shows a would-be lamp with a pneumatic regulator; at center, also from Edison's notebooks, is a slightly later version with an especially complex regulator; the doodles of the carbon spirals, at right, are by Charles Batchelor.

to find a way around Alexander Graham Bell's telephone patents, Edison devised the carbon telephone transmitter and other components for telegraphy's latest wrinkle. Experimenting with means for recording telegraph signals, he came up with his most surprising invention, the phonograph. With this last wonder, Edison became a celebrity.

The burdens of being a celebrity were little different in the 1870s from today. By the middle of 1878 Edison was described as "very tired and ill," worn out by traveling around the country showing off the "machine that talked." That summer he sought a break and took off to the West with a group of scientists who invited him to accompany them to Wyoming to view a solar eclipse. The vacation was, apparently, a great tonic, but conversations with the scientists turned Edison's attention to a new challenge: creating a practical electric light to replace the gas and oil lamps used everywhere.

When he returned east, Edison headed to the workshop of William Wallace in Connecticut. There Wallace, the country's premier brass founder, had on display an electric arc lighting system of his own devising. The newspaper reporter who tagged along described the scene: "Mr. Edison was enraptured . . . eight electric lights were kept ablaze at one time, each being equal to 4,000 candles, the sub-division of electric lights being a thing unknown to science. This filled up Mr. Edison's cup of joy. He sprawled over the table with the simplicity of a child, and made all kinds of calculations." The

other inventors. By the 1870s the availability of practical (though very inefficient) generators made the use of arc lights possible in large public areas, in lighthouses, and on streets. By its nature the electric arc was many times brighter than an ordinary interior lamp—perhaps four thousand candlepower as compared with the ten or twenty of gaslight. The other form of electric light used a current to heat up a material so hot that it became "incandescent." It was well known that an incandescent light, if sustained, could be made moderate enough for common indoor usage. But all substances that could be heated to incandescence were in the process either melted or burned up in the heat. This had been demonstrated by the futile efforts of inventors for several decades. Two distinct approaches emerged: one was to use a material with a moderately high melting point that did not oxidize, such as platinum. This substance, unfortunately, always got too hot and melted despite clever devices to prevent this. The other approach was to use a substance whose melting point was so high as to pose no problem. Carbon was the obvious candidate for this option, but despite the use of vacuum pumps or inert gases, no one had managed to sufficiently protect the carbon in a lamp from combustion.

This was the state of affairs that allowed the newspapers to remark that subdivision—the making of small electric lights —was "unknown to science." Here was a challenge that the superconfident Edison felt was both worthy and ripe. Upon his return to Menlo Park he plunged into several days of intensive experimenting. With the help of his closest assistant, Charles Batchelor, a clever and nimble-fingered Englishman, Edison constructed several lamps using spirals of platinum wire as "burners." These devices were distinguished by regulating mechanisms designed to cut off the current if the platinum approached its melting point. These regulators were combinations of electromagnets, switches, resistances, and levers, familiar features of Edison's telegraph inventions. Certain that finding the right sort of regulator posed little problem, Edison brashly announced that in a matter of weeks he would have all problems in hand.

Nothing emerges more vividly out of the laboratory records, letters, and newspaper interviews from Menlo Park in the early fall of 1878 than Edison's supreme confidence. The confidence was infectious, and Edison's announcement was greeted on the stock exchanges by a precipitious fall in gas stocks and by a clamor from some to secure a piece of the new technology.

Little time was wasted in organizing the Edison Electric Light Company, among whose backers were J. P. Morgan and the Vanderbilt interests. The company assured Edison the funds he needed to perfect his invention, including resources to expand Menlo Park and hire experts. All of this was comforting to Edison, and for several weeks the workers at Menlo Park went about constructing models of the new lamp, testing generators to power the system, and preparing patent applications. Only one problem clouded the picture—the light didn't work. Dozens of regulators were made, using several approaches, all designed to cut off current to the platinum wires or strips as they exceeded safe temperatures. The platinum was formed into a variety of shapes, with the intent of conserving the heat energy put into the lamp while allowing the maximum amount of light to be emitted. In every case the lamp flickered intolerably, the burner melted or broke, or the light was too faint. At this point Edison had made little effort to systematically investigate prior work on incandescent lights or to work out the various elements of the generation and distribution system that he would need. By late fall it was apparent that what he didn't know about electric lighting was at least as important as what he did.

Unfortunately for the inventor's giant ego, this was as clear to some of his financial backers as it was to Edison. In November, therefore, Edison was prevailed upon to hire a young Princeton-trained physicist, Francis Upton, recently returned from graduate training in Germany. In later years some claimed that Upton, with his advanced knowledge of mathematics and physics, was the key member of the Menlo Park team, and this claim has become part of the image of Edison's lab-

Nothing emerges more vividly than Edison's supreme confidence during the fall of 1878.

Edison made this drawing of the successful lamp shortly after its completion.

oratory as a modern scientific establishment. Upton was unquestionably valuable, for he was sharp, eager, and ambitious. But the electric light did not depend on the latest knowledge of physics. Upton's hiring was more important for what it said about Edison and his new line of attack in late 1878 than for the advanced learning it brought to the project. Edison now resolved to find out all he could about every aspect of lighting systems. He and his workers studied old patents, analyzed the work of current rivals, subscribed to the gaslight journals, and set about to begin all over again, still confident but now driven by both the challenges before them and the promises behind them.

At just this point, as the year was ending and the work in the laboratory began to take on the rhythm of a long, hard slog, a technical discovery was made that would set Edison's system apart from all others and provide a key to long-term success. In looking at some rival efforts, Edison and his associates noticed that the amount of electrical current required to operate the systems was quite large. Since Edison was determined to make a lamp that could be used with all the convenience of gaslight and, in particular, could be turned on and off without affecting other lamps, he realized that the lamps would have to be on a "parallel" circuit. In such a circuit, as opposed to a "series" circuit, electric current would be delivered independently to each lamp from the main wires of the circuit. This much was generally known, but the team at Menlo Park observed something else. If a circuit had many lamps on it (and Edison always felt that would be the only economical approach), the delivery of sufficient energy to light each lamp would require either a high voltage or a large current (energy equals voltage times current). Large currents, which everyone else's system relied on, could be carried only by large conductors—resulting in an enormously expensive use of copper. A combination of smaller currents and large voltages would require that each lamp have a high resistance (voltage equals current times resistance). Edison thus decided that his lamp would have to have a high-resistance burner.

This compounded the technical challenge, however. Short pieces of platinum had low resistances, so long spirals of thin thin platinum wire were required. The spirals, on the other hand, always broke easily once they were heated to incandescence. For many months in 1879 Edison and his co-workers struggled to make spirals that would last, all to little avail. Only one thing seemed to improve matters. When the platinum burner was enclosed in a glass globe and the best vacuum pump available had exhausted the air, the life of the glowing burner was measurably longer—reaching a few hours.

Edison's response to this discovery was typical: he insisted on having the finest vacuum pump possible and hired a glassblower to make it and keep it operating.

As 1879 dragged on, progress on the lamp was frustratingly slow. Still, Edison's confidence never flagged. He set his workers to designing and building the other pieces of equipment that would be necessary to make the light work. Much time and energy went into constructing a generator for a high-voltage system, and the result in the summer of 1879 was a radical new design that was the most efficient in the world. Smaller details were not forgotten as Menlo Park yielded fancied designs, at another earnestly watching the progress of some experiment. Sometimes he hastily leaves the busy throng of workmen and for an hour or more is seen by no one. . . . In these moments he is rarely disturbed. If any important question of construction arises on which his advice is necessary the workmen wait. Sometimes they wait for hours in idleness, but at the laboratory such idleness is considered far more profitable than any interference with the inventor while he is in the throes of invention . . ."

The main laboratory at Menlo Park was a two-story white clapboard building one hundred feet long and thirty feet wide.

A February 1880 group portrait at the Menlo Park laboratory shows the large second-floor room with the new electric lights hung in the gas fixtures. Thomas Edison is seated in front of the fabled pipe organ, facing into the camera; Batchelor is the third man from the left.

meters, switches, fuses, insulators, and other paraphernalia.

All this took place in the public eye. Even though Edison's early claims of the imminent demise of gas lighting were now discounted and a few voices of disenchantment could be heard, the general fascination with the happenings in the rural New Jersey laboratory was still lively. This was in part due to the continuing backing of Wall Street for Edison's efforts, although mutterings of dismay were being heard even there. The main source of wonderment, however, was Edison himself and the still fresh image of the Wizard of Menlo Park. The press loved it, of course, and Edison was ever mindful of the advantages of a reputation for working miracles. Eager readers devoured reporters' descriptions of laboratory life, as in this story from the New York *Herald* of January 17, 1879:

"The ordinary rules of industry seem to be reversed at Menlo Park. . . . At six o'clock in the evening the machinists and electricians assemble in the laboratory. Edison is already present, attired in a suit of blue flannel, with hair uncombed and straggling over his eyes . . . his hands and face somewhat begrimed and his whole air that of a man with a purpose and indifferent to everything save that purpose. By a quarter past six the quiet laboratory has become transformed into a hive of industry. The hum of machinery drowns all other sounds and each man is at his particular post. . . . Edison himself flits about, first to one bench, then to another, examining here, instructing there; at one place drawing out new

Most of the activity was on the second floor, a single room lined with bottle-laden shelves and filled with tables cluttered with electrical and chemical apparatus. The most conspicuous feature of the room was a large pipe organ on the back wall, a gift from an admirer who felt Edison and "the gang" needed some diversion in their long nights of work. The sound of organ music in the middle of the night coming from the hilltop building marked by the occasional strange glow from the windows heightened the mysterious atmosphere that seemed to surround Menlo Park. When, in May 1879, Edison publicly announced a worldwide search for new sources of platinum, a New York tabloid featured him on its cover, complete with wizard's robe and hat. Never before or since was one man or one place so closely identified with the strange miracles of the modern age.

In mid-1879, however, it looked as though only a true miracle would salvage the reputation of Menlo Park. The platinum lamp simply could not be made to work. When investors insisted on inspecting the work that had already cost them tens of thousands of dollars, Edison's staff made a number of low-resistance lamps that, at best, lasted a few hours. High-resistance devices were impossible to keep glowing for any time at all. The only thing that improved the behavior of the lamps was increasing the vacuum in their bulbs, so better vacuum pumps continued to be made. By fall Edison had reached the limits for improving the platinum lamp.

Such limits are constantly encountered in the chronicles of human creativity. An individual, driven by vision, imagination, and ambition into new and uncharted territory, will often reach the boundaries of the possibilities held out by a once promising direction. What then determines the changes in direction that yield up the special prize—the creation that makes a difference in the world and that marks the creator forever as different from his fellows? In the case of Edison's electric light, as in so many others, this is not an easily solved puzzle. In October 1879, faced with the unhappy results of more than a year of arduous and expensive labor, Edison changed direction. In a matter of weeks, the missing element of his invention was put in place; no one from that time forth was allowed to doubt the success of the electric light.

The missing element was carbon. But this time it was not the carbon lamp tried by dozens of inventors before, only to burn up or disintegrate—it was carbon in the incredibly high vacuum of Edison's bulbs. Carbon was a familiar material, indispensable to the telephone inventions that still occupied Edison's attention from time to time. In the middle of October, Batchelor and Upton jotted down in their notebooks measurements of carbon's resistance and some ideas on how it might be shaped into spirals. The efforts to make spirals, however, turned out to be fruitless—they always broke in the attempt to put them in bulbs. Finally, on the twenty-second of the month, Batchelor recorded "some very interesting experiments" using just a few inches of carbonized cotton thread. Put into a lamp, the short length of thread measured a resistance of a hundred ohms—many times that of platinum. What was more, the carbon lamp glowed almost as brightly as a gas lamp without flickering out.

One of the legends to grow up around the electric light was the story of a lamp, lit on October 21 and lasting forty hours, that provided a moment of clear triumph for the group at Menlo Park. For many years, electric companies celebrated the date as Electric Light Day, and October 21, 1929, was chosen as the day to honor Edison at Light's Golden Jubilee. But records from the laboratory give no evidence of this "breakthrough" lamp. The dramatic moment was perhaps a necessary creation of the memories of people who, understandably, recalled in later years their work as a romantic quest, capped by a single shining moment. We learn, however, that invention is rarely romantic but instead shares the messiness and uncertainty of most creative human endeavors.

After a few more days of testing it became clear that the carbon lamp was the answer. During the next few weeks Edison and his assistants made variations on the new lamp to learn all they could about it. They clearly marveled at the result, for the lamp that emerged was as wonderful for its sim-

We learn that invention shares the messiness and uncertainty of most human endeavors.

By 1880 Francis Upton could already depict the bulb as a glowing little tycoon.

plicity as for its light. A simple evacuated glass globe, in it mounted nothing but a short, black piece of carbonized sewing thread, the new lamp was very different from the bulky, expensive, and complex platinum devices around which the experimenters had built their hopes. Francis Upton, in a letter home in mid-November, exclaimed: "Just at the present I am very much elated at the prospects of the Electric Light. During the past week Mr. Edison has succeeded in obtaining the first lamp that answers the purpose we have wished. It is cheap—much more so than we ever hoped to have."

Little time was wasted in letting the anxious investors know that an important discovery had been made. Several of them took the Pennsylvania Railroad to the little Menlo Park stop to see for themselves that Edison was not bluffing. The inventor showed an unusual reluctance, however, to let the press in on the story—at least until he was ready. Finally he invited a reporter to get a full account of the invention, swearing him to secrecy. When the New York *Herald* for December 21 appeared carrying Marshall Fox's full-page story on the lamp, Edison was reported to be livid at the breach of confidence. The displeasure was short-lived, however, for, in truth, preparations for a public demonstration were well advanced. The workers in the laboratory had been kept busy for weeks making lamps, having discovered that bristol board made more reliable filaments than thread, while others had begun to install lamps in nearby homes, including Edison's and Upton's. A grand public display was scheduled for New Year's Eve, and hundreds of the curious, aroused by a steady stream of newspaper stories, flocked to the laboratory, heedless of a winter storm.

The crowds that thronged into Menlo Park were made up of curiosity seekers and newshounds after the latest sensation. But they represented something more; they stood for a new relationship between advanced technology and the common man. Edison's electric light was as mystifying and awe-inspiring as any invention of the age. Few things could have been more marvelous than the piece of charred paper glowing bright enough in its glass container to light up a room and yet not burning up. The magic represented by scientific technology was a source of unalloyed hope, not distrust. This attitude toward the powers of science and technology is one of the nineteenth century's most important legacies, and no single instance better represents it than the enthusiasm with which the crowds ushered in the new decade at Menlo Park. ∎

Robert Friedel, professor of history at the University of Maryland, is the author of *Pioneer Plastic: The Making and Selling of Celluloid* (Wisconsin, 1983) and *Zipper: An Exploration in Novelty* (W. W. Norton & Company, 1994).

Thomas P. Hughes sits atop a triumph of nineteenth-century technology in front of his 1961 Philadelphia home, designed by the architect Robert Venturi.

America's Golden Age

This historian believes the nation's technological flowering
from 1870 to 1970 will be compared someday to the Renaissance in Italy

An Interview with Thomas P. Hughes by Arthur P. Molella

Who are the real makers of modern America? Not the politicians or the business magnates, according to Thomas Parke Hughes, Mellon Professor of the History and Sociology of Science at the University of Pennsylvania, but the inventor-entrepreneurs, industrial scientists, and engineers who contributed to the golden age of American technology between 1870 and 1970. They created the vast systems shaping modern life—systems such as the Tennessee Valley Authority, the Manhattan Project, and the automobile industry. One of the pioneering practitioners of the history of technology, Hughes, sixty-five, has devoted a lifetime to understanding the people and institutions that have set America and Western Civilization on their current technological course. In his biography of the inventor and engineer Elmer Sperry, published in 1971, Hughes provided a case study of one of America's first professional inventor-entrepreneurs. In his next book, *Networks of Power* (1983), he developed the concept of technological systems that has become his hallmark. (Both these books won the prestigious Dexter Prize of the Society for the History of Technology.)

In his most recent book, *American Genesis: A Century of Invention and Technological Enthusiasm, 1870-1970* (Viking Penguin, 1989), he develops a sweeping new technological interpretation of United States history. Lavishly illustrated, *American Genesis* is addressed to general audiences as well as to historical specialists, in keeping with Hughes's determination to make the history of technology an integral part of general history. He describes America as a nation of builders and artifact makers—artifacts that have come to include the whole man-made landscape. And he reveals how the rest of the world has sometimes perceived this better than we Americans. In *American Genesis* Hughes—who is also Torsten Althin Professor at the Royal Institute of Technology in Stockholm—shows how figures as different as V. I. Lenin and Walter Gropius fashioned a modern European culture around American technological genius.

This interview took place last December in Hughes's home, a house in Philadelphia is designed by the postmodern architect Robert Venturi.

You were trained as an electrical engineer, and you obviously have a continuing interest in engineering. What induced you to shift to the history of technology?
I had two years of liberal arts college, at the University of Richmond, before I went into engineering, and I enjoyed the liberal arts very much. After three years in the Navy in World War II and getting my engineering degree at the University of Virginia, I had the opportunity to use the GI Bill to continue my education. Agatha and I had recently married; this was 1948. I was working as a manufacturer's representative, and we decided that we would like instead to have an academic life. So back we went to the University of Virginia. The people there told me I was foolish to give up a good job to go for a graduate degree in history, but we stuck it out.

Were there any figures who were particularly important in drawing you to the history of technology?
In the 1950s, while I was teaching, Lynn White gave lectures that were later incorporated in his book *Medieval Technology and Social Change*. I had the good fortune to meet him. Not only did White and his book give me a perspective on how encompassing the history of technology could be, but also it was very encouraging to find a scholar of his reputation and high standards doing the history of technology.

You are about to come out with a major new synthesis, *American Genesis*. The title suggests that you're dealing with something more than the history of technology, doesn't it?

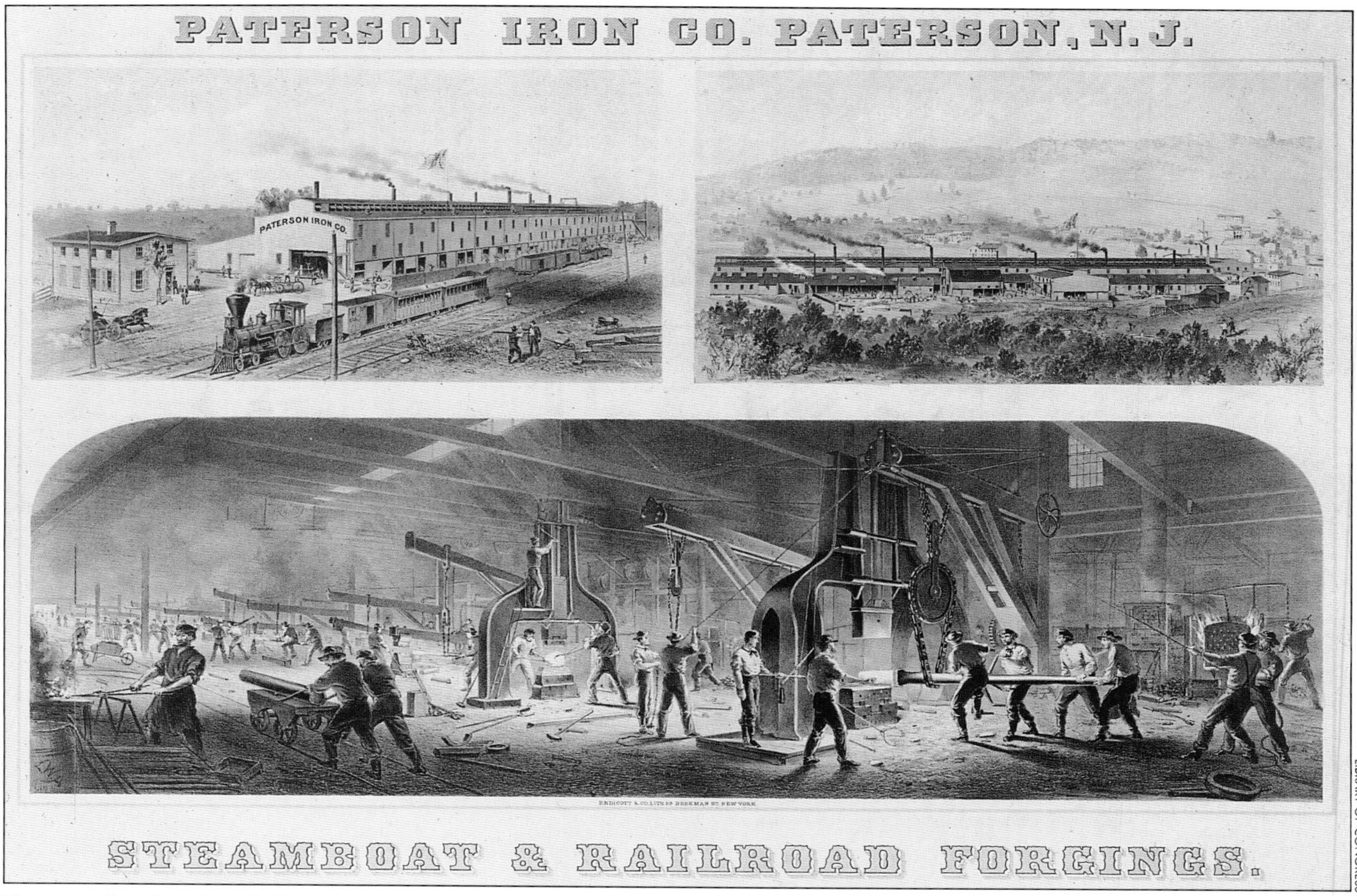

LIBRARY OF CONGRESS

The emerging American industrial landscape is depicted in an 1850s lithograph of the Paterson ironworks in Paterson, New Jersey.

Yes. I consider my new book a history that focuses on technology, rather than just a history of technology, which implies narrow specialization. My colleagues and I are historians who are interested in technology. There are other historians who are interested in politics and economics. I do not wish to see our field become—or continue to be—a field of specialization. It should be recognized as a part of general history, and a very important one. I think technology and science are at the core of historical developments in the twentieth century.

Over the centuries, we've made a wilderness into an artifact. We are a nation of builders.

It has been suggested that you are almost calling for a revision of Turner's frontier hypothesis. He said the grand theme of American history was the conquest of the frontier; you seem to say the grand theme now is the technological transformation of that former frontier.

I wouldn't go so far as to compare my theme to Frederick Jackson Turner's, which is a remarkably memorable one. But I would say that the theme of twentieth-century America could be encompassed by the expression "a nation of builders." I was careful not to use that expression too prominently in the book because "builders" suggests only bridges and railroads. By builders I mean people who wish to construct an artifact. And the world can be an artifact. A city can be an artifact. A painting can be an artifact. We have transformed a wilderness into an artifact in these several centuries of American history, so we're a nation of builders. I think this is an admirable theme for historians to rally about as they write of modern America.

***American Genesis* is to my knowledge one of the only scholarly surveys of American technology for the modern period. Why did you think it important to write such a book?**

I suppose the answer is the question, Why did I think it was important about fifteen years ago to begin teaching a course on American history since 1870? I did so because I think that when our history is looked back upon a hundred years from now, this century, roughly from 1870 to 1970, will be seen as one that was dominated by the creation of technologies. It will be compared to such remarkable eras as the Renaissance period in Italy or the Victorian period in Great Britain.

If the past one hundred years were indeed a golden century for America, why don't Americans themselves seem to want to celebrate it as such?

I'm of the opinion that most people who have been writing American history over, say, the past seventy-five years have concentrated on its verbal manifestations; they have tended not to be interested in *things*. They have been people who think of culture as artistic or verbal expression. So they have wished this country would express itself in high culture as it is traditionally defined—art and so on. But that's putting on blinders. I think that making artifacts—defined broadly—is highly creative, intelligent work.

I do think we're becoming a little more confident about ourselves. We're less deferential to the Europeans for their high culture, say, and for our supposed lack of high culture in the United States. And we're beginning to face up to ourselves as we are. When we fully realize that we are builders and creators, we'll begin to write more about this and analyze this characteristic more carefully and even celebrate it as a strength, without being sentimental.

There is the irony, however, that Europeans seem to identify us with the technological and to celebrate our culture of technology more than we do ourselves. Can you explain that?
The European architects, artists, and writers who flourished and were reaching the public between the wars felt, I think, that America was the modern technologically creative nation. But they also saw that we lacked the confidence to transform this creative activity of ours in America into a coherent cultural expression—that is, into a cultural expression in the traditional sense of architectural, artistic, and verbal expression, into the signs and symbols that capture the meaning of a people or a society. For instance, around 1910 the Italian futurist painters expressed the dynamism of the technological and industrial city. A few years later the German avant-garde architects developed the International Style architecture, which expressed itself through the use of the rectilinear and planar surfaces associated with machine design. These avant-garde Europeans knew we had the most advanced technology, but they also knew we had not yet articulated it culturally, and they believed they could do so because they understood that the essence of modernity was technology. This was a vision we lacked.

I'm puzzled because even though Europeans might perceive Americans as nonreflective or perhaps nonartistic, it's hard to believe that we're all that different from them.
We were that different in the first quarter of this century. Judging by what was being painted and the way it was being painted in this country, with notable exceptions, we were derivative. Of our architecture, for instance, Le Corbusier asked in the twenties, How can Americans work in an environment of modern technology yet be so derivative?

Would this imply that the true fulfillment of our golden age, as you term it, depended on what the Europeans made of us?
Definitely. I think people such as Marcel Duchamp, Le Corbusier, Gropius, Ludwig Mies van der Rohe, and others gave us the self-confidence to be aware of and reflect on our own remarkable characteristics. They contributed greatly to this self-confidence. Remember that both Gropius and Mies came over to the United States in the thirties. Others of the avant-garde had come over earlier, and they greatly influenced our artists, architects, and cultural critics.

And Europeans still appreciate the basic American genius that was involved in generating our technology?

Definitely. Even today they have not forgotten Henry Ford or Thomas Edison or the TVA. Europeans are no strangers to Route 128 or Silicon Valley. They see us as the creators of a technological world, and they greatly admire us for it.

***American Genesis* deals extensively with European developments. Is it really meaningful to speak about American technology per se, or are we actually dealing with nothing but differences in national styles?**
I don't recognize high or rigid borders between nations in technology and science. American technology, at least in the twentieth century, cannot be categorically distinguished from European technology. But it's meaningful to speak, for contrast, of American technology just as it's meaningful to speak of American art and American architecture. The essential, or primary, characteristics of modern technology ex-

Umberto Boccioni's *Unique Forms of Continuity in a Space* (1913) embodies the dynamic spirit of the futurist movement.

tend over the borders of industrialized nations and between Europe and the United States.

You describe American technology as a definite shaping force on modern Europe between the wars. Yet wasn't the United States politically and diplomatically isolationist in this period?
We had a remarkable influence on the Europeans between the wars, one deriving from our astounding ability to produce consumer goods for a mass—some would say democratic—market. Automobiles, radios, incandescent lights, and so on. But we were not so much offering ourselves to the Europeans for emulation as they were enviously looking in our direction. The Europeans were trying to fathom the workings of our great machine of production. It was easy for them to penetrate the political barriers of isolationism to obtain our technology. We exported technologies in large quantities in the interwar years, to the Soviet Union especially, and also to other parts of Europe. And not only were we exporting what is now called hardware, but we were exporting

A panel from James M. Newell's 1930s mural *The Evolution of Western Civilization* celebrates the achievements of twentieth-century man.

the ideas associated with our production, ideas that the Europeans then called Fordism, after Henry Ford, and Taylorism, after Frederick W. Taylor, the father of scientific management, who pioneered time-and-motion studies and strove to rationalize the workplace.

The American-Soviet relationship was very interesting in this regard.

In the pre–World War II period, the Soviet Union, under the influence of its Bolshevik leaders, Lenin especially, looked to us, as did other Europeans, as the epitome of the modern—not only of modern technology but also, potentially, of modern culture. The Russians desperately wanted and needed technology from the United States.

The leaders of the Soviet Union thought that they could remove the capitalistic characteristics from our technology, salvage the essential productiveness of America, and then transform it into a Soviet-Russian phenomenon, a Soviet modern technology that would be the great next stage in world technological development. So they were quite excited about the modernness of the United States, and they were great admirers of people such as Ford and Taylor. On the more intellectual level, many of the Soviet leaders admired the symbols and architecture and art of modern technological culture.

A unique aspect of your book is your interest in the story of European architecture, design, and even avant-garde painting and sculpture. What drew you in general into the study of these and their relationships with technology?

> Technology is not neutral; it imposes its own values, and they have permeated our culture.

My wife, Agatha, is a student of the history of art and architecture and is also a ceramic artist. She's had a great influence on me in this regard. Living in this house, we became good friends with the architect, Robert Venturi, and Denise Scott Brown, his wife and partner, and from them both I learned a great deal about postmodern and modern architecture. I learned from them that postmodernism is a reaction against the technological emphasis of the International Style architecture, which had its beginnings between the wars. This bolstered my conviction that the technological content of International Style architecture was worth exploring in detail. So motivated, I looked and found the technological content in Gropius, in Le Corbusier, and in others. For example, I went into the Gropius archives and found that Gropius in the twenties referred explicitly to Fordism and Taylorism, Ford methods and Taylor methods.

Do you believe that artists and architects helped articulate the cultural values inherent in technology?

Technology played a major role in the rise of International Style architecture and modern art because the values that are incorporated in technology were transferred to architecture and art. I do not accept the argument, and haven't for years, that technology is value-free. It's laden with values. And by values I refer in this case to technology's tendency to reinforce controlling, systematizing, ordering behavior. These values have permeated our culture in this century, and they were derived primarily from our technology. Artists have antennae out, and they sense the order, the control, the systemization, and the efficiency. And so you find artists and architects expressing these values in their work—people like Charles Sheeler and Charles Demuth, American artists of the first half of this century. Other artists react against these values, and that's still an influence of technology. These artists tried to break up, to deconstruct the order and control of modern technology in their paintings.

It seems here that your goal is to elucidate the human dimension of technology, to explore the moral values inherent in it. For example, in *American Genesis* you detail the eventful and tragic life of Samuel Insull, who built a vast electric-power network extending out from Chicago, greatly overextended himself, and died bankrupt and disgraced.

The moral element is certainly a major concern, again because I think of creating technology as one of our most fulfilling, creative activities. If one goes back to some of the basic books of Western civilization, including the Book of Genesis in the Old Testament, one will find that humans are defined by and find expression in making things. Hannah Arendt made a nice contrast between labor and work. She stressed that unlike mere labor, work is leaving something behind; it is changing the face of the earth in a way that is lasting. When we have human involvement, then we have morality, tragedy, mistakes, embarrassments, complexity, and contradiction. The human involvement that we take for granted in political history is just as important in the history of technology.

Is there a connection between technology and freedom?

I would say there is a tension between freedom and technology. Technology can greatly restrain our freedom. I think of technology as systems, as large systems with momentum. They can restrain our freedom much as can a bureaucracy in its hierarchical and high-inertia way. So we have to be very alert to make sure we use technology as a way of establishing and utilizing freedom. Technology can reinforce the value of freedom if we are cunning and energetic enough to make it do this. For instance, we can use communications technology to convey to people truthful information that they need in a democracy to make political decisions—or we can use communications systems to transmit the half-truths of a government wanting to manipulate and constrain. Energy technology can be used in environmentally benign ways to provide free access to clean air, water, and wilderness—or used so that our access to nature is severely constrained. This does not mean technology is neutral. Once in place, it can be inherently democratic or authoritarian.

Are you pessimistic about the future vitality of American technology? Do you perhaps see a life cycle to technological societies such as our own?

I'm primarily concerned about the vitality not of our technology but of our culture, since I'm arguing that our culture, especially our values, shapes technology. A major reason I'm concerned is because of the phenomenon that I've labeled "technological momentum." We become committed to the technological systems that we have created, and as a result, these technological systems have a high momentum, a high mass, a high velocity. Millions of people are committed to the way technology is being done in this country and used here. They live off the way it's done and used. Their values shape it and in turn are reinforced by it. Their skills depend on it. And it's hard for people who are so committed to

existing technology to change course. Consider how difficult it is now to change a system of nuclear-weapon production that emphasizes output and not the reduction of environmental hazards.

It's amazing how many of our leaders and thinkers are not well informed about technological change. They think technology is infinitely flexible, that you can change your technology tomorrow. That is not the case. Technology has all the momentum, the conservatism, of politics, and it takes years, even decades, to change it. Now, the question is, How deeply are we still committed to technological systems that may have taken essential shape in the twenties and thirties in this country—that is, mass-production technology, centralized technology, environmentally insensitive hierarchical technology, systematized technology? And if we are deeply committed to such systems, if we're conservatively dedicated to this kind of technology, we may be on a trajectory that does not allow us to solve new problems in new ways. A case in point is the military-industrial-university complex. Hundreds of thousands of people are committed to this way of doing technology and make a living from it. It will take a remarkable set of circumstances to move people off this trajectory, even if some of the problems that the technology was designed to solve no longer exist. Some argue that our aircraft carriers and long-range bombers are examples of that.

Your book compares today's huge technological systems to the dinosaurs. Environmental catastrophes destroyed them.

It may take technological catastrophe to make us rethink our patterns and our commitment. Take the great oil spills. They did make us think about the environment and what we were doing to it. Likewise Three Mile Island. And of course, Chernobyl recently forced people throughout the world to rethink the place of atomic energy.

When our technological systems have a high momentum, one needs a force of equal magnitude and velocity to change their character and direction. The demise of the dinosaur is comparable. Some scientists think a natural catastrophe eliminated the conditions needed for the survival of the dinosaur. Technological catastrophes could frighten us into changing our commitment to existing technology.

Knowing what we do now about the Chernobyl disaster and others, and with the wisdom of hindsight, how can you refer to the period between 1870 and 1970 as a golden age if these are the fruits of that century?

Well, there are problems in golden eras. There are problems in good lives and great lives, as we know. We no longer celebrate heroes uncritically. We shouldn't celebrate our golden age uncritically. In the beginning of the golden century, Americans were fantastically creative. They were dealing with a more or less open situation, and they embarked upon the creation of the systems of production that we associate with Ford and Taylor. By the twenties they had these systems in place, and the modern technological spirit of the century was being well articulated by engineers and managers and artists and architects. Then, as we moved into the period of World War II and after, there was a certain hardening of the arteries. We were producing well; we were in a groove. The American World War II effort was certainly an impressive expression of productive power even if it was necessarily focused on instruments of war. Since World War II we have moved into, shall we say, a postmature age, in which we are trying to repeat our successes, trying to recover the values of the past, and we're not willing enough to set out on a new course, to cast off some of the ballast of the past and move on to something new, possibly even dan-

The architect Le Corbusier applied a characteristically modernist look to the Dominican monastery of La Tourette, near Lyons, France, 1960.

gerous, but challenging. We are too often offering old solutions to new problems.

Throughout your writings you show an ambivalence toward the corporate and bureaucratic efforts that built the large technological systems like our electric-power grids. On the one hand, you see them as imposing order on chaos; on the other, you seem to have a very warm spot for the solitary inventor, who is increasingly an anachronism in our times.

W̲e are still deeply committed to systems that took shape in the twenties and thirties.

The people most responsible for the great burst of creativity in the early years of this century were the independent inventors. I admire them for their creative spirit. I associate them with Renaissance artists and the great Victorian engineers. You might call them free spirits. But their work was responsible for creating the systems that would make it difficult for those of us who live later to be as free in our creative activity. That's the paradox. In Thomas Mann's *Doctor Faustus* there's a wonderful section in which he describes the attitudes of a young composer toward music. The composer wants to discover a system of creation. And Mann uses Mephistopheles to show that if one finds a system for creativity, then one is no long-

er freely creating. Mephistopheles offers the young man a system. And in this way he destroys the young man's creativity.

We Americans have created a system, a remarkable system of mass production. And this in a sense restrains our creativity, at least along this trajectory. So I go back to the other question: What will we be able to do to break out from this constraint? I'd suggest, as did some socially responsible counterculture persons, that we concentrate on inventing technology to solve radically different problems, such as environmental ones.

You have long expressed admiration for the work of the cultural critic Lewis Mumford. In *American Genesis* you invoke him in your final chapters on the counterculture. How would you compare your own views with Lewis Mumford's?
I first read Mumford decades ago when I was in graduate school. I was impressed by the intellectual vitality of his concepts. But at the time I wanted my own concepts, my own generalizations, to emerge from the sources, so I was not inclined in my bones to accept Mumford's generalizations. I forgot Mumford for years. And then, as I began to write this book, I found myself saying, "Gee, now wait. I've run across this idea of mine somewhere before." For example, consider the social-construction idea that's so popular today among historians—the notion that society shapes the technology much more than the technology shapes society. When Mumford wrote *Technics and Civilization* in 1934, he argued that values shape technology. So as I was writing this new book, I began to reread Mumford, and I got reinforcement and stimulation and some refinement of my ideas.

Do you share any of his deep pessimism that emerged, for example, in the *Pentagon of Power*, in which he rails against the military-industrial complex?
I'm not as pessimistic as Mumford. He uses the concept of the megamachine, a technological supersystem such as the military-industrial complex. And at times he seems to think that the megamachine cannot be put off its course. I have confidence that if we become more aware of the nature of technology, of the humanness of technology, of the capacity we have to construct our technology socially, we can better control our large technological systems and redirect them.

I suppose I feel more confident than he because much of his pessimism came out of the immediate postwar period. I am writing decades after the war, and I see greater possibilities for getting control of, say, atomic energy, whereas he was laboring under the shadow of Hiroshima and Nagasaki. But his oppressive megamachine is my technological system. His megamachine has the momentum I discuss. Both he and I are deeply concerned. ★

Arthur P. Molella is chairman of the Department of the History of Science and Technology at the National Museum of American History, and is the former book review editor of the journal *Technology and Culture*.

SILVER from CLAY

by Robert Friedel

How a twenty-two-year-old in a woodshed developed the process that transformed aluminum from a precious rarity into one of the most inexpensive and common metals

The first pellets of pure aluminum produced by Charles Hall in February 1886 sit in a chest kept by Alcoa. They are known in the aluminum industry as the "crown jewels."

Aluminum is a paradox. It is a material associated with the most exotic of high technologies, such as space shuttles and jet aircraft, and—at the same time—it is used for the most mundane of objects, such as the cheapest pots and pans. It often seems weak and insubstantial, yet its strength by weight exceeds that of steel. It may gleam with a shininess rivaled by few other materials, or its surface may simply be dull, even drab. Aluminum reveals its greatest paradox, however, in its history, for while it is the most common metal in the earth's crust, it was completely unknown before the nineteenth century, and for much of that century it was considered one of the most precious materials in the world.

The great change in aluminum's status started a century ago in a couple of crude workrooms, one in the small Ohio college town of Oberlin, the other in the Paris suburb of Gentilly. In a striking case of simultaneous discovery, two amateur chemists, Charles Martin Hall in the United States and Paul L. T. Héroult in France, devised a means for using electricity to separate metallic aluminum from the oxygen that tightly binds to it in nature. Their 1886 invention was the culmination of a search that had frustrated some of the finest chemists in the world for several generations, and it laid the foundation for one of the mighty industries of the twentieth century.

The stories of Hall and Héroult are versions of a familiar tale of old-fashioned invention: ambitious young men working largely on their own, applying persistence, sweat, and a bright idea or two in search of the lucky chance. In 1886 both men were twenty-two years old and just starting out in their life's work. Both were well educated, though by no means of an academic bent. And both men were driven not by some deeply felt need for the new metal or by a professional challenge, but simply by the desire to become successful inventors.

The production of cheap aluminum was, in the late nineteenth century, the dream of many who sought to become rich and famous through invention. In 1884 *The New York Times* said that the "philosopher's stone has not been sought with greater eagerness than this cheap process." However, the magic of aluminum was rooted less in the uses to which the metal would be put than in a faith that aluminum was one of nature's greatest marvels, just waiting for the ingenuity of modern science to make it available. In fact, it took decades to develop the technologies that would make significant use of aluminum. But the dreams of the era still served to push the new metal to the forefront of the hopes and aspirations of men like Hall, Héroult, and the many experimenters who preceded them.

The dreams began, like many others, with chemistry. The first decades of the nineteenth century saw a great burst of chemical discovery as new techniques and new tools were exploited by some of the most imaginative and creative minds in science. At London's Royal Institution, from 1807 to 1809, Humphry Davy embarked on a spectacular series of experiments in which he isolated for the first time a host of elements, including potassium, sodium, magnesium, boron, and silicon. He theorized about the existence of other elements that his methods were not adequate to isolate. One of these was the supposed

Piles of aluminum ingots stretch into the distance outside a factory in Quebec. The Hall-Héroult process is used in almost all production worldwide.

STEVE DUNWELL/THE IMAGE BANK

metallic base of the common mineral alumina, and this Davy first dubbed *alumium*, later changing this name to *aluminum*. This was later changed to *aluminium*—the name still in use in Britain—since the *ium* ending seemed more consistent with similar element names. From Davy's time on, the search for metallic aluminum was a common goal of chemists.

It was almost twenty years before a detectable, though still very impure, sample was prepared. The great German chemist Friedrich Wöhler vaporized some aluminum chloride and reacted it with heated potassium. The little metallic flecks that appeared in the product were almost certainly aluminum, but they were too small and contaminated to study. Another

The magic of aluminum lay less in known uses for it than in a faith that it would be a marvel.

two decades later, in 1845, Wöhler returned to the aluminum problem and improved his method sufficiently to yield pinhead-size globules of the metal. With these he could determine some of aluminum's properties, and he was particularly struck by its lightness. The tiny pieces of metal, ex-

tracted with painstaking effort by a skillful experimenter in a well-equipped laboratory, were of considerable academic interest but otherwise caused no excitement.

Such was not the case a few years later, however, when Henri Sainte-Claire Deville, at Paris's Ecole Normale, accidentally made the first sizable chunks of aluminum. Deville had simply been attempting to make a new aluminum compound when he tried a variation of Wöhler's process that substituted sodium for potassium and ended up with enough aluminum to study the substance extensively. When Deville announced his results to the French Academy of Sciences in 1854, he was unabashedly enthusiastic about the prospect of

Julia Hall

The house in Oberlin. The woodshed where Hall did much of his work is probably the attached structure to the right.

Charles Hall

making aluminum commercial.

There followed a kind of aluminum craze; still, little was known about what the metal might be used for. The price was too high for all but the most luxurious applications. Deville was able, after much work, to sell his aluminum for about seventeen dollars per pound. An exhibit of aluminum at the Paris Exposition of 1855, where it was billed as "silver from clay," spurred popular interest. One of the first objects fashioned from Deville's aluminum was a baby rattle for the emperor's new son, and more objects were soon made—opera glasses, jewelry, and table items. Aluminum was indeed seen as a new kind of silver.

One English commentator predicted its usefulness for surgeons and the makers of piano wire and even, if it would ever be cheap enough, for the roofs of houses! An American lecturer described the day when the new metal would be used for everything from scientific instruments to bells—a little-known quality of pure aluminum is its wonderful musical resonance when struck. An American writer proclaimed that "just now, in this new metal, so long concealed in every hill-side, and even in the very dust of our streets, science seems about to make over to the arts one of her occasional bestowments, by which both the knowledge and power of our race are, at an instant, so widely increased."

These comments appeared in the popular *National Magazine* about six years before Charles Hall was born. They represented, however, an atti-

tude that was to influence Hall and many like him in the bustling world of post–Civil War America. The Oberlin in which Hall grew up was a small village built around its college, an institution that soon after its founding, in 1834, had become notable for its liberalism. Heman Bassett Hall graduated from the college in 1847, entered the ministry, and returned to Oberlin in 1874 with his wife, two sons, and five daughters.

A small-town minister's life was not a prosperous one, so it is particularly remarkable that the Halls sent to the college not only their sons but their daughters as well. Julia Hall, four years senior to Charles and a lifelong correspondent and friend to her bachelor brother, acquired a solid scientific training at Oberlin and was well prepared to be a full partner in Charles's experimental endeavors.

Julia was in the middle of her college education when Charles entered Oberlin in the fall of 1880. That year a new chemistry professor arrived at Oberlin, Frank F. Jewett, a graduate of Yale who had studied in Germany and at Harvard and had taught for four years at the Japanese Imperial University in Tokyo. Jewett was to provide Charles Hall with his education in chemistry and give him his first introduction to aluminum. He would tell his students of meeting the elderly Wöhler while studying in Germany and hearing directly from him what a wonderful substance aluminum seemed to be.

One other professor at Oberlin in-

fluenced the career and outlook of the would-be inventor. Elisha Gray taught the course in which Hall learned about electricity, which would be the key to solving the aluminum problem. And at the time Hall was his student, Gray was still trying to stake his claim as the inventor of the telephone. Four years previously, Gray's description of his invention had been delayed in getting to the U.S. Patent Office and thus had arrived several hours after the application of Alexander Graham Bell. This well-known cautionary tale taught Hall not only the importance of witnesses and records for establishing the priority of an invention, but also the need for quickly following up experiments that showed technical promise.

Charles spent his summers earning money for college expenses by selling books to farmers in the Ohio countryside, and during these trips he would write home, often describing inventive fancies. At the end of one such letter he promised Julia, "I really think I shall be a rich inventor some day."

During his later college years, Hall read about Deville's work and encountered the remark that "every clay bank was a mine of aluminum and that the metal was as costly as silver." From Professor Jewett he received access to working space in the college laboratory, and in various corners of the family home on East College Street he set up workbenches for his experiments and proceeded to duplicate most of the futile efforts of two generations of chemists.

The chemical reduction of aluminum from its oxide was a well-understood process. Deville's method consisted of making aluminum chloride by reacting chlorine gas with alumina and carbon. Adding sodium chloride (common salt) to this reaction produced sodium-aluminum chloride. In the next stage of the process, this double chloride was heated with sodium to yield more sodium chloride and aluminum metal. The problem was the high cost of producing the aluminum chloride and, even more significantly, the cost of metallic sodium. Many experimenters concentrated on trying to make these ingredients less expensive.

The first experiment of the college student–inventor was simply to mix clay with carbon and fire the mixture (just as one might heat iron ore with charcoal to reduce out iron). From this naive and futile beginning, Hall moved on to trying to make aluminum chloride more cheaply, just as had many before him. Seeing little

Hall wrote to his sister, "I really think I shall be a rich inventor some day."

progress, he then returned to what he felt was still the basic, if elusive, promise—making the metal directly from its abundant oxide. More mixtures of alumina and carbon, with various reducing agents added, were tried, all to no avail.

In his senior year at Oberlin, the would-be inventor experimented with new copper alloys, with an improved electric battery, and with better filaments for the Edison electric light (itself invented only five years before). "Whenever I get temporarily stuck on any other process," he

wrote his brother George, "I go to work on a cheap process for aluminum."

At this time events moved to bring aluminum back to the center of Hall's attention permanently. In November of 1884 publicity was given to the first significant effort to produce aluminum in America, by William Frishmuth in Philadelphia. A few weeks later, the Cleveland *Leader* carried a report that on December 6—Charles Hall's twenty-first birthday—the most important product of Frishmuth's work, a hundred-ounce cast-aluminum pyramid, had been placed atop the newly completed Washington Monument as a lightning conductor. So precious and rare was this piece that it had been displayed at Tiffany & Co. in New York.

When Charles Hall graduated from Oberlin on July 1, 1885, he gave a commencement address titled "Science and the Imagination." The joy of the occasion was dampened by the death of his mother only a couple of

The Making of an Industry

The Pittsburgh Reduction Company's first reliable customer was, ironically, the Pittsburgh steel industry; a small quantity of pure aluminum added to the giant crucibles of molten steel readily absorbed harmful gases without changing the quality of the steel. But a pound or two was adequate for a ton of steel, and the backers of the new metal had no intention of simply being minor suppliers to the makers of what they considered aluminum's primary rival.

The path by which aluminum became the world's second most important metal was tortuous. In 1893, when the aluminum makers showed a sample of a teakettle to one of the country's leading utensil

manufacturers, Ely Griswold, he refused to try to work the new metal himself but agreed to sell two thousand kettles if the Pittsburgh Reduction Company would make them. This forced the company into the fabrication business. But aluminum cookware in the late 1890s cost about six times more than comparable tin items.

From the beginning, the aluminum makers sought their key outlets in high technology. In the 1890s this meant electric power. But only in special situations was the metal attractive, such as in the 1897 installation of aluminum telephone lines around the Chicago stockyards, where locomotive fumes corroded copper wires. The development of steel-rein-

forced aluminum cable at the beginning of the new century finally offered an attractive substitute for copper, and more than 90 percent of overhead electrical transmission is now carried through aluminum.

Another high technology that aluminum rode to success was aviation. The gasoline-powered engine that propelled the Wright brothers' *Flyer I* off the sands at Kitty Hawk in 1903 contained aluminum, and the attraction of a light metal in flight was self-evident. The Liberty engine of World War I was one-third aluminum. By the 1930s aluminum was the primary material for aircraft, and its uses for other strategic needs multiplied rapidly.

Total aluminum production capacity in the United

Merle Oberon heads a World War II scrap-aluminum drive.

States increased roughly threefold from 1940 to 1945. It was this enormous capacity that made aluminum the ubiquitous material it has become in the second half of the twentieth century. Today, world production of aluminum exceeds twenty million tons a year.

months before, and Hall was leaving college with no job and no real plans for the future.

The woodshed attached to the kitchen of the Hall household became his workroom. With the death of their mother, Julia became mistress of the house and especially of the kitchen. More than ever, she became the key witness to and, almost certainly, an active partner in her brother's work. It is difficult to find a nineteenth-century inventor of importance who truly worked alone. From Edison's Menlo Park gang to the dozens of artisans working in the shops and laboratories that every inventor has relied on for special work, the lesser-known figures of technical progress have been indispensable to the success of the famous. The values of the Victorian era made it impossible for Julia Hall's contribution to be fully revealed, but we may be sure it was significant.

In the fall of 1885 Hall apparently concluded that chemical means for reducing aluminum must all rely on expensive ingredients such as sodium and aluminum chloride. At this point he turned to electricity. Since the time of Humphry Davy the possibility of extracting aluminum by electrolysis—the separating of compounds by passing a direct current through them—had seemed attractive but frustratingly elusive. Unlike the many substances with which Davy had been so successful, aluminum compounds dissolved in water would not break down with electrolysis. This is because aluminum combines so readily with oxygen that it never has a chance to separate out from a water-based solution. The challenge, therefore, was to find something other than water in which to dissolve the aluminum compound.

In his woodshed laboratory Hall rigged up a furnace. His approach was to seek out a mineral that he could melt and then use to dissolve alumina. The first success, in February 1886, was with cryolite, a soft, whitish mineral from Greenland. Chemically, cryolite is a fluoride of sodium and aluminum; more significantly, it can be melted. Using his crude furnace, Hall discovered that cryolite became clear when molten. When alumina was then added to the crucible, the white powder dissolved completely. A few days later Hall used a battery borrowed from Professor Jewett to see if a current through the molten solution would yield metallic aluminum. The experiment produced nothing.

At this point Hall showed the imagination, persistence, and insight that so often appear at the heart of invention. He surmised that the reaction taking place, at very high heat and with considerable electric current running through the vessel, might be too vigorous for the clay crucible he was using; impurities might be fouling his reaction. He then made a crucible from carbon, which promised to react only with the oxygen that the process might liberate. On February 23, about two weeks after his breakthrough with cryolite, he ran the current from Jewett's battery for two hours through a cryolite-alumina mixture in his new crucible. He poured off the mixture and, at the bottom, found metallic pieces the size of beads or marbles. A quick chemical test confirmed what the shininess and light weight of the pieces had already told him: he finally had aluminum.

Witnessing and assisting all of this was Julia. She was called in to confirm her brother's observations, and the two of them prepared letters with careful descriptions of the experiments that served as dated testimony of the invention's progress. Indeed, Julia Hall appears to have absorbed Elisha Gray's lessons about careful records for patent purposes even better than her brother, and her records served her brother well in court testimony in later years.

Investors were leery of a boyish chemist with an imperfect method for making a novel metal.

Hall's process was far from perfect. The cryolite did not always melt easily, the reaction consumed carbon at an alarming rate, the amount of current needed to extract even small pieces of aluminum was high, much fuel was consumed simply in keeping the mixture molten, and, after only a few runs, the reaction bath filled up with a black substance, making further work difficult or impossible. Nonetheless, Hall was convinced that he had the right principle and that only a bit of further experimenting and some financial backing were needed to make him a "rich inventor."

Getting this backing was not easy, for even in the expansive world of industrializing America, investors were leery of supporting a boyish-looking small-town amateur chemist with an imperfect method for manufacturing a novel material with an unknown market. Eventually Hall turned to a firm in nearby Cleveland.

The Cowles Electric Smelting and Aluminum Company used an electrothermal (as opposed to Hall's electrolytic) process that could not produce pure aluminum but extracted small amounts of the metal alloyed with copper. This "aluminum bronze," a handsome golden metal, had a small but stable market. After much negotiation, the Cowles brothers agreed to let Hall use their facilities to perfect his invention in return for an option to purchase his patents. Beginning in July 1887, Hall worked for a year, largely alone, at the Cowles factory in Lockport, New York. His progress was slow and, he felt, unappreciated, but he learned much about what would be needed to make his process commercially viable. The Cowles brothers, however, decided to let the arrangement with Hall lapse, and the young inventor found himself once again without backing or a properly equipped place to work.

At this point his fortune changed. A co-worker in Lockport introduced Hall to a Pittsburgh metallurgist, Alfred E. Hunt. Like many others, Hunt had tried his hand at making aluminum only to give up quickly. His interest in the metal was still lively, however, so upon hearing details of

After smelting—separation by the Hall-Héroult method—molten aluminum passes through a holding furnace and is poured into molds to form large ingots. Primary aluminum, smelted and unalloyed, has an average purity of 99.8 percent.

Hall's process, he agreed to gather together some friends and form a company. On July 3l, 1888, Hunt and his friends organized the Pittsburgh Aluminum Company (the name was soon changed to the Pittsburgh Reduction Company). A factory was built, and in November Charles Hall and his assistant, Arthur Vining Davis, began production. This was the beginning of the largest aluminum company in the world, whose name would be changed in 1907 to the Aluminum Company of America, universally known as Alcoa.

Some time still would pass before Charles Martin Hall could present himself back in Oberlin as a "rich inventor." The process that was carried out in the Pittsburgh factory left much room for improvement. The inevitable conflict between the claims of Hall's patent and those of Paul Héroult had to be worked out. Even the Cowles brothers caused further problems, as they claimed (with some justice) that Hall used techniques he had learned in Lockport. Above all, aluminum itself was a problem. Now that "silver from clay" was as plentiful as the prophets of science had once claimed it could be, it was not clear what it should be used for. Prices started at five dollars a pound—a third of the old price. This was quickly reduced to two dollars a pound, "in half-ton lots." But as Hall wrote to an associate, "practically no one wanted 1,000 pounds." In 1893 manufacturers produced the first cast-aluminum teakettles, and finally aluminum began to enter the consumer's world.

Until almost the time of his death in 1914, Charles Hall kept his boyish looks. He never married, for his shyness combined with an absorption in his work allowed little opportunity for romance. He amused himself with his piano playing; in his home at Niagara Falls, where he moved to oversee the giant aluminum works built to take advantage of the cheap electricity there, he had both a grand and a player piano. He wrote much less frequently to Julia in his later years; she stayed home in Oberlin taking care of their father until his death in 1911. She survived her brother and lived comfortably on the income provided by Alcoa stock he had given her. She also became the chief custodian of her brother's memory, saving (and censoring) the letters from him as a record of his achievement. As for Charles Hall's primary ambition, he was worth approximately thirty million dollars at his death—a rich inventor indeed. ∎

Robert Friedel, a professor of history at the University of Maryland, is the author of *Zipper: An Exploration in Novelty* (W. W. Norton, 1994).

AGAINST ALL ODDS

Jan Matzeliger, a poor black immigrant, struggled alone to become an inventor and in the early 1880s succeeded in devising a machine that revolutionized the industry

by Dennis Karwatka

If most nineteenth-century American inventors are forgotten today—which is undeniable—black inventors are especially obscure. Almost none of them were known even in their own times, and few books about technological history ever mention a black inventor. Jan Earnst Matzeliger is one of those who have been left behind. A solitary black immigrant, he invented a machine for use in manufacturing shoes that helped transform an industry, build a great corporation, produce several millionaires (himself not among them), and create work for thousands of Americans. Here is his story.

Matzeliger was born on September 15, 1852, in the Dutch colony of Surinam, on the northern coast of South America. His father, Carl Earnest Martzilger, was an educated white Dutch engineer who ran the government's machine works in the capital city of Paramaribo; his mother was a black slave on a plantation outside the city. Little can be learned about Matzeliger's earliest years, but it is likely he was initially reared by his mother. When he was still very young, the boy went to live with his father and a paternal aunt. Since blacks outnumbered whites fourteen to one in Surinam, culturally mixed households were not unusual. Matzeliger never mentioned his mother, and he probably never saw her after his earliest childhood. His fa-

One of two known portraits of Jan Matzeliger.

ther arranged for a machine-shop apprenticeship for the boy when he was ten, and it continued until the lure of the sea drew him from home at nineteen. Matzeliger left Surinam forever. He took with him a single memento: a small jar of nutmegs and coffee beans preserved in alcohol, which he kept all his life.

After two years of service on a merchant ship, the Dutch-speaking youth landed in Philadelphia in late 1873 or early 1874. At the time, Philadelphia was the intellectual mecca for black Americans. It had a black-owned and -operated hospital, black newspapers, several of the largest black churches in the country, and some of the fore-

most black musicians, artists, and entertainers in the world. Blacks made up about 4 percent of the population, more than in any other big Northern city. It was also a leading manufacturing city.

Nonetheless, the skilled twenty-one-year-old machinist found himself handicapped by his race, his foreign heritage, and his inability to speak much English. Competing with others who better understood the dynamics of racial interaction in America, and having arrived amid the severe economic crunch of the Panic of 1873, the soft-spoken newcomer was unable to find employment.

He developed no close relationships in Philadelphia; the people he lived among were mostly freed slaves with cultural backgrounds alien to his. But his acquaintances did eventually help him locate a series of unremarkable jobs that he held until he secured an apprenticeship in a shoemaking shop. The most important piece of equipment Matzeliger learned to operate was a McKay stitching machine. One of the first devices to bring automation to a part of shoemaking, it sewed the outer soles of shoes to the inner soles.

The five-year depression that followed the Panic of 1873 was one of the worst in American history. Eighteen thousand businesses failed, half a million workers lost their jobs, and by

1876 black unemployment in Philadelphia stood at 70 percent. Matzeliger probably was caught in a squeeze. In 1876 or 1877 he left for Lynn, Massachusetts.

He may have been inspired to move there by the 1876 Centennial Exhibition, held in Philadelphia. One of the dignitaries present at its opening was Frederick Douglass, a former resident of Lynn and the most influential black man in America. Whether or not Matzeliger heard Douglass speak, he almost certainly visited the shoe and leather exhibits that showcased Lynn as the shoe capital of the world.

Matzeliger arrived in Lynn almost empty-handed, but he had little trouble finding work. He had a plan of action. The city had too few trained shoe-machine operators, so rather than look for a machinist's job, Matzeliger took a job running a McKay stitching machine, at the M. H. Harney Company. He rented a room at the West Lynn Mission on Charles Street, in the black section of town, and enrolled in night school to learn English. Eventually he learned to speak the language with almost no accent. On October 29, 1878, he became a naturalized citizen. To further educate himself, he invested in a six-volume set of books titled *Popular Educator*, a five-volume series called *Science for All*, and a secondhand set of drafting instruments. These were very expensive items for him and certainly not casual purchases; he so highly regarded the books and drafting instruments that all three were specifically mentioned in his will.

As Matzeliger prepared himself to make the most of his opportunities, he tried to join three local white churches, Roman Catholic, Unitarian, and Episcopal. They all turned him away, and he never forgot the rebuffs. When asked about his background, he would only say that he considered himself a citizen of the United States. He was not interested in racial ties and never tried to join the only black church in town, the African Methodist Episcopal Church. In a community of

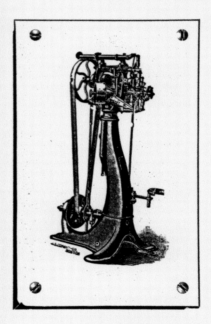
The machine in this 1896 advertisement was based upon Matzeliger's second patent.

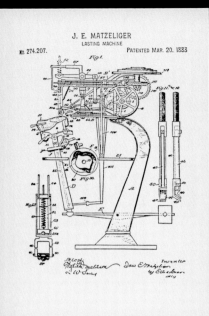

Matzeliger's first patent was so detailed . . .

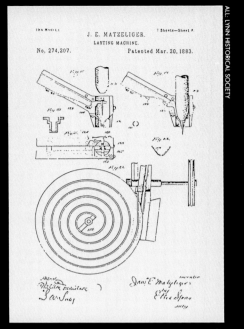

. . . that examiners needed him to explain it.

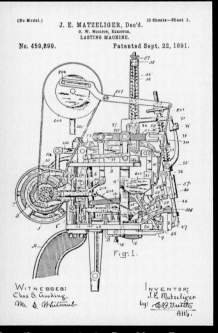

A posthumous patent refines his earlier ones.

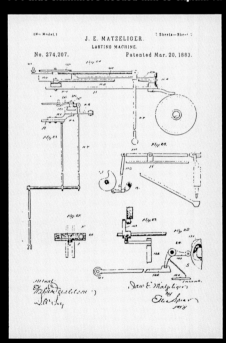

Additional details from the original patent.

One might sooner expect Matzeliger's detailed patent application from a large corporation than from an unproven young machinist.

35,000, 7 percent black, Matzeliger was a man in a cultural limbo, searching for recognition in a white world that would not accept him while rejecting a black world he could not understand. He found comfort in his evening technical pursuits.

He worked on several potential inventions, and there is evidence that he developed an automatic railroad-car coupler design that was stolen from him when he sought his employer's financial assistance. True or not, Matzeliger later solicited financing with caution, and he was careful to keep his inventions secret.

Shoe manufacture was still far from fully mechanized in the 1870s. Labor was divided so that shoes moved from person to person through the several rooms of a small factory as they were assembled. Stitching, or leather-sewing, machines had been introduced in the 1840s and were the most automated part of the process. The most successful one, on which Matzeliger had been trained, was named after its promoter, Gordon McKay, who owned the patent rights and manufactured the machine. It could stitch the outer sole to the inner sole on eighty pairs of shoes in the time a skilled worker needed to complete a single pair with awl and thread.

Factories increased their production by continually reducing the manufacturing process to simpler and simpler steps, but one intricate operation continued to defy mechanization: lasting, or fastening the upper part of a shoe to the inner sole. Shoes took on their final appearance while being shaped by hand over a wooden model of a foot called a last, and much manipulation was required to accurately form the leather around the last, especially at the heel and toe. Lasters were the aristocracy of shoe workers, both skillful and well paid.

A laster would place a leather inner sole, or insole, over the steel sole of an otherwise wooden last, then position the leather upper section of the shoe (the upper) over the last and carefully tug, shape, and wrap it around the insole. Tacks driven through both layers bent over and clinched when they hit the steel sole, and a McKay machine then stitched on the outer sole, or outsole. An efficient laster could process only fifty or sixty pairs of shoes a day, so shoe parts made by machine piled up while waiting for his attentions. This bottleneck kept shoes expensive.

Gordon McKay was a pioneer of early attempts to devise lasting machines and in 1872 organized the McKay Lasting Association to promote their improvement. He wanted to build a machine that could form, shape, tug, pleat, hold, and tack like a human laster. His company spent $120,000 developing one and an additional $130,000 fighting an alleged infringer for four years before dropping the case and joining with the competitor. But while the resulting Copeland-McKay lasting machine was fairly effective with heavy shoes and boots, it was useless for pointed toes or the thin leather used in fine women's shoes, the mainstay of Lynn's factories. It would take the black immigrant Jan Earnst Matzeliger to succeed where McKay, his engineering organization, and a quarter of a million dollars had failed.

Lasters liked to boast that no machine would ever replace them, for no machine could ever have fingers. Matzeliger must have heard the oft-repeated assertion within days of starting work in Lynn. He decided to think about a lasting machine—and embarked on a six-year struggle. He was doing more than merely rising to a challenge; he was skilled, intelligent, inventive, and ambitious, a potential mechanical genius, and he saw inventing an impossible machine as his path to recognition. Feeling the professional excitement of the chase, he invested too much of his nine-dollar-a-week wage on books and instruments, but that investment would ultimately pay dividends to everyone who wanted well-made, inexpensive shoes.

Matzeliger watched the delicate, complexly coordinated manipulations of lasters as they pulled the edge of an up-

Before automation, lasting was painstaking handwork that required a skilled laborer.

per around an insole with a pliers-like pincers and tacked the rolled-over edge to the insole, a nail at a time; they cut slots in the rolled-over edge of the upper at the heel and the toe so that the leather could lie flat on the insole. One shoe took five or six minutes to last.

Every night after his ten-hour workday, Matzeliger thought over and drafted his ideas. Since he had no family or friends, his encouragement came only from himself. By 1880 he had built a model mechanical laster out of wooden cigar boxes, elastic, and wire. It couldn't do any useful work, but it convinced him he was on the right track. He kept the details of the design secret, but several people learned of the project during the six months the model took to prepare. One of them offered him fifty dollars for the model sight unseen. Matzeliger rejected the offer but considered it all the proof he needed that he was making progress. The next step was to fabricate a far more ambitious and expensive working model.

A metal model would require greater working space and access to machine tools. Matzeliger knew how to get both. He capitalized on his mechanical abilities to get a job at the shoemaking factory of Beal Brothers, where he was given a secure working area for

his project and permission to use the company's machine tools.

He scrimped on food to have more money for the working model. Occasionally he got supper at a local restaurant in return for sweeping floors, but his staple was cornmeal mush. He took a part-time job driving coachloads of young people to a recreation area known as Raddin's Grove, near the Saugus River, and became good friends with two white women he met at the park: Bessie Lee, who operated a buttonhole machine at a shoe factory, and Enna Jordan, who worked at a restaurant. Seeing the slender Matzeliger grow thinner and certainly realizing why, they shared their meals with him; he in turn gave them dishes on which he had painted landscapes, and he made several toys for Bessie's younger brother. When Enna married, he gave her a large watercolor of a ship as a wedding present. The two women were the closest friends he ever had.

Matzeliger searched through junkyards and factory dumps for good parts from broken machinery—forgings, gears, pulleys, levers, and cams—and spent long hours altering existing parts to fit his requirements. It is scarcely surprising that he had some battles with depression and at times became extremely discouraged. He was, after all, trying alone to fabricate with parts cannibalized from broken equipment, a phenomenally complex machine that defeated able men who commanded all the machining talent money could buy.

Modification worked only up to a point; Matzeliger had to make several specialized parts using his employer's machine tools. After two years of unaided effort, all the while denying himself proper food, rest, and warmth, Matzeliger had completed his second machine.

It was a crude prototype, but it was quite capable of pleating the leather around a toe, the most difficult lasting task. He knew the model could not possibly withstand a severe factory test, but its success encouraged him to file for a patent, on January 24, 1882. A

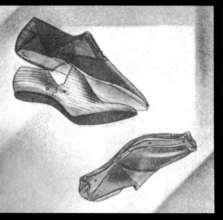
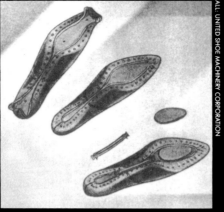

Illustrations from a 1936 pamphlet show stages in the making of shoes. At left, the upper, last, and insole before assembly; at right, the pieces have been fastened with tacks.

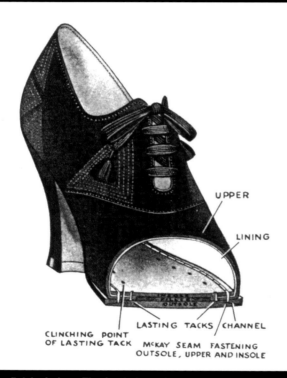

UPPER

LINING

CLINCHING POINT
OF LASTING TACK   LASTING TACKS / CHANNEL

MᶜKAY SEAM FASTENING
OUTSOLE, UPPER AND INSOLE

Cross-section of a finished shoe. The foot's irregular contours frustrated early inventors.

The Matzeliger laster became so popular that for forty years after 1885 nearly every shoe factory in America had one.

production model would be so simple to operate, he claimed in his patent application, that it would require "only the service of a boy or girl or other unskilled labor to attend the machine."

By one account, the officials at the Patent Office could not understand Matzeliger's complex text and drawings, and an inspector had to visit him to have the invention explained. The story is believable. Even by modern standards the fifteen-page patent is complex; one might sooner expect it from an engineering group at a large corporation than from a self-supporting and unproven young machinist working alone.

As always happens sooner or later with inventions, financing became a major issue. Time and money would be needed for a model durable enough to prove itself under factory conditions. It would require precision parts made in a professional machine shop. Matzeliger cautiously sought investment capital. His reputation as a machinist preceding him, he found help from two local businessmen, Charles H. Delnow and Melville S. Nichols. The price for their assistance was steep: they would fully support him in return for two-thirds of all eventual profits. Matzeliger agreed. His first lasting-machine patent was issued on March 20, 1883, and includes the names of Delnow and Nichols as assignees.

Matzeliger took three years to build an experimental machine and in the process made various engineering changes that would be reflected in his second patent several years later. The machine was finally ready for its first demonstration on May 29, 1885. Its main working component was a single pincers resembling an ordinary pair of pliers with the jaws thinned and bent. A worker placed an insole and an upper on a last and positioned the last on the machine. The machine drove a tack, turned the shoe, pleated the leather, drove another tack, and continued until the shoe was finished, exactly reproducing the technique used by hand lasters. The job took one minute.

Those who saw it could hardly believe their eyes. Working five times faster than a human laster, the device perfectly lasted seventy-five difficult pairs of women's shoes. Other machines had performed parts of these operations; this was the first to combine so many complex steps and produce shoes indistinguishable from handmade ones. And it could handle all shoe styles and any grade of leather.

Delnow and Nichols lacked the capital to set up a factory and a distribution system, so they joined with other investors to form the Consolidated Hand-Method Lasting Machine Company (CHMLMC). The company's name reflected an improvement incorporated in Matzeliger's second patent, which he filed for on August 14, 1885. The first model had used a gear drive to rotate the last; now it was supported and fed by the hands of the operator, making possible variations and corrections in the positioning of the upper. The improved machine also had a knee-operated control to adjust the pincers for different leather characteristics. As a result, it required so much skill to operate that the CHMLMC had to establish a training school. But Matzeliger's failure to meet his goal of being able to rely on unskilled labor was more than compensated for by the machine's high rate of production.

Around 1885 Matzeliger sold the company all rights in his patents for stock worth more than $15,000. By the next year 225 workers were manufacturing lasting machines at a plant in Beverly, Massachusetts, and could not keep up with the demand. The Matzeliger laster became so popular that for forty years after 1885 nearly every shoe factory in America had at least one. In the hands of a competent operator, it could last as many as seven hundred pairs of shoes a day, although two to three hundred was a more typical production rate. Shoe prices dropped by half.

Matzeliger's tombstone at the former North Congregational Church, Lynn, Massachusetts.

In 1899 the CHMLMC would merge with forty other companies to form the United Shoe Machinery Corporation. Thanks largely to Matzeliger's patents, the firm would become a virtual monopoly and earn fifty million dollars over the following dozen years. But by then Matzeliger would be dead, his name fading from memory. As so often happens with inventors, nothing had even been named after him. That would change only in 1984, when a Jan Earnst Matzeliger Bridge was dedicated in Lynn.

In 1886 Matzeliger bought a house on Albany Street, where Delnow and Nichols, his original backers, were his neighbors. He rented the house to the couple with whom he had previously boarded and continued to board with them there. His personal life had taken a turn for the better. Bessie Lee and Enna Jordan were members of Lynn's North Congregational Church and had spoken to officials there about membership for Matzeliger. Partly because of his gentlemanly demeanor, the church accepted him in 1884, and he immersed himself in its activities—attending services, teaching Sunday school, instructing in oil painting, and participating in church fund-raising bazaars.

Matzeliger earned but a fraction of the money realized by some of his fin-anciers, but his happiest years were the few that remained after he gave up control of his patents. He enjoyed pleasant surroundings, good friends, financial security, and local recognition. Not all successful inventors have been so fortunate. He filled his days by working on an improved tack-delivery system for shoemaking and a final design for his second machine. He was granted five patents in all, three of them posthumously.

His years of self-deprivation had taken their toll on his health, and in 1886 he was diagnosed as having tuberculosis. Despite extensive medical treatment, he died on August 24, 1889, just a few weeks shy of his thirty-seventh birthday.

Matzeliger had signed a will four months before he died. He was generous with his friends but harsh with those who had spurned him. He left about a third of his estate to the North Congregational Church, requiring that "it shall not knowingly be given or expended for any member of the Roman Catholic, Unitarian or Episcopal churches." His books went to two young church members. Enna Jordan was remembered with two watercolors, a Bible, and some shares of stock; Bessie Lee also received a small amount of stock, and her brother was given his drawing instruments. A few Matzeliger artifacts remain in the possession of Lynn's First Church of Christ, which merged with North Congregational many years ago, but most have been lost to history.

For his part, Gordon McKay willed six million dollars to Harvard to be used for "the great subject of mechanical engineering in all its branches and in the most comprehensive sense." Harvard's Gordon McKay Laboratory of Applied Science provides facilities for research in solid-state physics, electronics, and physical metallurgy.

The jar of nutmegs and coffee beans was never accounted for.   ★

Dennis Karwatka is an associate professor of industrial education and technology at Morehead State University, in Kentucky.

RAISING GALVESTON

by Don Walden

To get out of the way of hurricanes, the entire city of Galveston had to be lifted as much as eleven feet, buildings and all, and walled off from the sea

The worst natural disaster in American history struck Galveston, Texas, on September 8, 1900, when a hurricane covered the whole seaside city with surging water, leveled a third of its area, and took an estimated 6,000 lives. The city had been ravaged by hurricanes before and would certainly be devastated again, but never had Galveston been so helpless and desperate.

Nevertheless, within a few months the city fathers responded with a grandly, confidently technological form of salvation. They would build a wall against the Gulf of Mexico and raise the entire city above harm by reshaping the island on which it sat. They would move 16.3 million cubic yards of sand and defeat the sea.

Galveston Island is a barrier island 2 miles off the coast of Texas, about 28 miles long and 3 miles wide at its widest. Along its south side a wide beach faces the Gulf of Mexico; on the north, toward the coast of Texas, lies a natu-ral harbor. Galveston early became Texas's principal port, and in 1889 the United States chose it for a deepwater harbor on the Gulf.

By 1900 the city, at the eastern end of the island, was a thriving seaport with 37,789 inhabitants. The metropo-lis had an esplanade-lined boulevard, fine houses, churches, and public build-ings; its beach along the Gulf was lined with hotels, bathhouses, and restau-rants. Galveston also had a major prob-lem: hurricanes. The highest spot on the island was only 9 feet above mean low tide, and by 1900 eight hurricanes had flooded the island. Storm surge would raise the level of water in Gal-veston Bay, on the north, as much as 10 feet and inundate the island, while waves poured over the Gulf beach on the other side. In 1886 a commission considered building a sea wall but re-jected the idea.

So Galveston was vulnerable in the first week of September 1900, when a hurricane roared through the Caribbe-

Large photograph: Strollers walk down a newly completed section of the sea wall before the land has been raised behind it, about 1905. Inset: A similar view after the work was done.

an, hit Florida, and headed west, gathering strength. Joseph Cline, the climatologist in Galveston, received two telegrams telling him a hurricane was heading his way.

Friday the barometer changed little, but by midnight Cline noticed long swells on the beach and a higher tide than usual. By dawn the tide was flooding lower parts of the island, heavy rain was falling, and the barometer was dropping. The city had been through storms before. How bad could this one be? Men went to work that morning; mothers and children went to the beach to watch the pounding waves.

Nonchalance was a mistake. By noon the water was two feet deep in some streets. At 3:00 P.M., when Cline sent his last report to the Weather Bureau, the barometric pressure was 29.22 inches, and the wind was blowing at 42 miles an hour. At 5:15, when the gauge blew away, the wind had reached 84 miles an hour; later it was estimated at more than 100 miles an hour. But flooding was the worst problem. About 7:30 P.M. Cline was standing in 8-inch-deep water in his house. Suddenly it was 4 feet deep—"above my waist before I could change my position." Eventually the entire island was under water 10 to 15.7 feet deep.

At least Galveston was built for floods. Because of frequent flooding, many houses stood on stilts, out of the water. This night was different, though. Besides 20-foot waves battering houses along the beach, the storm tore loose streetcar tracks and sent 50-foot

The 1900 hurricane put the entire island underwater, killing at least six thousand.

lengths of railroad line, lashed together with ties and crosspieces, hurtling into the city. They battered down the first row of houses and swept them into the next row, which joined the wreckage moving into the city. By the time the storm was over, 3,600 houses had been destroyed.

Debris kept moving until it was about six streets inland, and there it piled up in a wall more or less parallel to the beach and strong enough to resist the waves. Some water seeped through to flood the area between there and the bay, but the wall protected the rest of the city from battering. "Except in rare instances," a report after the storm recorded, "the line of debris marks the limit of total destruction." At 1:45 A.M. the water began to subside.

When the sun rose on Sunday morning, the sky was cloudless, as if nature had spent all its energy. But the death and damage were enormous. At St. Mary's Orphanage each nun had tied eight infants to her body. The women were found Sunday with the dead infants still strung to them. Similar scenes were found all over Galveston.

By various estimates between 6,000 and 8,000 people had died during the night. At first bodies were buried, some at sea. As the toll mounted, they began to be burned, and observers on the mainland could see the fires at night until November.

A few Galvestonians moved away, including one man who had lost twelve of his fourteen relatives; but no one talked openly of abandoning the island, and most resolutely decided to rebuild. It was to technology that they turned. On November 22, 1901, the city appointed a board of engineers to make recommendations on three objectives: protecting the city generally against overflows from the sea; raising the city above overflows; and building a breakwater or sea wall along the Gulf.

The members of the board were outstanding engineers, Brig. Gen. H. M. Robert is best known today for having written *Robert's Rules of Order*; he was the head of the Army Corps of Engineers and had experience in harbor works. Alfred Noble was from Chicago and had helped design that city's breakwater and raising. H. C. Ripley had lived in Galveston and was familiar with its sand and soil, tides, winds, currents, storms, structural materials, contractors, and carriers.

The board started its work by gathering information about the storm. But how do you measure a hurricane? In a downtown hotel the board established a public forum that asked citizens for information on six topics: the direction and force of currents that had washed over the island; the effect of the breakwater formed by the debris; whether the water began to fall before or after the wind changed; sudden rises in water when the wind veered to the east and southeast; the relative effects of the wind, waves, and wreckage in destroying property; and whether a current from the bay toward the Gulf had been observed. Citizens brought in anecdotes, snippets of information, and data. On January 25, 1902, the engineers delivered their report.

It begins by making Galveston's vulnerability clear. The highest point was on Broadway, which runs lengthwise

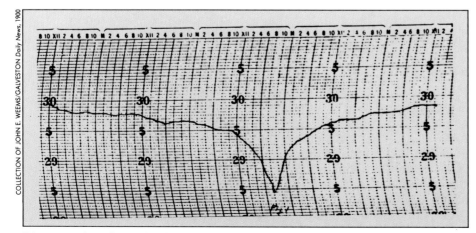

A barogram from September 6 to 10, 1900, shows the barometer's plunge during the storm.

AWFUL CALAMITY—GULF TIDAL WAVE. SEPTEMBER 8TH 1900.

A popular lithograph made before the year was out details—and sensationalizes—the havoc and destruction caused by the hurricane.

along the island. Its elevation was 9 feet above mean low tide. The average elevation of most of the city was only 5.8 feet above mean low tide. Eight storms had flooded the city since 1834. In 1837 a vessel drawing perhaps 10 feet of water had been blown inland to a spot where the elevation was 5.5 feet, and in later storms water had risen to 9.3 feet deep in the city. But the 1900 storm had been the worst, with water from 10 feet deep in Avenue A, along the bay, to 15.7 feet deep at one point along the Gulf. Water first came in over the east end and south side of the island—by the Gulf—but before that water could get across the island, water from the bay met it, and the currents merged and ran northwest. Although wind damaged houses all over the island, currents and waves did the most damage, some carrying streetcar and railroad tracks and mounting debris. Such waves appeared suddenly.

The board concluded that it would be possible to protect Galveston from

storms like those before 1900 and to prevent serious damage from a storm as severe as the 1900 one. That could be accomplished, the board members said, by raising the city's grade so that it sloped upward from the bay to the Gulf. Avenue A would be raised to 8 feet, and the slope from there would

A couple walk past the debris of collapsed buildings shortly after the hurricane.

be at 1 foot in 1,500 feet. To protect the new shape of the island, a concrete wall should be built, 3 miles long and 17 feet above mean low tide, or 1.3 feet above the highest water in the 1900 storm. One end would be on the bay side of the island; it would swing around the east end of the city to the beach, then turn west and run for twenty-three blocks to the Fort Crockett reservation. It would be 16 feet wide at the bottom and 5 feet wide at the top, its face concave at the bottom, rising to a vertical line, so it would throw the storm waves upward rather than let them wash across the island. It would sit on timber piles driven into the sand, and an apron of riprap 27 feet wide would protect it in front.

On top of the filling behind the wall would sit an embankment, level with the top of the wall and sloping up an additional foot 200 feet behind the wall and then descending to the surface of the city.

This embankment was considered part of the sea wall and essential to it. A boulevard and sidewalk along the sea wall and grass elsewhere would help protect the embankment. The embankment was needed not only structurally but also because without it the wall, 4 feet higher than the new grade, "would very much obstruct the view of the Gulf." A levee would protect the western end of the city.

The rationale for the project was simple. "The raising of the city grade is necessary to get the streets and lots sufficiently high for safety to life and property in severe storms," the engineers wrote. "The sea was is necessary to protect this filling from the force of the waves." Had the city had the new grade in 1900, the bay water would have been only 2 feet deep at Avenue A. South of Broadway the land would have sloped above the elevation of water from the bay. The new elevation also would have decreased the danger from the Gulf. Even without a sea wall, the deepest water from the Gulf would have been 3.5 feet. "Still, even in such shallow water there would have been some damage from the waves of the Gulf had there been no sea wall to break their force." The curve on the face of the sea wall would "give the wave an upward direction and prevent to a great extent its running up and over the embankment behind the wall." The embankment would prevent water from undermining the sea wall from behind. "Doubtless some of the Gulf water would slop over the sea wall and embankment from wave action and run down the slope in a thin sheet," but only when the water was at its highest point.

The project would cost $3,500,000: $1,300,000 for the sea wall and $2,200,000 for the filling—an amount that was not large considering the results obtained. But the city had defaulted on interest payments on bonds, and its credit was bad, so a financial plan almost as complex as the project itself was devised. The county, which had good credit, took on the sea wall project and embankment

The city would be elevated above storm level: the wall would protect the fill.

and sold $1,500,000 worth of bonds at 5 percent interest. The state legislature had promulgated a new charter for the city, establishing the Galveston Commission as its government: the city would be allowed to keep various taxes and sell its own $2,000,000 in bonds to pay for the grade raising.

On March 20, 1902, the voters approved the country's sea wall bonds overwhelmingly—3,119 in favor to 22 against. In a banner headline the Galveston *Daily News* exulted GRAND JOLLIFICATION LAST NIGHT. The firm of J. W. O'Rourke and Company of Denver got the contract with a bid of $1,198,318.80 and agreed to take $350,000 in sea wall bonds.

As usual with large projects, there were delays, and they started at the very beginning. The pilings were to be longleaf yellow pine from the forests of East Texas. Piling was expected in Galveston about the last of September 1902, but for some reason the shipment didn't leave Beaumont until October 4 or 5. The first two carloads arrived on October 27, apparently without warning. They were promptly hauled to the work site, and at 2:00 P.M. that day the first pile was in the ground. In about twenty minutes it was driven to the clay stratum. Only about twenty people were present, but they "cheered the

The map at right shows the extent of the hurricane's devastation. The storm pushed northward a wall of debris, destroying virtually everything to the south; the debris helped protect the area to its north, including much of the business district. The area east of the end of the original sea wall, as well as much of Pelican Island, is new land, filled during this century. (The lowest numbered street in 1900 was Eighth Street —the eastward enlargement of the island was already planned.)

christening of the first construction work on the sea wall," as the *News* reported the next day. Eight piles were driven that day.

Pile driving never became a routine matter; weather and tides kept interfering. The piles were to stand 4 feet apart between centers in four parallel lines 3.5 feet apart. A trench 16 feet wide and 3 to 4 feet deep was excavated, and two pile drivers on railroad tracks forced the timber down to the clay, so that the tops were at 2.5 feet above mean low tide. The top 6 inches were then sawed off. Next three thicknesses of plank, 3 inches think and 1 foot wide, were driven down just behind the row of piles nearest the Gulf, to protect the piles from undermining. The work started on December 10, but only because there weren't enough round piles to keep the men busy. Forty men worked on the pilings.

When enough piles were driven, a little mixer on rails poured concrete into the trench for the foundation, and men beat it down along the heads of the piling.

Galveston Bay

Avenue A

Broadway

51st Street

33d Street

Fort Crockett
Avenue S

Key

—— Original Seawall
━━ Extended Seawall
〰 Wall of Debris
▢ Total Destruction
▢ Partial Destruction
▢ Post-1900 Fill

PHILIP SCHEUER

Before the upper part of the wall was poured, the riprap was laid in an apron 27 feet wide in front of the foundation. The specifications had called for granite, limestone, or sandstone riprap. They all cost the same per ton—$2.10—but sandstone was much lighter, only 86,700 tons, as opposed to 110,000 tons of granite, so the county chose sandstone. By the time the work started, though, O'Rourke found that good sandstone was scarce, and "we will not be able to get it fast enough." So he made the county a deal: If he could use granite and the extra tonnage added more than $6,000 to the cost, "we will complete the riprap at out cost."

Oone reason why he wanted granite was that it was in copious supply nearby. A little more than 200 miles away in central Texas lies the Llano Uplift, a dome of Precambrian rock that covers hundreds of square miles. O'Rourke took a group of the county commissioners to Granite Mountain there and to a nearby sand

The New York *World* and the Red Cross set up offices in this building within days.

stone quarry, and as one of them observed, "The Sandstone quarries looked like gopher holes in comparison with the granite mountain." The county bought O'Rourke's suggestion, and the riprap became granite. To prevent delays, the railroad assigned two hundred cars to the sea wall project and

labeled them so that as soon as they were emptied, they could return to the mountain. At Galveston a steam crane sitting on the foundation lifted the rocks out of the railroad cars. The specifications required that at least half of the stones weigh more than 200 pounds each and one-fifth weigh 1,000 pounds or more.

Early in 1903 rain and wind caused more delays. In February it rained nineteen out of twenty-eight days, and a strong southeast breeze blew for fifteen days, so work was suspended several times. One time the weather cleared and a long section was excavated, but that night the wind raised an extra high tide that filled the excavation with sand. The high tide prevented work the next day. The third day the trench was dug again, and another high tide filled it. Wet weather also interfered with work at Granite Mountain, so riprap arrived more slowly than planned.

Finally enough riprap was in place for the wall itself to begin to rise above the Galveston beach. On March 16, 1903, concrete for the first monolith was poured into a wooden box 16 feet wide, 16 feet high, and 25 feet long. Inside, the tamping crew packed it down. Steel reinforcing rods, 10 feet long and 4 feet apart, were held in position by light ropes. Neighboring monoliths followed.

Railroads along the wall were useful here too. On parallel lines railroad cars carried crushed granite, sand, and cement, and on the line beside the foundation, a big mixer turned out 300 cubic yards of concrete a day. A steam crane picked up materials from the cars and dumped them into the mixer. At the mixer's discharge funnel, another crane received the mixed concrete and poured it into the box. As the work progressed, several different sizes of monoliths were built.

It took one day to pour a monolith and a week for it to cure. The crew built alternating sections, and by the time the seventh was poured, at the end of the week, the first would be cured. The workers could then go back

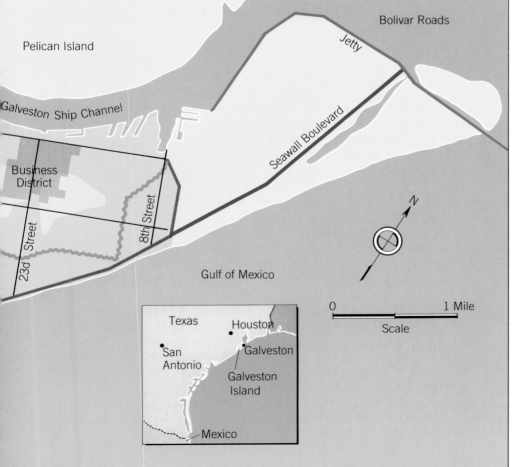

and fill in all the intervening gaps.

By July 29, 1904, less than two years after starting, the colossal wall stood 17,593 feet long and weighed 40,000 pounds per foot. Eighteen thousand railroad cars had passed the site, carrying round pilings, sheet pilings, riprap, crushed granite for the concrete, sand, cement, and steel rods. While the work on the county's wall progressed, the federal government decided to build 4,935 additional feet of sea wall to protect Fort Crockett west of town.

Building the wall was almost easy compared with raising the island's surface to the wall's height. Sand would have to be piled from a few inches to 17 feet high. The Board of Engineers estimated that the job would require 11,244,000 cubic yards of sand, and one writer said seven hundred steamships the size of the *Baltic*, the world's largest at the time, would be needed to carry that much sand.

By itself such a task would be a fairly simple matter of hauling in sand and pouring it on the ground; that had been done before. But never had it been done in such a densely populated area. Almost 3,000 buildings stood on

A temporary railroad hauled eighteen thousand cars of material for the wall.

the ground to be raised, including churches, schools, 1,226 cottages, 413 one-story houses, and 162 stables. There were also water and sewer lines, streetcar lines, electric lines, streets, sidewalks, fences, shrubs, trees, gardens, and outhouses. Working around those problems challenged everyone, exciting debate over where to get the sand (from the bay, the Gulf, or land) and how to deliver it (through pipes over the sea wall or by cars). Each solution presented problems.

On October 27, 1903, three men came to Galveston to inspect the situation. One, Lindon W. Bates, had invented a system he thought might work. With him were his partner, P. C. Goedhart, and their engineer, D. Brand, and they toured the city with the secretary of the Grade Raising Board, E. R.

Cheesborough. They headed to the bay front and then, after getting on the sea wall, which was under construction, walked along it for a way. Near Eighth Street the three stopped and told Cheesborough they wanted to bid on the job. Only two bids were submitted, and theirs was $74,000 lower than the other, so they got the contract.

Their method was little short of audacious. Bates had invented a self-propelled dredge, and the partners eventually brought four to Galveston. They dredged a slurry of sand and water from the bay, then steamed into the city via a canal, which had to be excavated. There the slurry was pumped into pipes that led to whatever section was being raised at the moment. As the sand settled, the water ran off through drainage ditches to the bay.

Excavating the canal was a major undertaking in itself. It ran from the bay around the city's east end and south side, following the curve of the sea wall. On maps it looks like an arm partway around the city with a turning basin for a fist. It was 3 miles long, 18 feet deep, and wide enough for two dredges to pass each other. Buildings, trolley car tracks, utility lines, and other improvements were removed from its way, and bridges were built so wagons, pedestrians, and the trolley could cross the canal. After the grade raising was completed, the canal was filled in and all the improvements were returned.

After the dredges arrived, they worked night and day pulling up the sea bottom with centrifugal pumps and suction pipes with cutters on the ends. They did this 6 miles out at sea, taking forty minutes to load and fifteen to thirty minutes to unload back in town. The largest dredge, the *Leviathan*, made five trips a day, and the others made six trips a day. The *Galveston*, a typical one, had a hopper that held 1,500 cubic yards, and it could

Workmen pose with a new section of the sea wall and a crane riding on the rails behind it.

move 6,000 cubic yards of sand a day.

Photographs show the 42-inch slurry pipes in street intersections spewing sand and seawater 10 feet into the air. On the ground lies a muddy film, but that passed in a few minutes, leaving the sand hard and firm. In nearly every picture a man stands atop the pipe looking down in fascination.

Certainly the work was fascinating. Even today Galvestonians tell their grandparents' stories of the grade raising with a kind of affectionate awe. Most stories deal with the buildings that had to be raised. When it was time to fill a section, a dike was erected around it to hold the sand. Then the engineer in charge, H. T. Wilson, stenciled white marks on telephone poles and fire alarms at intersections to show where the new grade in that section should be, and owners hired contractors with jacks to raise their houses 2 feet above the level. In some sections houses were raised 8 to 12 feet.

Just before the filling began, the *Daily News* published a list of house movers and said that although raising homes would not be expensive, owners should band together to hire contractors. Raising some houses was

Building the wall was almost easy compared with raising the island.

enormously expensive. It cost $6,000 to raise W. L. Moody's brick mansion 3 feet—and took two weeks just to place the three hundred jacks in position. St. Patrick's Church weighed 3,000 tons, and it had to be raised 5 feet. That took seven hundred jacks, but services were never interrupted.

Some owners did not raise their houses. Where houses stood on stilts, the sand might fill only the space under them. Other owners just didn't want to bother. The owners of Ashton Villa, now one of the attractions on a tour of Galveston, decided not to raise, and that's why the top of the wrought-iron fence in front stands only a foot or so above ground. Of the grand stair to the front porch, only three or four steps are left above the ground. To get to some doors, visitors step down.

There were also houses that appeared "perilously high," according to the *Daily News*. The ends of porch steps hung in the air, and extensions had to be built to reach the ground until the ground could reach the house. Along the canal many properties were cut into, just as properties are cut into today when an expressway is built, so owners kept their cows tied to the back railings of their houses or found themselves, as the *News* put it, "keeping the pig in the parlor."

Getting around while the houses were on stilts was a project in itself. Along the streets being raised temporary boardwalks were built. Some were just planks attached to fences. The *News* said they didn't give much assurance to the corpulent or to those "with the downtown club habit." Connecting to them were planks leading to the houses and to the sheds and outhouses in the backyards. Photographs show a rickety maze of foot trestles such as Dr. Seuss might have drawn. Getting from place to place was tricky because the maze sometimes led three or four blocks out of the way. And routes changed as new sections were raised.

Fences had to be removed and stored so they could be reinstalled on the new ground, but the corner posts were left so the lot corners could be found without a new survey. After the filling, fence posts could be seen sticking up 1 to 5 inches. Where the filling covered the corner posts, planks were nailed to them to reach above the new level.

A widespread worry was that the filling would ruin lawns. It was 45 percent sand and 55 percent salt water, and it added to the damage the hurricane had done. Some homeowners dug up their topsoil, put it in bins or on platforms, and replaced it after the filling. Some took soil from their backyards, put it on their front yards, and put all the sea sand on the backyards. But they needed to build 1-foot dikes around the front yards to hold out the salt water. In one area that needed only about 6 inches of filling, the homeowners decided to do it themselves so they could save their trees. The filling

A woman enters a building that has been lifted on stilts from the old ground level to the new.

Galveston on two levels: the area at the right has already been raised; on the left the houses are lifted and ready but the land is still low.

was pumped nearby, and the homeowners brought it to their lots themselves. In many cases there was no way to protect the ubiquitous oleanders and the trees. Besides the salt, in some sections the filling was deep enough to smother roots. The Women's Health Protective Association led an effort to plant trees and oleanders, and one family with a 14-acre farm offered free cuttings of oleanders.

But Galveston took its problems with a sense of humor. One day, while the engineer H. T. Wilson was inspecting the work, a woman asked if he had any hooks with him, saying, "That is such a beautiful hole to go fishing in. I thought you fellows were raising the grade, but it looks to me as if you were raising duck ponds." Someone else asked, after the sand dried, when the camels would arrive.

The project took almost seven years. On August 8, 1910, the last cubic yard of sand was in place, and Galveston had risen above the sea. The first test came even before the project was finished. In July 1909, as the grade raising progressed, a hurricane bore down on the island. Five people died. Six years

later, after the grade raising had been finished, the island was hit by a hurricane some think was as severe as the 1900 storm. Only eight died. That storm beat the schooner *Allison Doura* to pieces against the sea wall, and evidence of the encounter can still be seen in two large chunks broken off the top of the wall.

Over the years the wall has been extended several times. The federal gov-

A small crowd watches sand and water for the fill spew from a slurry pipe.

ernment built a section 10,300 feet long in the 1920s to protect Fort San Jacinto, east of the city. This section continues along the beach, starting at the place where the original sea wall curves to the north. The land behind the extension became available for filling and building, and today it is as high as the rest of the island. This filling has buried the old wall, but at several points what looks like a sidewalk is the top of the sea wall, identifiable because of the red granite in the concrete. In 1927 and from 1950 to 1963, extensions were built that carried the wall far to the west. It now covers 10.04 miles, 9.74 of them along the Gulf, and Galveston advertises the longest sidewalk in the world. Building the wall has cost a total of $15,465,000.

The sections have noticeable differences. The first mile of the federal wall, built right after the county's 3 miles, is made with sandstone concrete, and instead of red granite, it shows gray spots of sandstone. The faces of both sections are deeply pitted after standing up to eighty-six years of storms, but the federal section seems more so. The first sections of the wall stand on untreated piles that would be vulnerable to teredo, a marine organism that could destroy the pilings and let the wall sink into the mud. But a beach keeps the worms away, and groins help hold the beach in place. Later sections are built on treated pilings and on concrete pilings that are not vulnerable to teredo; in those sections there are no groins and no beach. Longtime residents of Galveston can show visitors places where the beach used to stretch hundreds of yards in front of the sea wall but where today the waves of the Gulf crash over the riprap and lap at the foot of the wall itself. There are places that used concrete riprap, large flat blocks that were supposed to fit together like pieces of a puzzle; while they were being placed, a storm undermined the beach, and the riprap is buckled like a waterlogged driveway. In some lengths the riprap is beginning to subside into

I
t has been said that Galveston could not exist without the wall. You can see it's true.

the Gulf; in others the wall itself has sunk a foot or so.

It has often been said that without the sea wall Galveston could not exist. If you stand on the west end of the sea wall, you can see that the unprotected beach beyond the end has eroded about 50 yards back. That erosion is itself a testimony to the importance of the wall.

Today the sea wall is an arena of life. Joggers buck the wind; bicycles and pedal-powered surreys with fringed

tops weave among the strollers; surfers and fishermen unload gear. At Fort Crockett's old gun emplacements, now a park, people sit watching the surf or, at night, the lights of shrimp boats out in the Gulf. Always there's a wind.

In 1961 Hurricane Carla struck Galveston three days after the anniversary of the storm of 1900. Tides from the bay flooded part of the city, and tornadoes spawned by Carla damaged buildings. But in the protected area no one died and no homes were destroyed by the storm surge. The sea wall had proved itself once more. ★

Don Walden is pursuing a graduate degree at the University of Texas after a career in journalism.

HERMAN KOKOJAN/BLACK STAR

A postcard view (above) shows the wall—and the raised town behind it—where it originally turned north at the eastern end of the island. At right, Hurricane Alicia batters against the sea wall on August 18, 1983.

At five-thirty on the afternoon of August 29, 1907, a steelworker named Ingwall Hall was perched high on the partially constructed south cantilever arm of the Quebec Bridge, a few miles from Quebec City. The bridge was to have a span of eighteen hundred feet when completed—the longest in the world. The first whistle signaling the end of the workday had just blown, and Hall was waiting out the few minutes before the final whistle that would send the men on the structure home for the night.

Instead of the final whistle, the workers heard a loud report, like a cannon shot. Two compression chords in the south anchor arm of the bridge had failed, either by the rupture of their latticing or by the shearing of their lattice rivets, and as the distress of mortally tortured steel spread through the entire superstructure, the nineteen thousand tons of the south anchor and cantilever arms and the partially completed center span thundered down onto the banks of the St. Lawrence River and into the water the bridge had been designed to cross. One eyewitness likened the collapsing columns to "ice pillars whose ends were rapidly melting away."

Swallowing water and fighting the river's sudden turbulence, Hall had to struggle in order to breathe. After a few

A DISASTER IN THE MAKING

It took only fifteen seconds for the massive south arm of the Quebec Bridge to fall into the St. Lawrence in 1907, but the prelude to the catastrophe began years before

by John Tarkov

long minutes, a rescue boat reached Hall, and he was dragged aboard. He had lost two fingers, but of the eighty-six men on the bridge when it went down, he was one of only eleven who survived.

No bridge collapses quickly. Just as the safe completion of a bridge is measured in years, the failure of a bridge can be reckoned in the same way. Though the chaotic physical dismemberment of the south arm of the Quebec Bridge took no more than fifteen seconds, the more orderly prelude to the catastrophe began long before.

It began in the summer of 1897, when the consulting engineer Theodore Cooper attended the annual convention of the American Society of Civil Engineers in Quebec City. A former director of the society, Cooper was one of the most respected bridge builders of the time. He made an excursion to the proposed site of the Quebec Bridge and within a week expressed an interest in giving the Quebec Bridge Company the benefit of his expertise.

Cooper's tender of interest was hardly unbidden. The Quebec Bridge Company had been sounding out American bridge engineers as consultants because its own chief engineer, Edward A. Hoare, had never worked on a bridge with a span longer than three

hundred feet. Cooper was a proud, confident man, fiercely devoted to his calling. He had been graduated as a civil engineer from the Rensselaer Institute (now Rensselaer Polytechnic) in 1858 at the age of nineteen. Enlisting in the Navy in 1861, he served as an assistant engineer of the gunboat *Chocura* for the last three years of the Civil War, then moved on to a teaching post at the United States Naval Academy. After a tour of duty in the South Pacific, he resigned from the Navy in July 1872. In May of that year, Capt. James Eads appointed Cooper the inspector of steel manufacturing for Eads's most important engineering work, the St. Louis Bridge.

If the Navy laid the groundwork for Cooper's career, the St. Louis Bridge launched it along a high trajectory. Captain Eads moved Cooper up quickly, placing him in charge of erection at the bridge, which was the most ambitious use of the cantilevered method of erection yet attempted. Cooper performed his duties admirably—once going without sleep for sixty-five hours during a crisis, another time wiring Eads at midnight to warn him that the arch ribs were rupturing, a potentially disastrous condition that was remedied by following the instructions Eads immediately wired back. Upon completion of the work in 1874, Cooper found himself much in professional demand. By 1879, after resigning as the

Six days before its collapse, the bridge reaches delicately out over the river. The first three panels of the center span extend to the left of a temporary tower.

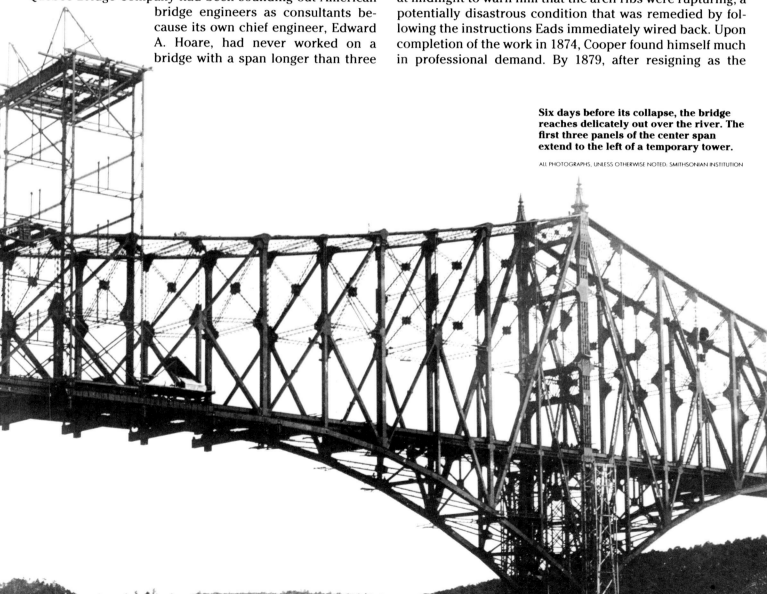

superintendent of Andrew Carnegie's giant Keystone Bridge Company in Pittsburgh, Cooper was able to set up as an independent consulting engineer in New York.

The projects he undertook there were notable and prestigious. His works included the Seekonk Bridge in Providence, the Sixth Street Bridge in Pittsburgh, and the Second Avenue Bridge in New York. He moved through the most rarefied atmosphere of his profession, but unlike his mentor Eads, he never oversaw a truly heroic masterwork. The Quebec Bridge, viewed in that light, was irresistible to Cooper. He said the bridge would be his last work. It would stand as the crowning achievement to an elegant career.

Almost two years would go by before Cooper's affiliation with the Quebec Bridge Company became formal. The financially troubled company had a history of moving slowly—or not at all. Incorporated by an Act of Parliament in 1887, it had accomplished virtually nothing in its first eleven years. In March 1899 officials of the company met with Cooper in New York and arranged for him to review the bids for the long-awaited bridge contracts. All prospective contractors' plans and tenders were sent to him, as well as clear instructions on how he should proceed. He was especially urged to keep in mind the weak financial position of the Quebec Bridge Company.

I ts huge size cried out for preliminary tests and studies, but none were ever conducted.

The Quebec Company had been in close touch with the Phoenix Bridge Company of Phoenixville, Pennsylvania, since 1897, and the Phoenix Company had already submitted preliminary plans for the bridge. Now that the bidding was open, the Quebec Company's desire to give the Phoenix Company the contract for the superstructure was barely concealed.

On April 14, 1899, John Sterling Deans, the chief engineer of the Phoenix Bridge Company, wrote to Edward Hoare, his counterpart in Quebec: "Dear Mr. Hoare—Mr. Szlapka [Phoenix's chief design engineer] and I were with Cooper the greater part of yesterday, and you will be glad to learn that there was not a single vital or important criticism or mistake found in our plans. . . . Mr. Cooper, however, somewhat upset me, by making the following remark, which of course I understood was entirely personal and without any full knowledge of the situation. He said: 'Well, Deans, I believe that all of the bids will probably overrun the amount which the Quebec Bridge Company can raise, and that the result will be . . . that all of the bids will be thrown out and a new tender asked on revised specifications and plans.' Mr. Cooper undoubtedly desires to be perfectly fair, but . . . does not fully understand the situation. I trust, therefore, that you will give his report the most careful scrutiny, and get it in the right shape before it is submitted."

There were more collegial letters between Phoenixville and Quebec, and both Deans and Hoare stayed in close touch with Cooper. Later Cooper would maintain that no

pressure had been brought to bear on him. In any event, on June 23, 1899, he sent his findings to the Quebec Bridge Company. "I therefore hereby conclude and report," he wrote, "that the cantilever superstructure plan of the Phoenix Bridge Company is the 'best and cheapest' plan and proposal."

Those three words—"best and cheapest"—became a touchstone for Cooper in his approach to the bridge. His subsequent letters to Quebec and Phoenixville are seasoned with references to the fiscal consequences of major design decisions. None of the parties involved ever placed costs before safety outright, but their aim was clearly to build a bridge that could bear the twin loads of its own mechanical burden and the Quebec Bridge Company's financial burden.

The Quebec Company had no cause to be dissatisfied with Cooper's scrupulous concern for its ledger books—and had every reason to be confident of his ability to oversee the

Theodore Cooper in old age. His career ended with the tragedy.

building of a good bridge. On May 6, 1900, Cooper was appointed the company's consulting engineer for the duration of the work. He had become, finally, the master builder on a project of historic magnitude.

Five days before his formal appointment on May 1, Cooper exercised his authority by recommending that the span of the bridge be lengthened from sixteen hundred feet to eighteen hundred feet. His explanation for this major design change revealed an attentiveness to both engineering and expense. Piers constructed in deeper water would be subject to the heavy ice floes of the main channel. Closer to shore, they would be less vulnerable—and quicker to build, speeding up the completion of the entire work by at least one year. The change would also make the bridge the world's longest. To keep down the increased cost of steel in the superstructure for an eighteen-hundred-foot span, Cooper recommended another major design change: modified specifications that would allow for higher unit stresses.

His recommendations were approved at Quebec almost as a matter of course. And then, for the next three years—as work proceeded on the substructure, the anchorages, and the approach spans—practically nothing was done to prepare for the engineering difficulties posed by the eighteen-hundred-foot span and the higher allowable stresses.

Once again, money was the root of inaction. Short of funds as usual, the Quebec Bridge Company was making no promises to anybody about its capacity to pay for the bridge's superstructure once the preliminary work was done. For all the goodwill between Phoenixville and Quebec, the Phoenix Bridge Company was politely declining to enter into a contract until payment might be assured.

And so, while the huge size of the bridge cried out for pre-

Nineteen thousand tons of steel lie twisted and smashed on the south bank of the St. Lawrence River shortly after the bridge's collapse. Several people can be seen gazing at the wreckage.

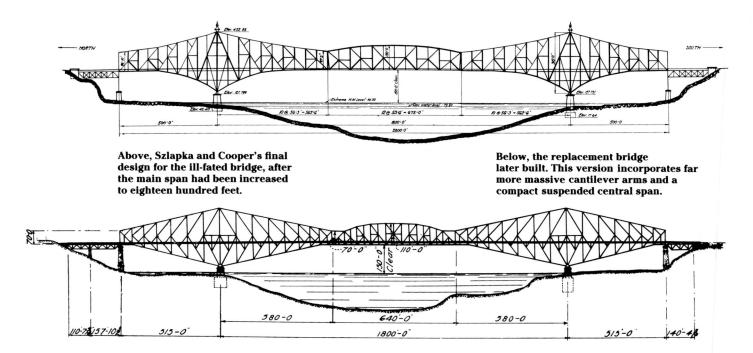

Above, Szlapka and Cooper's final design for the ill-fated bridge, after the main span had been increased to eighteen hundred feet.

Below, the replacement bridge later built. This version incorporates far more massive cantilever arms and a compact suspended central span.

liminary tests and research studies, none were conducted during the long slack period between 1900 and 1903. It was not in the interests of the Phoenix Bridge Company to go out-of-pocket on research costs it might never recoup, and it was plainly impossible for the Quebec Bridge Company to provide the funds. An unspoken assumption became necessary instead: Theodore Cooper's experience and authority were sufficient to confer success upon the untested work.

Then in 1903 the Canadian government guaranteed a bond issue of $6.7 million to pay for the work. With that, the torpor enveloping the project turned into humming activity. Phoenix and Quebec entered into serious contract discussions while design engineers and draftsmen struggled to meet the urgent demand for detailed drawings.

Three years of opportunity for deliberate preparation had been lost. In the rush to provide drawings so that the steel for the bridge could be fabricated with little loss of time, there was no recomputation of assumed weights for the bridge under the revised specifications. It was an oversight of critical importance, and Theodore Cooper did not intervene. He decided to accept the theoretical estimates of weight that the Phoenix Bridge Company had provided.

During the three languid years that preceded the project's lurch into progress, Cooper visited the site of the bridge three times. His third visit, in May 1903, when he was sixty-four, would be his last. After that, he would decline requests that he come to Quebec. His health was poor, he said, and his physician had advised him not to travel. From that point

As the bridge crept out over the river, the stresses on members farther back become intolerable.

on, he would oversee the construction of the world's longest spanning bridge from his office in New York.

Cooper's health may indeed have been fragile, but he was hardly an invalid, commuting almost daily to his office at the foot of Manhattan Island from his home on West Fifty-seventh Street. The only specific references to illness in his letters to Quebec and Phoenixville cite "the grippe" and "fatigue" as his reasons for not being able to be there.

In fact, he had never much appreciated being there in person as a consulting engineer. He regarded on-site visits as unproductive and largely devoted to atmospherics. From his earliest days in private practice, Cooper had insisted on a clause in his contract that limited his on-site responsibilities to a maximum of five days a month. When the Quebec Bridge Company's secretary, Ulric Barthe, at one point brought Cooper's attention to that understanding, Cooper replied that the five days were not an obligation but a limit, implying that it was a limit not to be abused. With his health now weakened, the five-day limit became academic.

The question of his health also caused Cooper to offer what amounted to a *pro forma* resignation in 1904. On a visit to New York, S. N. Parent, the president of the Quebec Bridge Company, asked Cooper when he might see him in Quebec again. Cooper's answer was never. He then asked to be relieved of his responsibilities, but Parent would not hear of it. A short time later Cooper made the same offer to John Deans of the Phoenix Bridge Company, who also refused to treat it seriously. The matter was laid to rest, and Cooper refrained from pressing it. Feeling, as he later said, "a pride and a desire to see this great work carried through successfully, I took no further action."

In the summer of 1903, while Cooper was still well enough to travel, his pride in the great work took him to Ottawa. He was incensed. Collingwood Schreiber, the chief engineer of the Department of Railways and Canals, had suggested that the department hire its own consulting bridge engineer to review and correct the detailed drawings of the Quebec Bridge—after Cooper had seen them—and then submit

Bridge Failure In, Bridge Failure Out

The building of great bridges has changed since Theodore Cooper's day, but as Professor Philip J. Harris of the Department of Civil Engineering and Applied Mechanics at McGill University points out, "Human beings really haven't changed that much." Honest human error in the face of the unforeseen—or the unforeseeable—is ultimately what brings bridges down, as it did in 1940 when the overambitiously designed, four-month-old Tacoma Narrows suspension bridge over Puget Sound writhed sinuously in a high wind until it broke apart. Human error was also the underlying cause in 1967 when the seemingly sturdy, forty-year-old Silver Bridge over the Ohio River at Point Pleasant, Ohio, collapsed without warning, plunging forty-six motorists to their deaths.

The collapse of the Silver Bridge proved such an enigma to investigators that it took four years of study, using state-of-the-art technology, to determine the reason: metal fatigue had caused one eyebar to crack and fail, bringing the rest of the bridge down with it. The fatal crack was so thin that it could not have been detected in the standing structure by even the most sophisticated methods available.

Far less subtle was the collapse of the West Gate Bridge at Melbourne, Australia, in 1970. In trying to connect the main lengthwise splice of the bridge, engineers started removing bolts from the main transverse splice at midspan to correct for misalignment. Before they had taken out enough bolts to correct it, they removed so many that the bridge suddenly collapsed. "You can hardly believe," says Harris, "that anyone, let alone qualified engineers, could make such a mistake."

But while human error will be a major variable as long as human beings build bridges, improvements in other areas—more reliable materials, greatly expanded technical knowledge, a much larger pool of qualified engineers, and organizational schemes in which a number of expert opinions weigh in—have taken some of the uncertainty out of bridge work.

The most novel improvement comes as no surprise: computer technology. "Cooper and Phoenix had good analytical capabilities for their time," says Roger Dorton, who manages the Structural Office of the Ontario Ministry of Transportation and Communications, "but they lacked the speed to rerun changes and test out their assumptions. They extrapolated from smaller bridges, with no perception that with the Quebec Bridge they were getting into a new realm of knowledge."

Computer modeling and analysis, however, can have its pitfalls. "It can give you a false sense of security," says Professor Emory Kemp, who heads the Program of the History of Science and Technology at West Virginia University. "With computers you can end up working along the fine edge of safety, and there may be those one or two key factors you haven't thought of." Or to paraphrase a data processing maxim: Bridge failure in, bridge failure out.

At the University of Maryland, a computer data base is being used in the new field of forensic engineering. Founded in 1982, the university's Architecture and Engineering Performance Information Center (AEPIC) makes available information on past structural failures as a preventive tool for architects and engineers. Data are available on about thirty bridge failures.

A problem confronting AEPIC, says its director, Donald Vannoy, a professor of civil engineering at Maryland, is that the center receives a lot of complaints but not enough information. The center has prepared a four-page data-gathering form designed to preserve the anonymity of engineers providing basic facts about failures. "No one likes to wash their dirty linen in public," says Vannoy, "but except in rare cases where the basic facts themselves are a tip-off, it's a nonsensitive form. We're hoping to double the data base in a year."

No group is more acutely aware of the calamity of bridge failures than the people who build bridges. And no one realizes better than they that the cardinal thing any bridge builder—in 1907 or 1986—must stand watch over is his own human frailty.

---

them to Schreiber for final approval. Robert Douglas, an engineer in Schreiber's department, had reviewed Cooper's new specifications for the eighteen-hundred-foot-span bridge and had criticized the high unit stresses. "Considering that the American government in several cases appointed four or five engineers to consider and determine unit stresses of unexampled magnitude," Douglas would say later, "I thought that this matter was too important to be left to the judgment of Mr. Cooper." But confidence in Cooper was the byword just then, and foresight was at a premium.

Upon learning of Schreiber's proposal, Cooper wrote angrily to Quebec: "This puts me in the position of a subordinate, which I cannot accept." His brisk discussions with Schreiber in Ottawa yielded a decidedly one-sided compromise, much to the relief of Cooper's worried colleagues in Quebec and Phoenixville. It was agreed that plans and specifications would pass from Cooper to Schreiber for final approval; as it would turn out in practice, Schreiber's initials could just as well have come from a rubber stamp.

"I think," Cooper wrote to Hoare upon his return from Ottawa, "this will allow us to go on and get the best bridge we can, without putting metal where it will do more harm than good." By now, whether he wanted it or not initially, Cooper had attained virtually absolute authority over the engineering of the Quebec Bridge. He would say later that the burden had been imposed upon him by the circumstances, and that it was an onerous one. But in 1903 he had journeyed in haste to Ottawa to block Schreiber's attempt to have drawings independently reviewed; in 1904 he had quickly acceded to the protestations of Deans and Parent that he not resign; and in 1905 he insisted that a young, recently graduated engineer be installed at Quebec to serve, in effect, as his eyes and ears on the bridge.

The young engineer's name was Norman McLure, and though nominally he answered to both Cooper and Hoare, he was in fact Cooper's personal representative, communicating with Cooper frequently. McLure's intelligence, energy, and loyalty suited Cooper well. He was well trained and well recommended, and he had enough technical competence to keep Cooper accurately informed and to execute Cooper's instructions, but not nearly enough experience to act without Cooper's authority.

Any great bridge builder is a figure of hubris. Here is what happened when the hubris went unchecked.

The practical effect of all this, after the contract between Quebec and Phoenix was signed and erection of the superstructure got under way late in the summer of 1904, was to leave the day-to-day, hands-on building of the most technically ambitious bridge project in the world to a group of men utterly unprepared to grasp the scope of the work. No one at the site knew enough about what he was doing to act with authority. Everything of import was referred to Cooper.

Work on the superstructure proceeded uneventfully at first. The few difficulties that occurred were minor. The first sign of potentially serious trouble surfaced in 1906.

The best opportunity for the critical computation of weights, during the waiting period from 1900 to 1903, had long since been missed, but early in 1905 the shop drawings of the south anchor arm were practically complete, and it would have been possible to recompute the weight of the arm to within a few percentage points of its actual weight. Neither the Phoenix Bridge Company nor Theodore Cooper bothered to do it—now for the second time.

On February 1, 1906, they began to pay the price. Cooper received a report from E. L. Edwards, the Phoenix Bridge Company's inspector of materials, revealing that the actual weight of steel put into the bridge had far exceeded the original estimated weight. (By June the projected weight for the complete structure would have to be raised from sixty-two to seventy-three million pounds.) Cooper concluded that the increase in the already high stresses, due to the error reported by Edwards, was between 7 and 10 percent.

By this time the south anchor arm, tower, and two panels of the south cantilever arm had been fabricated, and six panels of the anchor arm were already in place. Cooper decided that the increase in stresses was safe, and he permitted work to continue. The only alternative would have been to start building the bridge all over again.

By the summer of 1907 the consequences of allowing the bridge's actual dead load to go uncalculated for so long began to show up on the structure itself, in the lower chord compression members—the lower outside horizontal pieces running the length of the bridge.

On June 15 McLure wrote to Cooper: "In riveting the bottom chord splices of [the] south anchor arm, we have had some trouble on account of the faced ends of the two middle ribs not matching. . . . This has occurred in four instances so far, and by using two 75-ton jacks we have been partly able to straighten out these splices, but not altogether."

Cooper replied: "Make as good work of it as you can. It is not serious. It would be well . . . in future work to get the best results in matching all the members before the full strains [forces] are brought upon them."

When work on the central, suspended span began in July—as the span crept out over the river—the rapidly increasing stresses on the compression members farther back became intolerable. The instability of built-up, latticed compression members in a major work under construction was poorly understood then, so key portions at the ends of the Quebec Bridge's weight-bearing lower chords were still unriveted, even as the stresses upon them grew insupportable with the steady outward advance of the span.

By early August the end details of the compression chords began to show signs of buckling. On August 6 McLure reported to Cooper that lower chords 7-L and 8-L of the south cantilever arm were bent. Cooper was troubled. He wired back with instructions, and with the almost plaintive question: "How did bend occur in both chords?"

On August 12 McLure informed him that the splice between lower chords 8-L and 9-L was now bent as well. Cooper's concern grew, but it was not shared in Phoenixville. Chief Engineer Deans insisted that chords 7-L and 8-L had already been bent when they left the shop. McLure insisted that they only began to show deflection after being installed on the bridge. The debate over chords 7-L and 8-L occupied the greater part of August. Meanwhile work continued, and the stresses on the lower chords grew.

On August 20 chords 8-R, 9-R, and 10-R showed distortion. On August 23 the joint between chords 5-R and 6-R showed a half-inch offset. The bend in chord 8-R was increasing. The bridge was collapsing with glacial slowness, but no one—not even Cooper, for all his concern in the face of the Phoenix Bridge Company's almost cavalier attitude—appreciated fully what was happening.

On August 27 the crisis should have been obvious to all. A week before, chord 9-L of the south anchor arm had been only three-quarters of an inch out of line. On the morning of August 27 McLure measured it again. The deflection was now two and one-quarter inches. McLure wrote to Cooper immediately. Had he been more experienced, he might have sent a telegram, the way a younger Theodore Cooper had once wired Captain Eads at midnight years before.

As word of what had happened to chord 9-L of the anchor arm swept the bridge, gusts of anxiety swept along with it.

By the end of the day B. A. Yenser, the Phoenix Company's general foreman on the bridge, decided to suspend work, saying that he feared for his own life and the lives of the men under his charge. The next morning he changed his mind and ordered work to continue. Chief Engineer Hoare of the Quebec Company endorsed this decision—there is some evidence that he may have requested it. He saw no immediate danger, and he was afraid that stopping work then might mean that it would not resume until spring.

Officials of the Phoenix Bridge Company continued to insist that *all* the bends detected in the lower chord members had been present before installation. They made no effort at all to explain how the deflection of chord 9-L had grown by an inch and a half in the past week.

Fear was everywhere on the bridge on August 28, while the men in charge at the site were paralyzed by a vacuum of authority. Hoare, the Quebec Company's responsible engineer on the project, was technically unqualified—and thus unable—to take command. After much discussion, he dispatched McLure to New York to brief Cooper in person.

Shortly before 11:30 A.M. on August 29, Theodore Cooper arrived at his Manhattan office and found Norman McLure waiting for him. McLure's letter of August 27 had arrived as well. Cooper read it, spoke briefly with McLure, and at 12:16 P.M. he sent a terse telegram to Phoenixville that read: "Add no more load to bridge till after due consideration of facts. McLure will be over at five o'clock."

Cooper was unaware that work was still going on at Quebec. He was under the impression, based on McLure's letter, that construction had stopped two days before. In his haste to catch a train to Phoenixville, McLure neglected to wire Cooper's decision to Quebec as he had promised to do, and so work continued through the afternoon.

Cooper's telegram reached Phoenixville at about 3:00 P.M. John Deans read it—and disregarded it. The workers stayed on the bridge. When McLure arrived at five o'clock, Deans and Peter Szlapka met with him. They agreed to meet again in the morning, when a letter from Phoenix's field engineer at Quebec was due to arrive. The letter would support the Phoenix Company's position that the chords had left Phoenixville slightly bent but serviceable. Almost precisely as the meeting adjourned, chords 9-L and 9-R of the anchor arm buckled, and the Quebec Bridge collapsed.

The members of the Royal Commission of Inquiry investigating the collapse wrote in their 1908 report, "We are satisfied that no one connected with the work was expecting immediate disaster, and we believe that in the case of Mr. Cooper his opinion was justified. He understood that erection was not proceeding; and without additional load the bridge might have held out for days."

John Deans was excoriated for his abysmally poor judgment during the final crisis, and the Quebec Bridge Company was criticized for appointing the unqualified Edward Hoare as the responsible engineer at the site. But the brunt of the blame was placed on the shoulders of Theodore Cooper and Peter Szlapka. Cooper had examined and approved Szlapka's design for the bridge. "The failure," said the commissioners, "cannot be attributed directly to any cause other than errors in judgment on the part of these two engineers.... A grave error was made in assuming the dead load for the calculations at too low a value.... This error was of sufficient magnitude to have required the condemnation of the bridge, even if the details of the lower chords had been of sufficient strength."

The second Quebec Bridge was completed in 1917. Weighing two and a half times more than its ill-fated predecessor, it has stood without any additional reinforcement since the day it opened. It did undergo a calamity of its own, however. In 1916 its prefabricated central span dropped into the river while being raised into place, killing eleven.

Theodore Cooper's career ended with the collapse of the first Quebec Bridge. He testified twice before the Royal Commission, speaking candidly and with some bitterness toward both the Phoenix and Quebec bridge companies. His

On opening day, October 17, 1917, the first train crosses the completed second Quebec Bridge.

testimony brought forth a fusillade of countercharges from officials at Phoenixville and Quebec. With that last tremor of the tragedy behind him, Cooper retired from public life. He died at home on August 24, 1919, at the age of eighty.

Several months after the disaster, a party of engineering students from McGill and Laval universities made an excursion to the site of the ruins that had been the first Quebec Bridge. There was little they could learn from the tortured steel; the Royal Commission had already pronounced it of strictly limited value to its own investigation.

What lessons the debris contained had to be gleaned on levels other than the purely technical. And if the twisted metal spelled out anything to the young engineering students as they made their way around it, the message was this: Any great bridge builder is by nature a figure of hubris. Here is what happens when hubris goes insufficiently checked by deliberation and exquisite care in the face of the little known. You may not think this could happen to you, but it can. It can happen to anyone who dares to build. It happened here to the best of them. ■

John Tarkov, a free-lance writer, was a senior editor of *Geo.*

Radio Revolutionary

by Thomas S. W. Lewis

Edwin Armstrong's innovations, culminating in the introduction of FM, made modern broadcasting possible, but his life ended in tragedy

Just before Christmas in 1913 three engineers from the American Marconi company crowded into a cluttered basement room in Philosophy Hall at Columbia University to see a young man demonstrate his new invention, a regenerative, or feedback, circuit, which he confidently declared had made possible the most effective wireless receiver in the world. This was a time of extravagant claims—and not a little fraud—about the new technology coming to be called radio, and the visitors were suspicious as they heard a wireless telegraph transmission from the Marconi company's station three thousand miles away in Clifden, Ireland, a station normally picked up with great difficulty in the eastern United States. That the inventor, a recent graduate of Columbia named Edwin Howard Armstrong, had hidden the receiver in a black box made the listeners all the more skeptical. But a few days later, after confirming the authenticity of the messages, the assistant chief engineer of the party, a young man named David Sarnoff, declared the invention "the most remarkable receiving system in existence." This occasion marked the first meeting of Armstrong and Sarnoff, men who were to become two of the most important figures in radio. Each was to have a profound influence upon the other when their careers became intertwined.

The history of radio in the United States is one of strong and often eccentric personalities. Armstrong, as one friend described him, was "all focussed in one direction." Son of the American representative of the Oxford University Press, he was born in 1890 and grew up in Yonkers, New York. At the age of fifteen, after reading a copy of *The Boy's Book of Inventions*, he declared his intention of becoming an inventor in the field of radio. Soon he had filled his attic bedroom with coils, coherers, crystals, Leyden jars, and condensers, and he busied himself experimenting with electrical circuits. In the still of the night, when signals were clearest, he listened to faint sounds from transmitters as far away as Key West. In 1910 he erected single-handedly a 125-foot vertical antenna in his yard.

Almost nobody at the turn of the century had the prescience to understand the potential of a technology so new, imprecise, and as yet unsophisticated as radio. It seemed more a hobby for amateurs than a serious commercial venture. Transmissions were limited to laboratory demonstrations or experimental efforts over distances of less than two hundred miles. Wireless communications had begun only a few years before: Heinrich Hertz had successfully transmitted electromagnetic waves across a room in the late 1880s; Guglielmo Marconi had sent his first wireless message across the Atlantic in 1901, an accomplishment that was shortly understood to be due partly to the reflection of radio signals off the upper atmosphere—a discovery that was crucial to all later work in radio. With the hope of increasing the capability of wireless receivers, Lee De Forest was developing the first three-element vacuum, or audion, tube at the very time young Armstrong was reading tales of great inventors.

Aside from radio, Armstrong developed few passions: tennis, fast cars, and high places. Tennis he played whenever he could, spending hours charging his barrel-chested six-foot frame about the court. To indulge his craving for speed, he would travel to the private Long Island Motor Parkway, where for the fee of a dollar he drove at speeds of up to a hundred miles an hour. He liked nothing more than to climb hundreds of feet to the tops of radio

Opposite, Armstrong shows off atop a transmitting tower 450 feet above Forty-second Street in 1923. Right, a billboard for an early FM station.

transmission towers or to install radio equipment on the roofs of tall buildings. For relaxation he read books about mountaineers.

Armstrong's stubbornness and interest in difficult problems led him to his most important inventions. He realized that receivers and transmitters might benefit from radical design changes, and he challenged virtually every fact of radio technology that others accepted. As his technical papers reveal, he enjoyed showing up the experts, be they eminent professors at Columbia University, where he studied electrical engineering; mathematicians, whose elegant solutions and theorems he inherently distrusted; or, later, heads of corporations whose commercial interests ran counter to what he was trying to develop.

The idea for the regenerative, or feedback, circuit came to Armstrong in a moment of revelation while he was mountain climbing in Vermont in 1912, between his junior and senior years at Columbia. Upon his return to the university he built the circuit and thereby greatly enhanced De Forest's audion as a detector for wireless signals.

Resembling a small light bulb fitted with a grid placed between the filament and a metal plate, De Forest's 1906 audion tube had helped amplify a radio signal but did little else; a half dozen years later the inventor was still struggling to make the tube practical. Understanding the tube's capacity even better than De

Armstrong's "superhet" was adopted in the 1930s. It is still the basic radio receiver.

Forest did, Armstrong found that by looping the signal from the audion plate circuit back to the grid via suitable coupling coils, he could increase amplification enormously. And when he increased the feedback beyond a critical level, the tube became a transmitter.

Inventing his regenerative circuit proved to be easier than having it accepted commercially, at least before broadcasting became a business. American Marconi and the Atlantic Communication Company bought the right to use it in limited applications; licensing the invention to smaller manufacturers proved more profitable. By 1922 the inventor had issued twenty-four licenses, and royalties reached some ten thousand dollars a month.

The idea for Armstrong's second major invention came to him in another moment of insight, while he was stationed in France as a captain in the Army Signal Corps during World War I. Watching a German bombing raid, he pondered a way of locating the positions of airplanes by tracking the weak high-frequency waves emitted by the engine's ignition systems. He envisioned a superheterodyne receiver, based on the electrical mixing of frequencies. The technique of mixing frequencies had been introduced to radio technology by the Canadian engineer Reginald Fessenden in about 1903. It was Armstrong, however, who developed its commercial practicality.

In the superheterodyne the incoming signal is mixed, or heterodyned, with the steady output of a local oscillator to produce a signal of intermediate frequency that can be much more cleanly and effectively amplified. Armstrong's laboratory constructed an eight-tube receiver which included three intermediate-frequency current, and two audio frequency amplifiers. Over the next few years Armstrong designed some very elegant devices using this circuitry to achieve improved sensitivity and selectivity.

By the mid-1920's the regenerative receiver and crystal sets began to decline in popularity as the transitional Neutradyne receiver and its variations came on the market with better fidelity and amplifications; after 1930 there was widespread adoption of the "superhet" as wider patent licensing became available and it became easier to tune—with a single dial—than its predecessors. Today the superheterodyne constitutes the basic receiver in practically every radio.

When Armstrong returned to the United States after World War I, nearly everyone recognized him as foremost in his field. The Radio Club of America gave a dinner in his honor at New York's Hotel Ansonia in 1919. His large, melon-shaped head, which had been prematurely balding before the war, had been made into a complete dome by an anthrax infection contracted in France; his firm mouth, long upper lip, and blue eyes, his modest and laconic speech, and the occasional involuntary twitch of his neck and shoulders (a reminder of a bout with chorea in childhood) remained unchanged.

Not all thought him preeminent, however. Just before the war Lee De Forest had claimed the prior invention of the regenerative circuit, and now he was eager to press his suit. The litigation quickly became acrimonious, taking up much of

Armstrong, who developed an airplane radio during World War I, waves from a biplane.

Armstrong's time and energy until its resolution years later, and it helped determine his bitter attitude toward patent law. Fees for his defense lawyers began to force him into debt, and when, in 1920, the Westinghouse company offered him $335,000 for exclusive rights to the regenerative and superheterodyne circuits, Armstrong decided to sell. The sum was substantial; even after paying his creditors, Armstong was now wealthy.

Armstrong's next invention, the superregenerative circuit, made him a millionaire. He developed it as a consequence of his litigation with De Forest. When preparing his regeneration apparatus for a demonstration to the court in 1922, Armstrong said he "accidentally ran into the phenomenon." The superregenerative circuit greatly improved the feedback process (although the device would not become fully practical for another decade). The Radio Corporation of America paid Armstrong $200,000 in cash and sixty thousand shares of stock for the invention. Later the corporation added twenty thousand shares for consulting work, making Armstrong the largest stockholder in the company. Just before the stock market crash of 1929 Armstrong sold most of his stock for $114 a share.

Armstrong's association with RCA drew him close to the corporation's president, David Sarnoff, and even closer to Sarnoff's tall, charming and intelligent secretary, Marion MacInnis. He courted her in the manner of the twenties, taking her for drives on the Motor Parkway in a new Hispano-Suiza, on trips up the Hudson, and to dinner and theater parties. Perhaps it was this growing relationship that inspired Armstrong to perform his most daring stunt. On a May afternoon in 1923 he scaled the transmitting tower of RCA's station WJZ, 450 feet above Forty-second Street. Hanging over the street from one of the aerial's crossbeams, he posed for a photographer he had brought along. That evening he returned to stand atop the large, banded iron ball crowning the tower. Sarnoff was not amused, and for a while he barred Armstrong from his offices. Marion MacInnis married Armstrong in December. For their honeymoon, they traveled in the Hispano-Suiza to Florida. His wedding present to his bride was the first portable superheterodyne radio—a huge mechanism that they lugged onto the beach with them.

Early in 1924 Armstrong returned to Columbia to continue an effort he had begun a decade earlier to eliminate static from radio. Conventional wisdom held the problem insoluble. "Static, like the poor, will always be with us," the chief engineer of AT&T had declared. But Armstrong labored persistently, sometimes taking several months to set up an experiment that involved as many as a hundred vacuum tubes. He worked a seven-day week and usually a fifteen-hour day, broken only by a lunch of a sandwich and a glass of milk. Though he held a chair of electrical engineering at Columbia, he taught no courses. His salary was one dollar a year.

Shortly before Christmas 1933 David Sarnoff returned to the same cluttered basement room of Philosophy Hall where twenty years earlier he had witnessed Armstrong's demonstration of the regenerative circuit. Armstrong and Sarnoff had become friends, but not intimate ones. Armstrong was tall, slow-speaking, cerebral, and gentle; Sarnoff was short, talkative, and aggressive. Armstrong's background was middle-class, Presbyterian, and American; Sarnoff's, lower-class, Jewish, and Russian. In 1906 Sarnoff had become an office boy for the company's chief telegraph operator, running a wireless station atop Wanamaker's department store in New York, where on April 15, 1912, he helped relay North Atlantic radio messages bearing news of the *Titanic* disaster. This brought radio—and Sarnoff—to the attention of the general public. From then on the enterprising Sarnoff was the self-appointed spokesman for and prophet of radio as a mass medium. When RCA was formed in 1919, he quickly assumed a leading role; by 1930 he was president.

Armstrong had called Sarnoff to the laboratory to witness a demonstration of his invention to eliminate static from radio. Sarnoff had long expressed the hope that an inventor would come forth with a "little black box" to do just that. What he found was not a simple device to be added to existing radios or transmitters, but an entirely new radio system: frequency modulation, or FM.

In the previous decade radio had become a major presence across the country. The number of homes with radios in 1922 stood at 60,000, with many of these radios home-built; by the Depression year of 1933, when Franklin Roosevelt broadcast his first fireside chat, the number was 19,250,000. Automobile radios were first introduced in 1930 and numbered 500,000 three years later. The use of Armstrong's superheterodyne circuitry in receivers had grown rapidly. When people were not listening to the President, they were hearing shows with stars like Amos and Andy, Ted Mack, Fred Allen, and Bob Hope. On Broadway, Cole Porter acknowledged radio's impor-

The inventor and his wife enjoy his unwieldy wedding present to her on their honeymoon.

tance in the title song of his musical *Anything Goes*:

*Just think of those shocks you've got
And those knocks you've got
And those blues you've got
From that news you've got
And those pains you've got
(If any brains you've got)
From those little radios.*

All "those little radios" worked on the principle of amplitude modulation. The invention Armstrong demonstrated to Sarnoff, however, introduced some fundamental changes. *Modulation* refers to the way in which voice and music information is impressed on a radio wave. In amplitude modulation (AM) the information signal varies the amplitude of the wave; what Armstrong proposed was a method of modulation that would vary the wave's frequency. By analogy to waves of water, AM imparted the signal through changes in the heights of the waves; FM did so by varying the spacing of the wave crests. Since most noise affected wave height, or amplitude, much more than frequency, FM was much less vulnerable to interference. But FM would require entirely new transmitters and receivers and would need a fairly wide channel spacing—up to two hundred kilohertz—space for which was not readily available in the already crowded five hundred to sixteen hundred kilohertz AM band. The inventor

The inventor resolved to introduce FM himself, bankrolling it with his own money.

proposed VHF (very high frequency) allocations, where plenty of room was available. It was in this part of the spectrum, furthermore, that FM's promise of improved high fidelity might best be fulfilled.

Sarnoff was presented with an enormous dilemma. The industry had a considerable investment in medium-band AM, and a move simply to abandon it and switch to VHF FM seemed financially disastrous. It clearly represented a major threat to any company already committed to AM. Sarnoff hoped for some sort of compromise, though, and was not averse to a little experimenting. In March 1934, therefore, Armstrong's equipment was moved to the top of the Empire State Building for definitive broadcasting tests. Receiving sites were set up first at Westhampton Beach, Long Island, New York, and then at Haddonfield, New Jersey.

What the experimenters showed was a truly substantial improvement in the signal-to-noise ratio with the new technique. An FM signal twice as strong as a noise pulse would suppress the pulse; in AM a signal had to be one hundred times as strong. Also, FM displayed a capture effect—that is, if two stations on the same frequency arrived at the receiving antenna with different signal strengths, the system would grab the stronger one rather than pick up both at once. The capture effect, together with the fact that VHF signals cannot be received farther than about fifty to seventy miles from a transmitter, suggested that FM stations in not-too-distant cities could operate on the same channel.

Thus, the advantage of FM resided not simply in its high fidelity, with which AM could compete, but in a combination of effects, the most significant of which was its spectacular ability to suppress atmospheric and internal electronic noise. In notes written in the receiving log at Westhampton Beach on June 9, 1934, Armstrong reported: "1 PM. W2XDJ signed off. All tests performed exactly according to Hoyle. This experiment concludes just twenty years of work on this problem. . . . An era as new and distinct in the radio art as that of regeneration is now upon us. After ten years of eclipse my star is again rising."

In fact, the worst was yet to come. On May 21, 1934, the Supreme Court resolved the long-festering and bitter battle over the invention of the regenerative circuit by deciding in De Forest's favor (the matter was a complex issue of priority in which each side had presented a strong case). Though the Institute of Radio Engineers refused Armstrong's offer to return the medal it had given him in 1918 for the regenerative circuit, it could not restore the inventor's loss of dignity.

However serious the wound was, Armstrong would not let it deter him from his work with FM. But in April 1935 RCA asked Armstrong to remove his apparatus from the Empire State Building so that the company could use the space for its experiments with television. Not wanting to postpone the introduction of FM indefinitely, Armstrong then resolved to establish the medium himself, bankrolling it with his own money and licensing the patents to small companies, just as he had done twenty years before with regeneration. In preparation he enlarged his laboratory staff, moved into a spa-

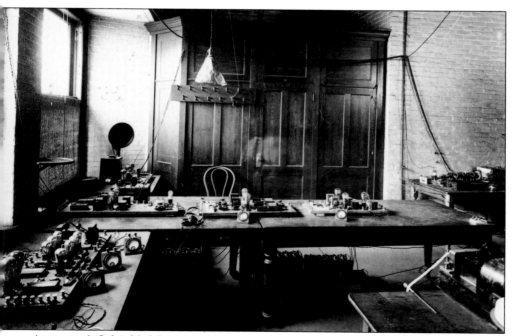

Armstrong's Columbia laboratory, 1927. As the sole chair suggests, he usually worked alone.

Harnessing the Airwaves: From Hertz to Armstrong

In the late 1880s Heinrich Rudolf Hertz (1857–94), a German physicist, proved an earlier theory of the English physicist James Clerk Maxwell that electromagnetic waves could move through space. To do this, Hertz attached copper plates to two separate metal spheres. When he generated an alternating current between them, sparks jumped from one sphere to the other. As crude as it was, this device served as the first transmitter. For a receiver Hertz held a loop of copper wire a few feet away. When a spark jumped between the original two spheres, another, smaller spark jumped through this receiver. Before his death, at thirty-seven, Hertz was also able to measure the length and velocity of electromagnetic waves and determine that they had similar properties to waves of heat and light. His machinery became the basis of early spark-gap transmitters.

In the summer of 1896 a young Italian inventor named Guglielmo Marconi demonstrated an improved Hertzian transmitter linked to an elevated antenna system, which made it possible to send radio waves several hundred yards. For a receiver, Marconi employed a coherer—a tube of silver and nickel filings that exhibited lowered electrical resistance and "cohered" when subjected to currents from radio waves. The receiver was connected to an apparatus that could print the dots and dashes of Morse code. In December 1901, Marconi sent a signal from Poldhu, Cornwall, England, to a receiving site in Newfoundland. In 1902, Marconi developed a magnetic detector that used a band of iron wires inside a coil to pick up signals. The "Maggie," as it came to be called, was considerably more reliable and faster than the coherer. It was widely adopted by the Marconi Wireless Telegraph Company.

In 1906, in Massachusetts, Reginald Fessenden successfully impressed voice and music information on a radio wave by using a high-frequency alternator as a transmitter. The alternator's great advantage was that it generated truly continuous waves, unlike the earlier transmitters. This device was improved further by Ernst Alexanderson of the General Electric Company. By 1918 the alternator was the state of the art in radio transmitting appliances.

Also in 1906, two Americans —Henry C. Dunwoody and Greenleaf W. Pickard—independently developed the first crystal detectors. Consisting of a wire impressed against a piece of crystal, the device removed the audio-frequency component from a radio signal and allowed it to be picked up by a set of headphones. In the early broadcasting era this "cat's-whisker" galena detector was fairly popular.

In 1904 John Ambrose Fleming of England had developed a diode, a two-electrode vacuum tube capable of detecting wireless signals, based on an effect observed two decades earlier by Thomas Edison. While perfecting the incandescent bulb, Edison had noticed that a weak current would pass across a space between the bulb's filament and a metal plate placed above it. Fleming discovered that the bulb-plus-plate would pick up a radio signal and transform it into pulsed direct current, which then could be used to indicate telegraph signals.

Two years later Lee De Forest, a Yale-educated entrepreneur and inventor, placed a zigzag grid between the filament and plate of a two-element tube and discovered that a small voltage change on the grid would create a much greater one in the plate circuit. This made possible the amplification of weak radio signals.

In the regenerative detector developed by Edwin Armstrong between 1912 and 1914, a portion of the amplified signal in the plate circuit was fed back to the grid in phase with the incoming signal, thereby reinforcing it.

Armstrong's superheterodyne circuit (from the Greek *heteros*, meaning "other," and *dyne*, "beat"), the basic component of all radios today, amplified weak signals more than ever before. Each block in the first diagram below represents a stage in the process. The incoming signal is mixed with a second frequency, which remains constant. The resultant signal is then amplified and sent to a detector, where it is converted to an audio frequency and sent to an audio amplifier.

The receiver in Armstrong's frequency modulation system consisted of the same circuits found in the superheterodyne circuit, plus additional limiter and discriminator circuits. The signal passes through a mixer and intermediate amplifier (as is the case with the superheterodyne) to a limiter circuit that cuts out any amplitude variations caused by static. The FM wave is converted into an AM wave in the discriminator and then (again as in the superheterodyne) passes through the detector to the audio amplifier.

SUPERHETERODYNE RECEIVER

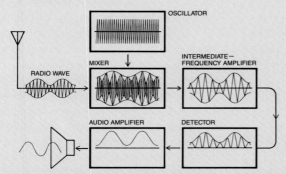

The incoming signal (upper left) is mixed with a constant signal from an oscillator, amplified, and converted to an audio signal.

FM RECEIVER

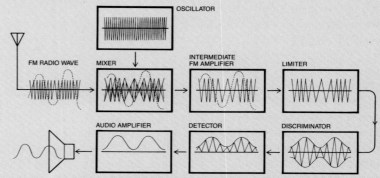

The signal is similarly mixed and amplified but then, after static is removed by a limiter, is converted to AM and then audio.

Edwin Armstrong in the early 1940s.

cious apartment overlooking the East River, which became both home and office, and secured additional patents on a number of improvements to FM. On July 18, 1939, he began broadcasting from the first FM station, W2XMN, which he had built entirely with his own money in Alpine, New Jersey. That year General Electric began manufacturing—under Armstrong's license—the first commercially available FM radios. By the end of the year the five-year-old Federal Communications Commission (FCC) had received 150 applications for permits to establish FM stations.

In 1940 RCA offered Armstrong one million dollars, with no payment of royalties, for his FM patents, but by now the inventor was stubbornly determined to hold onto them and continue licensing. Full commercial FM broadcasting was authorized by the FCC on May 22, 1940, and forty channels were allocated in the forty-two to fifty megahertz range. But then the commission began to express concern about sky-wave interference in the designated FM range—the possibility that signals reflecting from the ionosphere (a layer of electrified air in

the upper atmosphere) would cause interference in receivers. This later became a major issue in battles between Armstrong and RCA.

In 1940, the National Television Systems Committee, which was recommending standards for television, chose to back FM for the television sound signal and AM for the picture. The FCC went along with this when it authorized commercial television service on July 1, 1941. This use of FM was a coup for Armstrong, but the economic benefit for him was slight.

World War II halted FM aural broadcasting progress early in 1942, and Armstrong devoted himself to research in FM radar for the Signal Corps. By now RCA had an FM station on the air in New York that used a transmitter slightly different from Armstrong's; by 1944 there were forty-seven FM stations in the country and five hundred thousand FM receivers.

At the close of the war a Radio Technical Planning Board (RTPB) representing industry interests was formed to advise the FCC on postwar standards and channel allocations. The board supported the FM frequencies that had been established earlier as well as the use of FM for television sound, but the FCC, citing a study warning of sky-wave interference, recommended moving the FM band to 92 to 106 in the megahertz range.

This proposal was generally favored by the television industry, which would gain flexibility from the higher channel allocation. But television manufacturers that also made FM radios, including Zenith and General Electric, opposed the move. Also against it were the Radio Technical Planning Board, existing FM broadcasters, and Edwin Armstrong. Nonetheless, the decision was made to move the FM band to 88 to 108 megahertz, where it remains today. The FCC

allowed a number of stations to operate on both high and low FM bands during a transitional period until new receivers were generally available. But to the FM industry the "FM shift" seemed more like an FM bust, the major effect of which would be to render all existing FM radios and transmitters obsolete, thus crushing the industry and benefiting companies that had been late to get involved with FM.

Sarnoff and RCA, meanwhile, were focusing mainly on television but continued to carry out their own research with FM. After being rebuffed in its attempt to buy out Armstrong's patents, the company decided to try to get around them. RCA's first commercial FM receiver, in 1946, used a supposedly new circuit to remove noise pulses, or unwanted amplitude-modulation signals. The circuit was very effective, but it could easily be seen as simply an adaptation of the limiter-discriminator component of Armstrong's own FM system. Armstrong made an impressive argument to this effect in an ingenious paper before the Radio Club of America. The inventor already believed RCA would emerge a big financial winner—and he a big loser—as a result of the FM band change; now his dismay at the company and its chairman, Sarnoff, increased.

RCA's tight control of its own radio patents provoked resentment among competing companies, and in 1946 Zenith repudiated an RCA license package, ceased to pay royalties, and brought triple damage suits against RCA, GE, and Western Electric, among which there had been interlocking patent-rights agreements. Litigation multiplied swiftly into suit and countersuit, and other manufacturers brought charges of patent infringement and restraint of trade against the big corporations.

So Armstrong was not alone when, on July 22, 1948, he filed suit in federal district court against RCA and other companies, charging them with infringing his five basic FM patents and violating the antitrust laws. The case was to be a test of endurance, a Dickensian legal battle that a single man—even an Armstrong —could not hope to win. Though represented by one of the finest Wall Street law firms, he found the opposition prepared to fight. "They will stall this along

Zenith radios roll off one of the first FM assembly lines, and their performance is checked in special listening rooms, about 1941.

until I am dead or broke," he said. Stall they did. Legal fees mounted steadily while at the same time income from patent royalties dwindled. The financial and emotional strain on Armstrong grew until it became too much.

By 1953 Armstrong was caught in a tragic drama from which he would not escape. His health deteriorated; his once-robust frame now appeared gaunt, and his face haggard, and the twitch in his neck and shoulder became more pronounced. The pressure proved too much for his wife; at Thanksgiving she left their apartment in New York City to live with her sister in Connecticut.

Late in January 1954 Armstrong confessed to his lawyer that he had "made a mess" of his personal life and said he was ready to settle a twenty-one-patent infringement suit that had just been instituted by him. But he could not bear defeat, and the thought of retiring a beaten man was abhorrent. On the night of January 31, Armstrong—then sixty-three years old—penciled a two-page note to his wife, Marion, concluding, "God keep you and Lord have mercy on my soul." Fully dressed in his hat and

scarf and overcoat and gloves, he went to the window of his apartment and plunged ten stories to his death.

His widow pressed on, continuing the litigation. One by one, favorable agreements and court decisions began to appear. Late in 1954 RCA agreed to a $1,040,000 settlement; the twenty-one-patent infringement suit was decided in Armstrong's favor in September 1959. The legal proceedings did not come to an end until October 1967, when the Supreme Court refused to review a lower court judgment against Motorola. Eighteen years after he had brought suit and thirteen years after his suicide, Edwin Howard Armstrong had won.

Armstrong's inventions and ideas have also triumphed. Today virtually every radio, television, and radar system employs the superheterodyne circuit. Frequency modulation has become the standard of high-fidelity broadcasting all over the world, thanks in part to subsequent developments in the high-fidelity industry and innovative regulatory procedures. Having declined in number between 1950 and 1958, FM stations in the United States began to multiply after

the introduction of stereo on records. In 1961 the FCC authorized the modern stereo-FM system and extended an earlier authorization permitting FM stations to sell a background music service to banks, stores, and supermarkets. Finally, the FCC ruled in 1965 that FM stations broadcasting to audiences of more than one hundred thousand had to offer original programming at least half the time, rather than simply duplicate AM schedules.

These developments led to a dramatic increase in the number of FM stations, from 990 in 1961 to the current total of 4,965. The FM industry has been given an additional boost by the proliferation of receivers in automobiles. And improvements in solid-state engineering and microelectronics have lent a crowning touch to the fulfillment of Armstrong's dream of realism in the transmission of sound. FM has reached a healthy adulthood, but only after a birth and early life whose turbulence its inventor could not survive. ∎

Thomas S. W. Lewis is Professor of English at Skidmore College.

THE LETTER THAT CHANGED THE WAY WE FLY

TRANSCONTINENTAL & WESTERN AIR, INC.

10 RICHARDS ROAD
MUNICIPAL AIRPORT
KANSAS CITY, MISSOURI

August 2nd,
19 32

Douglas Aircraft Corporation,
Clover Field,
Santa Monica, California.

Attention: Mr. Donald Douglas

Dear Mr. Douglas:

Transcontinental & Western Air is interested
in purchasing ten or more trimotored transport planes.
I am attaching our general performance specifications,
covering this equipment and would appreciate your advising
whether your Company is interested in this manufacturing
job.

If so, approximately how long would it take
to turn out the first plane for service tests?

Very truly yours,

Jack Frye

Jack Frye
Vice President
In Charge of Operations

JF/GS
Encl.

N.B. Please consider this information confidential and
return specifications if you are not interested.

TRANSCONTINENTAL & WESTERN AIR, INC.

General Performance Specifications
Transport Plane

1. Type: All metal trimotored monoplane preferred but
   combination structure or biplane would be considered.
   Main internal structure must be metal.

2. Power: Three engines of 500 to 550 h.p. (Wasps with 10-1
   supercharger; 6-1 compression O.K.).

3. Weight: Gross (maximum)   14,200 lbs.

4. Weight allowance for radio and wing mail bins   350 lbs.

5. Weight allowance must also be made for complete instruments,
   night flying equipment, fuel capacity for cruising range
   of 1080 miles at 150 m.p.h., crew of two, at least 12 passengers with comfortable seats and ample room, and the usual
   miscellaneous equipment carried on a passenger plane of this
   type. Payload should be at least 2,300 lbs. with full equipment and fuel for maximum range.

6. Performance

   Top speed sea level (minimum)   185 m.p.h.
   Cruising speed sea level - 79 % top speed 146 m.p.h. plus
   Landing speed not more than   65 m.p.h.
   Rate of climb sea level (minimum)   1200 ft. p.m.
   Service ceiling (minimum)   21000 ft.
   Service ceiling any two engines   10000 ft.

   This plane, fully loaded, must make satisfactory take-offs
   under good control at any TWA airport on any combination of
   two engines.

Kansas City, Missouri.
August 2nd, 1932

The letter and general performance specifications TWA vice-president Jack Frye sent to airplane builder Donald Douglas in 1932.

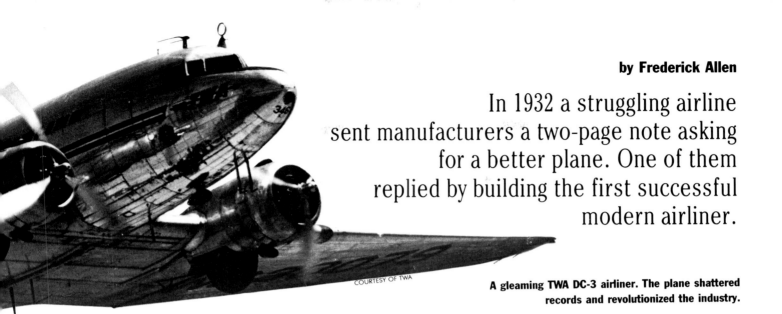

by Frederick Allen

In 1932 a struggling airline sent manufacturers a two-page note asking for a better plane. One of them replied by building the first successful modern airliner.

COURTESY OF TWA

A gleaming TWA DC-3 airliner. The plane shattered records and revolutionized the industry.

A brief letter mailed on August 2, 1932, led to the emergence of modern airline travel. It was a form letter sent to airplane manufacturers and was just three sentences long, with a postscript and an accompanying single-page list of general specifications for a possible future airplane. But it sparked a project that pulled together the best aeronautical engineering and design work of the previous decade to produce a line of airplanes that represented a culmination of everything before them and a breakthrough to the future. For a brief while they made everything else in the sky obsolete, and they brought commercial air travel to maturity.

The letter was sent by Jack Frye, vice-president of Transcontinental & Western Air, Inc. (TWA), to a handful of airplane manufacturers. The planes that grew out of it were the Douglas DC-1, DC-2, and DC-3. The letter read simply:

"Transcontinental & Western Air is interested in purchasing ten or more trimotored transport planes. I am attaching our general performance specifications, covering this equipment and would appreciate your advising whether your Company is interested in this manufacturing job.

"If so, approximately how long would it take to turn out the first plane for service tests?"

The attached single page of specifications — its brevity seems preposterous today, when the specs for a new aircraft might fill several trucks — asked for an all-metal three-motor monoplane that could cover 1,080 miles at 150 miles per hour, seat twelve passengers comfortably, land at under 65 mph, and take off from any TWA airport with one engine out. Maximum gross weight: 14,200 pounds.

Donald W. Douglas's Douglas Aircraft Corporation had never built an airliner, but he jumped at the chance the letter gave him. His company put out in just ten months a plane that far exceeded TWA's hopes. Two years after that, the plane had evolved into the DC-3, a craft so universally preferred to anything else in the skies that by 1939 three-quarters of all passengers were flying on it, and the skies themselves were starting to look the way they do today.

Jack Frye wrote the letter because his airline was desperate. Commercial aviation was still virtually in its infancy. Planes were slow; with top speeds of around 100 mph they could hardly even beat the railroads. They had to land for fuel every couple of hundred miles. They were noisy, uncomfortable, cramped, and expensive. There was little wonder that almost nobody flew. The successful airlines paid their way with government contracts to fly airmail.

TWA was in an especial bind. It depended for its long-distance flights on Ford and Fokker trimotors. The boxy, wooden eight- or ten-passenger Fokker monoplanes, each with an open cockpit and overhead wing, had served the airline well until March 31, 1931. Then a single accident had destroyed them. A TWA Fokker on a scheduled flight plunged out of the sky into a Kansas pasture, and among the seven bodies pulled from the wreckage was that of the legendary Notre Dame football coach Knute Rockne. An investigation revealed that the insides of the wooden wing had rotted away where it joined the fuselage, and the way the plane was constructed, routine inspection could not even have detected the problem. The experience marked the beginning of the end not only for the Fokker but for all wooden aircraft. TWA was going to have to find a new metal plane.

To make matters worse, United Air Lines, which, like TWA, held one of three transcontinental air routes (determined by airmail-handling contracts), had just ordered a big, new metal plane from Boeing that was going to fly faster and need fewer refueling stops than any existing airliner. With its rounded, streamlined aluminum-alloy body, the Boeing 247 would be the first modern passenger plane, and TWA knew it. What's more, TWA couldn't have it. Boeing and United Air Lines were sister companies under the same holding company, and while Boeing wasn't unwilling to sell its new plane to TWA, TWA was going to have to wait until United had received all sixty it had ordered. That wouldn't be for several years, and by then TWA might be out of business.

So just to stay alive, TWA would need a competitive craft, and none existed. The Boeing 247 was a step in an evolution toward the modern airliner, but it was a big enough step that nothing earlier could compete with it. Passenger planes had been improving rapidly and dramatically in the last decade; a plane just a few years old — like a Fokker — was a dinosaur. The modern single wing had been developed just fifteen years before, during World War I, by the German aeronautical scientist Hugo Junkers, who found that a metal wing with separate upper and lower surfaces could be cantilevered and braced entirely from within, eliminating the drag caused by the familiar messy biplane systems of struts and guy wires.

The only DC-1 ever built attracts onlookers in California.

A Ford Tri-motor, one of the most popular airplanes of the 1920s.

Another German, Adolf Rohrbach, had taken this innovation a step further. By stretching aluminum-alloy sheeting tight over the wing structure — Junkers had used heavy corrugated steel — he could streamline the wing while actually strengthening it so that far less internal support was needed.

Henry Ford's Ford Tri-motor, of 1925, introduced metal construction to commercial transport, and the "tin goose," as it was called, became the most popular passenger plane of the late twenties. But it was noisy and poorly heated and could rarely carry its twelve passengers faster than 105 mph. By 1932 it was as obsolete as the Fokker. Another late-twenties craft, the Lockheed Vega, was America's first streamlined airline plane, with a stretched skin rather than Ford's corrugated surface and a brisk cruising speed of 135 mph. But it seated only four, and it was made of wood.

Boeing meant to incorporate every recent breakthrough in aircraft design into the new 247. The company had already broken ground in 1930 with its Monomail, an all-metal plane with a fuselage of advanced semimonocoque design. *Monocoque* meant that, as in a lobster's shell or a Ping-Pong ball, the smooth, tight, curved outside skin carried the bulk of the structural load; *semi* meant that, unlike in the shell or ball, some internal support was still needed. The design —descended from Rohrbach's wing — both created a much stronger structure and freed up inside space that had previously been clogged with girders and spars. Modern as it was, the Monomail had an open cockpit, a concession to pilots who just a few years before had been flying canvas-and-wire biplanes. The 247 was going to have a streamlined, semimonocoque, all-metal body and internally braced single wings; a closed cockpit; and retractable landing gear, a detail that by cutting drag could increase air speed by 6 to 8 percent. It

would seat ten, and, powered by two 600-horsepower Pratt & Whitney engines, it would cruise at an unprecedented 155 miles per hour. The 247 stood to make Boeing the nation's leading manufacturer of airline planes.

Jack Frye's letter sought a plane to match the 247. He thus solicited an all-metal monoplane with a metal internal structure; however, he was willing, in extremity, to consider a partly wood plane, or even a biplane. He asked for three rather than two engines to reassure passengers. The weight, range, and cruising speed he requested were comparable to those projected for the Boeing, and he wanted the latest in high-tech controls — "complete instruments, night flying equipment." The 65-mph landing speed would guarantee that the plane could land on as short a strip as the slow Ford Tri-motor. To ensure the safety of the craft in case of engine failure, Frye added at the end: "This plane, fully loaded, must make satisfactory take-offs under good control at any TWA airport on any combination of two engines."

He sent the letter to all the leading airline manufacturers and a few smaller ones. One of the smallest took the bait. Donald Douglas had founded his company in 1920, when he was twenty-eight; it had done a good business turning out planes for the military but had never built a large transport plane, and Douglas was eager to break into the potentially lucrative civil market, especially in the throes of the Depression. The son of a Brooklyn bank teller, Donald Douglas had become infatuated with flight in 1908, when as a teen-ager he saw Orville Wright fly above Fort Myer, Virginia. Four years later he dropped out of the United States Naval Academy to study aeronautics at the Massachusetts Institute of Technology. By 1915, when he was twenty-three, Douglas had enough of a reputation to be hired sight unseen as chief engineer for the aviation pioneer and plane builder Glenn Martin. When Martin saw his new employee, he exclaimed, "Why, you're just a boy. A boy engineer."

Douglas had less than a thousand dollars in savings when he cut out on his own in 1920, and he started off in a room in the back of a Los Angeles barbershop. Within a year he had designed the first plane in the world that could carry more than its own weight in cargo, and he managed to sell a variation of it to the Navy as a torpedo bomber. He followed that with a succession of Army observation planes, postal mail planes, and flying boats.

Donald Douglas's company had never built an airliner, but he jumped at the chance the letter gave him.

When Jack Frye's letter arrived, in August 1932, Douglas's company occupied an old movie studio in Santa Monica, where a dozen young airplane designers worked in shirt sleeves and knickers and all knocked off for picnic lunches together. As soon as Douglas received the letter, he and his engineers began looking for ways they could design a plane to outdo the specifications and outperform the 247 too. With the Depression squeezing every manufacturer, Douglas knew he would have to work extremely fast to have a chance at winning a contract.

Immediately Douglas's engineers decided to dispense with the trimotor idea. As the chief engineer, James H. ("Dutch") Kindelberger, later said, "Why build anything that even looks like a Fokker or Ford?" According to Kindelberger's assistant, Arthur Raymond, "We all thought, Doug, Dutch and I, that we had a chance to meet the requirement with two engines. The simplicity of that solution appealed to us. It would clean up the whole front of the airplane. You would not have the propeller in front of the pilot; you would not have the aerodynamic drag of the engine up there. . . . You'd have less noise and vibration in the cabin, and no gas lines or fumes in the fuselage. You'd have a simpler, less costly design. It was just a better solution." As it happened, Raymond had been studying new methods of calculating airplane performance at Caltech, and he was able in just five days to determine that a two-engine plane could indeed meet TWA's demands, even though it would mean being able to take off from a four-thousand-foot-high airport on only one engine.

The designers also agreed to give the plane a rounded, all-metal, stressed-skin semi-monocoque fuselage, backed by aluminum-alloy stiffeners that ran around its inside like barrel hoops; recently introduced cowlings in front of the engines to reduce drag; retractable landing gear; and wing flaps, which had never been used on a large plane but held the key to being able both to fly fast and to land slow. They also decided to take advantage of an advanced, lightweight, multicellular wing structure that had been designed by Jack Northrop, a brilliant young airplane designer whose company and inventions Douglas had recently bought out. They named the plane they were sketching out the DC-1, for Douglas Commercial No. 1.

Just ten days after Frye's letter had arrived, Arthur Raymond and Douglas's general manager, Harry Wetzel, boarded a transcontinental train for New York to present a proposal to TWA. Raymond did some final calculations, and by the time the two reached the East Coast they had the whole plane designed and specifications ready for everything down to the width of the aisles.

In New York they met with Frye; TWA's president, Richard Robbins; and TWA's celebrity technical adviser, Charles Lindbergh. As intense discussions got under way, the TWA people came to like the general design of the plane, especially its strong yet roomy fuselage. But they were skeptical about

Donald Douglas, aviation innovator.

Workers in the early years of the Douglas Aircraft factory, 1920s.

its ability to take off from any TWA airport with an engine out. Then, in the middle of the talks, Lindbergh made matters worse. He decided that the plane should be able not only to take off on a single engine but then to continue on and climb above and fly over the highest mountain on any TWA route. Raymond did some calculations showing a 90 percent certainty that the plane could do this. He telephoned Douglas and confided, "The other 10 percent is keeping me awake nights." Douglas turned to Kindelberger and was told: "There's only one way to find out. Build the thing and try it."

Raymond and Wetzel thus promised TWA that their plane would meet the requirement, and TWA decided to give them a shot at it. On September 20, 1932, the airline offered Douglas Aviation $125,000 to build a prototype (the specifications had said nothing about price) and took an option to buy up to sixty planes in production for $58,000 each. Douglas would have to sell at least that many to break even. To be safe, TWA also gave a contract to General Aviation, a much larger manufacturer, to build a traditional trimotor.

Back in Santa Monica, the Douglas engineers went at it. Their wing was refined in tests of miniature models in the big wind tunnel at Caltech, which had been installed in 1930. But the shape of the wing had to be changed dramatically not because of aerodynamics but because the plane was becoming heavier and its center of gravity was moving back. Arthur Raymond decided that rather than displace the whole wing, it would be simpler just to taper its leading edge and move back some outer panels. This gave it a swept-back shape no previous wing had had.

Unlike the fuselage, the wing was not semimonocoque; it used Jack Northrop's weblike internal structure of spars and ribs. It was built in three pieces, and a simple flanged and bolted joint, also invented by Northrop, allowed it to be taken apart or replaced almost effortlessly. In flight the wing would carry the whole weight of the plane, its upper surface working under compression and its lower surface in tension.

FASTEST · SHORTEST · FAIR TO FAIR

UNITED AIR LINES MAINLINERS

THE MAIN LINE FAIRWAY

STOPOVERS ALLOWED AT YELLOWSTONE... BOULDER DAM... GRAND CANYON AND OTHER NATIONAL PARKS

ONLY UNITED'S MAINLINERS LINK THE EAST WITH EVERYWHERE WEST

A 1939 United ad offers service between World's Fairs by DC-3.

Since it was flexible, passengers on the DC-1, as on virtually all subsequent large planes, would become used to seeing the tips of the wings flap and shudder as the plane moved through the air, absorbing turbulence that would otherwise shake up the fuselage and the passengers themselves.

Like the wings, the engines could be easily removed. The engineers improved on cowlings to fit over the front of the engines that had been designed by the National Advisory Committee on Aeronautics (the early predecessor to NASA), and they housed the engines in streamlined nacelles out in front of the wings, where turbulence would be reduced.

The choice of the engine itself became a hot contest. Pratt & Whitney's Hornet and Wright's similar Cyclone, each a nine-cylinder air-cooled radial, were both available, and both companies took space in Douglas's erecting shop to work on adapting and selling their engines. A white line across the floor separated them. Wright finally won the battle with a 690-horsepower supercharged power plant that was said to have the lowest specific weight of any airplane engine yet designed. Onto the engine Douglas's engineers fitted a two-pitch propeller, a new invention that allowed the pilot to angle the blades for maximum power at takeoff and then to straighten them for more efficient travel in level flight.

In February 1933, as the DC-1 was being assembled, the sleek Boeing 247 had its first flight. It was smaller than first planned, but the ten-seater could cruise at 155 mph, making it the fastest airliner existing. Watching it soar through the sky, Boeing's chief engineer, C. N. Monteith, marveled, "They'll never build 'em any bigger." Meanwhile, the engineers in Santa Monica raced to complete their bigger plane. The "excitement helped your morale," one of the engineers later recalled. "In the same rooming house with Eddie Allen [the Douglas test pilot] lived Al Reed and Gene Root, fresh out of Cal Tech. They rode bicycles to work and arrived in a sweat. We all had some responsibility for structure—I did stress analysis on the engine nacelle."

The DC-1 was wheeled out for its first test flight on July 1, 1933, less than ten months after TWA had signed the contract for it. The pilot was Douglas's vice-president for sales, Carl Cover. As Donald Douglas and hundreds of his employees watched from the grass beside the airstrip at the Santa Monica airport, the just-completed plane accelerated down the runway, lifted into the air, rose — and then fell. One engine had gone out.

Cover banked sharply, and as he descended, the engine came back to life. He started climbing again, and then both engines went dead. For a moment it looked as if the whole project was over. Cover again dropped the nose, and both engines came back. He then began gingerly coaxing the plane higher, repeatedly dipping downward to bring the engines back as repeatedly they died, until finally he had enough altitude to circle and make a safe landing.

He emerged from the plane dazed and baffled, but it didn't take Douglas's mechanics long to figure out what had happened. A new type of carburetor had been installed on the engines with its floats on backward, so that the fuel was cut off every time the plane tilted up. The carbs were set right, and within days the plane was rolled out again. This time everything worked. It was run on two engines and run on one engine, and it performed flawlessly. After it had landed, a telegram went off to TWA in New York: "This is it."

The next hurdle was the promised takeoff on a single engine. This produced more drama. The plane was taken to TWA's highest airport, in Winslow, Arizona, and loaded down with sandbags to give it a maximum laden weight of eighteen thousand pounds. Pilot Edmund Allen took the controls; on board as a representative of TWA was the well-known flier Tommy Tomlinson. The cautious plan was to start with full power and cut one engine back to half-power just after the plane left the ground; if the plane then rose without strain, a second takeoff would be tried with the engine cut back all the way. But as the plane began its first lift-off, Tomlinson

The DC-2 and -3 exceeded in almost every respect the original specifications set by TWA.

reached up and flipped not the throttle but the ignition switch on one engine. The landing gear was already being retracted, so there was no playing safe. The plane sank at first—to within six inches of the ground, Tomlinson later said. Allen shoved the throttle down all the way on the remaining engine, and the plane steadied and started to rise. It kept climbing, and when it had reached eight thousand feet, Tomlinson was asked to explain his rash action. "You work for the manufacturer," he told Allen. "I work for the customer. I just wanted to see if the old girl is as good as you guys claim she is." The plane kept going all 230 miles to Albuquerque, and it was almost ready to take off again for the return flight to Winslow when an old Ford Trimotor that had preceded it out of Winslow landed behind it.

That prototype plane was the only DC-1 ever built. TWA liked it, but before it went into production, Douglas's engineers realized that they could stretch the fuselage a foot and a half, cut a bit off the cargo space, and seat fourteen instead of twelve. That would well surpass the airline's original request that the plane seat "at least 12 passengers" and make the plane significantly more attractive economically. They also put on more powerful new engines, which increased the cruising speed to 196 mph. Now the plane exceeded in almost every respect the original specifications set by TWA and those of the 247 as well.

TWA put its first DC-2s in service on May 18, 1934. By the end of the month it had broken the New York–to–Chicago speed record four times and had cut the Boeing 247's five-and-a-half-hour time between the two cities by half an hour. In August the DC-2 began transcontinental service between Newark and Los Angeles, with stops at Chicago, Kansas City, and Albuquerque. Its eighteen-hour coast-to-coast schedule cut an hour and a half off the record set by the 247 the year before. Not only did the DC-2 fly faster and carry more passengers than the Boeing, but it also avoided, by its low placement of the wing, the Boeing's inconvenience of a wing spar

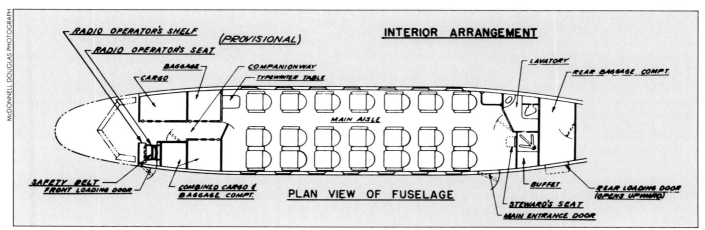

The DC-3's wider fuselage gave it a roomy cabin capable of seating twenty-one passengers.

across the cramped fuselage, which passengers had to step over to get down the aisle. Within a year all the leading airlines except United, wedded to its 247, had ordered DC-2s.

The DC-1's evolution was not complete, however. The impetus for the crowning advance came again from an airline in a fix, but this time it was not TWA but American. American Airlines was saddled with a roundabout transcontinental route (determined by its airmail contracts) that brought its passengers within sight of both Canada and Mexico (at Buffalo and El Paso). It simply couldn't keep up with the faster and more direct flights of TWA or United. Cyrus R. Smith, American's sharp-talking, Texas-born president, saw sleeper service as his airline's only hope, but to make sleeper service attractive in 1934 would mean finding a plane that combined the spaciousness of old Curtiss Condors — wide biplanes used as sleepers — with the speed of the new DC-2. Of course, no such plane existed.

Smith decided Douglas should build one. In his no-nonsense personal style of doing things — a style not then uncommon in the young airline business — he simply called up Douglas on the phone. He told him he needed a wider DC-2 with sleeping berths. He didn't have any money to pay for it, but he promised he could secure a $4.5-million government loan to cover it. Douglas's response was: "We can't even keep up with the orders for the DC-2s." Smith stayed on the phone, promised to buy twenty planes sight unseen, and argued that the wider plane could also be used as a regular passenger craft with twenty-one seats — seven rows of three seats across instead of the DC-2's two across. After two hours of Smith's cajoling, Douglas gave in. He later said to Raymond: "So they want to buy twenty? We'll be lucky if we break even. Who the hell is going to buy a sleeper plane? Night flying is about as popular as silent movies."

The Douglas Sleeper Transport, or DST, was rolled out in December 1935, but all eyes were already on the day-flying version being prepared, with twenty-one seats. That was designated DC-3, and it soon became the most popular plane existing. At first Douglas hoped that widening the DC-2's fuselage and extending its wings a little would do the whole job, but it wasn't that simple. As he later explained, "We added five feet more to the wing on each side of the fuselage. . . . We soon found out however that just putting on more wing didn't give us the lift and stability we needed. It was really a case of redesigning the wing." Extensive tests in the Caltech air tunnel using eleven successive miniature models of the plane led gradually to a truly new wing — thinner, narrower,

An icebound DC-2 from the 1937 film *Lost Horizon*.

and ten feet longer tip to tip.

In addition, the enlarged plane was given better, hydraulic landing gear, new 1,000 - horsepower Wright engines, a skin of a new stronger and lighter aluminum alloy, cabin soundproofing designed by an acoustical engineer, and an interior in mellow colors specially chosen to avert airsickness.

When the DC-3 entered scheduled service, on June 25, 1936, it was the biggest thing in the sky, the equivalent in its era to a Boeing 747. One airline official called it the "flying whore" because it had no visible means of support. C. R. Smith described it more aptly as "the perfect airplane for its day." With its unmatched speed and capacity it swiftly came to dominate the air routes. To fly a DC-3 between New York and Chicago cost an airline about eight hundred dollars, just slightly more than sending a DC-2, but with the additional seats, that meant a savings of 30 percent per passenger. A United pilot recalled, "United tried to advertise that its Boeings were just as fast as the DC-3s but you knew it wasn't true when you saw them pass you up in the air. . . . There's nothing that makes passengers madder than arriving late all the time. So United got rid of its 247s and bought DC-3s too." By 1939 DC-3s were carrying three-quarters of all airline passengers, and they were doing it so efficiently that the number of domestic airline planes had actually dropped from 460 to 358 while the number of passengers had quadrupled.

The DC-3 soon became legendary. In World War II it became the C-47 transport—and in Britain the Dakota — which served as an all-purpose, ubiquitous aerial truck, hauling not only cargo but also paratroopers, personnel, and gliders. The planes that flew over the Himalayan "hump" from India into Burma were DC-3 "gooney birds"; so were the planes that flew the airlift to Guadalcanal. More than nine hundred DC-3s helped deliver the troops that invaded France from England in June 1944; a similar number towed gliders over the Rhine for the advance into Germany in March 1945—the greatest airborne invasion of all time.

After the war more advanced airliners began to be designed, with pressurized cabins and, before too long, turboprop engines, but the old DC-3 was too good to disappear. It remained a staple short-hop airliner throughout the fifties and sixties. And it was still one of the nation's major military planes in the Vietnam War, where it found new jobs as propaganda leafletter, electronic surveillance ship, night photographer, Agent Orange dispenser, and, most oddly, heavily armed flying gunboat.

The last American military DC-3 was decommissioned in 1982, but air forces around the world still use them.

DC-3s are still flying on scheduled airline flights everywhere too; in this country just one passenger line continues to use them: Provincetown-Boston Airlines, whose fleet of a dozen includes the most traveled one of all, a DC-3 that has clocked more than eighty-seven thousand hours of air time, or almost ten years in the sky. DC-3s fly as cargo planes and private planes as well. One reason hundreds survive is that the plane is virtually indestructible. No DC-3 has ever been lost as the result of a structural failure. And the DC-3's presence is still felt in jets many times larger and faster; it is their common ancestor as the first truly successful, all-metal, streamlined, semimonocoque modern airliner.

After the war, more advanced airliners were designed, but the DC-3 was too good to disappear.

The singular career of the prototype DC-1 that answered Jack Frye's letter suggests the versatility of the entire breed. In February 1934 the government canceled all its airmail contracts with private carriers in favor of a short-lived experiment with Army mail delivery. Frye made a valiant show of defiance. He climbed into the DC-1's cockpit and, with the great Eddie Rickenbacker in the copilot's seat, sped TWA's final load of airmail from Los Angeles to Newark in thirteen hours and four minutes, setting a new coast-to-coast record. The feat prompted a New York newspaper to observe, "This plane has made obsolete all other air transport equipment in this country or any other." A year later, with larger engines, the DC-1 broke its own record by almost two hours — and within three days set eighteen other world records.

In the summer of 1936 TWA sold the DC-1 to its largest stockholder, Howard Hughes. He planned to fly it around the world, but then he chose instead to make the flight in a racy Lockheed 14, a plane designed to compete with the DC-3, and he sold the DC-1 to an Englishman. The Englishman sold it after several months to a French company; the French firm sold it to the Republican government of Spain, where it was pressed into Civil War service. When Barcelona fell in 1939, the top Spanish Republican officials escaped to France in the DC-1. Then it was taken over by the new nationalist Spanish government, which put it into regularly scheduled airline service for one last time. In 1940 it crashed on its belly after engine failure at takeoff. Nobody inside the sturdy craft was hurt, but the plane was so banged up it was scrapped.

Monks from the nearby Málaga Cathedral gathered spars and skin from the wreck of the DC-1 and used them to make an *andas*, a portable platform for moving the image of the Blessed Virgin through the streets of the city on holy days. Thus transfigured, the DC-1 lived on. ★

Frederick Allen is the editor of *Invention & Technology*.

THE IMAGE BANK. © GORDON KALLIO

Many privately owned DC-3s, like this one in California, remain in service around the country, as do a handful in commerical use.

A Silver Streak

by Margaret Coel

The Zephyr brought new life to railroading in the thirties, introducing diesel power, lightweight construction, and streamlining

At 5:04:40 on Saturday morning, May 26, 1934, the first diesel-powered, stainless-steel, streamlined train pulled out of Union Station, Denver, on a dawn-to-dusk race for Chicago. Called the Zephyr, it had been delivered to the Chicago, Burlington & Quincy Railroad in Philadelphia just six weeks earlier and had traveled west in a series of short trips. To reach Chicago before sunset, it had to cover 1,015 miles nonstop in less than fourteen hours. No train in railroad history had run more than 775 miles nonstop, and the Burlington's crack passenger train, the steam-powered Aristocrat, took twenty-seven hours from Denver to Chicago. Newspapers called the Zephyr's race "chancy."

Sleek and shiny in the early morning sun, the Zephyr looked like a rocket in a Buck Rogers cartoon. Its technology, as novel as its appearance, had been developed over the previous three years, the result of major breakthroughs both in metallurgy and in the

design of the diesel engine. Such breakthroughs had seemed so unlikely as the thirties got under way that most railroad officials had assumed high-speed, diesel-powered trains were "decades and millions of dollars away."

Four industrial leaders of the day had set out to develop and manufacture the revolutionary train. They were: Ralph Budd, president of the Burlington; Edward G. Budd, founder of the Philadelphia auto-body plant that bore his name (the two Budds were not related); Harold L. Hamilton, president of the Electro-Motive Corporation, a division of General Motors; and Charles Kettering, research vice-president of General Motors. With the nation in the grip of the Depression, these capitalists were betting that the Zephyr would win its race to Chicago, lure passengers back to the railroads, open new markets for stainless-steel and diesel

The Zephyr pulls out of Denver in the first few minutes of its race to Chicago in May 1934. All along the route people stood by to watch the gleaming train speed past.

engines, and reverse the downward side their corporate profits had been taking since the Crash of 1929.

Shoring up profits at the Burlington took top priority for Ralph Budd, the man who ordered the Zephyr. Genial and soft-spoken, with wire-rimmed glasses, the fifty-two-year-old Budd had taken the helm of the Burlington in 1932 after apprenticeship as the boy wonder of the railroad industry. Born on a farm in Iowa in 1879, he had raced through high school and college in six years, earning a civil engineering degree from Highland Park College in Des Moines. After a decade in the engineering departments of Midwestern railroads controlled by James J. Hill, Budd was tapped to be Hill's assistant and chief engineer on the Great Northern Railroad. In 1919, at the age of forty, he succeeded Hill as the railroad's president.

By the time Budd moved to the Burlington, the Depression had bought the nation's trains almost to a standstill. Long lines of empty cars and coaches rusted in the railyards as annual freight revenues dipped to two billion dollars, half the amount of a decade earlier. The number of passengers on the Burlington alone declined from eighteen million annually to seven million

The decline in passengers could not be laid wholly at the feet of the Depression, however. By 1930 Americans were driving twenty-four million motor vehicles of 920,000 miles of improved roads. While most Americans still preferred trains for cross-country trips, they drove their automobiles on shorter jaunts, putting the railroads in a bind. As Ralph Budd explained, railroads had to continue running trains on short routes to handle mail and baggage. "whether or not anyone rides the trains." At the same time, steam locomotives were becoming more and more expensive to operate. With fuel prices rising, they gobbled enormous quantities of coal and oil. Weighing 250 tons apiece and thundering down the track at sixty miles per hour, they destroyed both rails and themselves. The result: costly repairs and unproductive time in the shops.

In the mid-1920's, railroads tried to cut operating costs on short routes and lure back passengers with railcars—

What the railroads needed, Budd concluded, was a fast, luxurious, ultramodern train.

Ralph Budd, of the Chicago, Burlington & Quincy Railroad, ordered the Zephyr.

self-propelled single cars. By 1930 six hundred railcars were at work on the nation's railroads, fifty-five of them on the Burlington. The majority were designed by Cleveland's Electro-Motive Corporation, the engineering firm that Harold Hamilton had founded in 1922. Hamilton, a Californian, had started in the railroad business as a callboy on the Southern Pacific and moved up quickly to locomotive engineer. Still ambitious, he had hired a retired Berkeley professor to tutor him in mathematics. Eventually he became a motor-truck salesman, gaining experience that later allowed him to design railcars with features from both the automotive and railroad industries.

Hamilton was a pioneer in putting the internal-combustion engine in a railcar. The gasoline-fueled engine ran an electrical generator, which in turn produced electricity to drive traction motors and provide an electric transmission, thereby eliminating mechanical gears and making the railcar easy to operate.

Despite the railroads' hopes for railcars, the traveling public still preferred automobiles. With 275-horsepower engines, railcars lumbered along at about forty miles per hour. By the late 1920s, the railcars had become about as costly to operate as steam-powered trains and weren't any more popular.

As long as freight business increased during the 1920s, railroads absorbed the loss in passenger revenues. But when freight revenues fell with the Depression, railroads started casting about for ways to bring Americans back to the trains. As Ralph Budd observed, "People were still traveling in the Depression, but not by train."

What the railroads needed, Budd concluded, was a new kind of train, an expanded railcar that was fast, convenient, ultramodern, and luxurious enough to fire the public imagination. To operate economically, it would have to be lightweight yet capable of hauling a maximum amount of "pay weight." The Burlington had just the route for such a train: the 250-mile stretch between Kansas City and Lincoln, Nebraska. The route had been nearly deserted by passengers, yet a train made the round trip every day, carrying mail and baggage.

Just as Ralph Budd was reaching this conclusion, the Edward G. Budd Manufacturing Company began constructing a lightwight, stainless-steel railcar. With automobile-body orders down, the company president was counting on the railcar for new business. Born in Delaware in 1870, Edward Budd had started out as a machinist's apprentice in 1887. Twenty-five years later he was president of his own auto-body manufacturing company. By 1932 the White-haired, whit-mustachioed Budd was about to cap a long career with his greatest achievement, the Zephyr.

Not long before, the company's research team, headed by Col. Earl J. W. Ragsdale, had introduced Shotwelding, the first successful method of welding stainless steel. Since its development by Krupp in 1914, the thin, lightweight alloy of low-carbon steel, 18 percent chromium and 8 percent nickel, had been used only for cutlery and surgical instruments; ordinary welding and riveting destroyed its two main properties—strength and resistance to corrosion. With Shotwelding, sections of stainless steel were electrically fused, creating rustproof joints stronger than the adjacent metal. Stainless steel could now be used as a major structural material.

In September 1932 Ralph Budd visited the Budd auto-body plant and took a ride in the new stainless-steel railcar, a ride he later called the first step in the creation of the Zephyr. Asked why a railroad president had turned to the automobile industry, he replied, "having taken our patrons from us, we may adopt some of [their] popular ideas to win them back."

Convinced that the automobile company could build a lightweight, three-car train. Budd began looking for a high-speed, economical engine. For economy and thermal efficiency, he knew that nothing could beat the diesel, which burned crude, inexpensive petroleum and used from one-fifth to one-tenth as much fuel as an oil burning steam locomotive. But he also knew that the diesel was heavy, slow, and erratic. Since 1898, when its inventor, the Munich professor Dr. Rudolf Diesel, had first successfully demonstrated the engine, railroads had tried with only limited success to adapt the diesel to locomotives.

Sluggish and massive—some weighed as much as three hundred pounds per horsepower—the early diesel locomotives used most of their power hauling themselves around. The diesel's heavy metal construction was necessary to withstand high temperatures and pressures. In addition, the engine's four cycles, in which the pistons took four separate strokes—fresh air intake, compression, fuel ignition, and gas exhaust—demanded a maze of weighty pipes and pumps that turned diesel locomotives into metal-bound monsters.

Still, the diesel's fuel economy continued to attract the railroad industry. At Cleveland's Winton Engine Company, which built engines for Electro-Motive railcars, Carl Salisbury, the chief research engineer, hit upon the idea of a separate unit injector for each cylinder, thus eliminating the heavy plumbing of the diesel. Each unit injec-

During construction at the Budd Manufacturing Company, the train's frame of hollow beams is covered over with a skin of stainless steel as little as one-fiftieth of an inch thick.

tor would act as a pump, putting the fuel under fifteen thousand pounds of pressure before spraying it into the piston.

While Salisbury went to work on the unit injector, Charles Kettering, one of the great inventive geniuses of the twentieth century, was also looking at ways to make the diesel more efficient. Born in rural Ohio in 1876, Kettering had armed himself with both mechanical and electrical engineering degrees from Ohio State University before setting out on a engineering career that spanned half a century. Among his inventions were the automobile self-starter, leaded (ethyl) gasoline, balancing machines, and variable-speed transmissions. By 1928 the middle-aged Kettering had turned his attention to a two-cycle diesel, generally dis-

missed by other engineers as impractical. Kettering believed the intake and exhaust strokes could be combined in the ignition, or power, stroke, making the diesel fast and smooth.

When Kettering heard about Salisbury's unit injector, he ordered a Winton diesel engine, complete with the injector, for his yacht the *Olive K*. He then spent as much time as possible on Lake Michigan, not relaxing but tinkering with the diesel engine. Kettering's method was to throw away the books and let the diesel tell him how it wanted to work. "The trouble with the diesel," Kettering later explained, "is that everyone tried to make it like a steam engine. If folks had made the diesel the way it wanted to be made, they might have gotten somewhere."

In 1930 Kettering's two-cycle engine seemed promising enough for General Motors to buy both the Winton Engine Company and the Electro-Motive Corporation, giving the automobile company a diesel-engine plant and a staff of railroad designers. With orders falling off for new automobiles, GM hoped an efficient, high-speed diesel engine would open up new markets. The U.S. Navy, interested in using a lightweight diesel engine for submarines, cooperated on research that continued over the next two years. Kettering headed the project.

Toward the end of 1932 Ralph Budd got word from Hamilton that General Motors was building a pair of two-cycle diesel engines. The new engines were slated to power the GM exhibit—an actual Chevrolet assembly line—at the Century of Progress Exposition, due to open in Chicago the following May. Budd lost no time in calling on Kettering at his Detroit laboratories to inquire about putting a diesel engine in the new Burlington train. "We wouldn't dare sell you this thing," Kettering told him. "We don't even know if it will run."

When the exhibition opened, Budd and other Burlington officials were on hand to see if the diesel engines would run. The new engines were constructed of Cromansil, a new, strong yet lightweight steel alloy of chromium, manganese, and silicon developed by Lukenweld, Inc., of Pennsylvania. With Cromansil and the two-cycle design, the diesel had finally shed its excess weight. The eight-cylinder engines developed between seventy-five and eighty horsepower per cylinder yet weighed only twenty-two pounds per horsepower. As Electro-Motive's historian, Franklin M. Reck, put it, "To engineers who understand their significance, these innovations were nothing short of sensational."

Still, not all the bugs had been worked out. As soon as the exposition closed each night, two engineers went to work repairing and overhauling the engines. So experimental were the engines that General Motors wanted no attention whatsoever called to them. Visitors strolled by the Chevrolet assembly line unaware that the diesels fenced off to one side represented the most advanced technology at the exposition. But Ralph Budd grasped their

Budd saw the new Cromansil diesel engines and "immediately was set afire."

significance. "Immediately I was set afire," he said later, "because I knew that the diesel was something completely revolutionary, and better—so much better—than anything we had ever had."

On June 17, 1933, Budd ordered a three-car, stainless-steel train from the Budd Manufacturing Company. And even though the new diesel had not been tested in railroad locomotives, he ordered a General Motors Model 201A diesel engine with 600 hp, capable of 110 mph. The order prompted Kettering to call Budd "a very nervy railroad president," but Budd disagreed. "I knew that if General Motors was willing to put the engine in a train, the national spotlight would be on the corporation," he said. "They'd simply have to stay with it until it was satisfactory. Actually, I wasn't taking a chance at all."

That summer the Budd automobile plant geared up to produce its first train. Paul Cret, a Philadelphia architect, headed the design team, which included the Chicago architect John Holabird and Budd employees Earl Ragsdale and Walter and Albert Dean. Burlington historians credit the young Albert Dean, who had graduated from MIT only two years earlier, as the main designer.

To ensure hundred-mile-per-hour speeds, the team borrowed the concept of streamlining, developed by airplane designers who had discovered that bullet-shaped fuselages gained speed by cutting through head winds. The results of wind-tunnel tests conducted on miniature train models at MIT showed that with equal size and weight, a con-

ventional train traveled 75 mph, while a streamliner reached 100 mph. Streamlining's advantages dictated the train's shape, with a sloped front, a rounded roof, lower fluted sides, flush windows and doors, and flat sheathing along the lower edge.

Next, the designers jettisoned all unnecessary weight. Cars were articulated, which meant that the ends of adjacent cars rode on the same truck. Instead of thirty-six wheels, the usual number for three cars, there were sixteen. Brakes, manufactured by Westinghouse, went directly on the trucks, eliminating heavy metal brake riggings.

But it was the almost paper-thin stainless steel, manufactured by United States Steel, that made the train a featherweight compared with conventional ones. The frame was constructed of hollow U-shaped beams, with walls just 0.012 inch thick. Additional pieces of stainless steel were welded at points of stress so that, as Edward Budd explained, each beam had exactly the "right amount of metal to stand the strain to which the section is subjected, and no more." The side and roof frames carried their weights like a bridge, resting on the end trucks instead of sitting on the underframe. Completed, the frame weighed 20 ounces per linear foot, yet had a tensile strength of 150,000 pounds per square inch.

On the lower sides went fluted sections of stainless steel, 0.02 inch thick, or about as thick as five sheets of paper stacked together. The thickest sheets—seven-sixteenths of an inch—covered the roof and slanted nose. Panels between the safety-glass windows were constructed of quarter-inch-thick Armorply, plywood sheathed with copper on the inside and stainless steel on the outside. Stainless steel acted as a natural insulator, and since stainless steel was rustproof, no paint was needed. Polished by wind, rain, and dust, the train would become more beautiful with age.

Up front behind the driver's compartment sat the Winton-built Cromansil engine, on a chassis also constructed of Cromansil. Designed with rounded contours to avoid stress on angles or squared joints, the chassis was welded together, marking the first time welding was used on a railway

Ralph Budd (left) and Edward G. Budd stand in front of the train at its formal dedication, in Philadelphia, April 18, 1934. The ceremony took place just ten months after the train had been ordered.

At the rear of the train, a tapered, window-wrapped solarium contained seats for twelve.

engine bed. Weighing only three tons, the chassis supported thirty tons of the engine and the front motor truck.

Behind the engine was the rest of the power plant, designed and assembled by Electro-Motive. The main generator, built by General Electric, transformed the engine's mechanical energy into electrical energy for the traction motors. It also provided the electrical transmission and supplied the electricity for two General Electric air compressors on the brakes. An auxiliary generator supplied current for the battery, train lights, and air conditioning.

From the slanted nose to the rear solarium the new train stretched 196 feet and weighed 200,000 pounds, one-eighth as much as the hefty Aristocrat. With its low center of gravity it could hug the track and sweep around curves without swaying. Rubber pads placed around the bogies absorbed vibrations and noise.

The train's interior received just as much design attention as the engine and running gear. After the engine compartment came the railway post office,

while the baggage and express compartment took up the first section of the second car. Next came the modern electric grill and the smoker's lounge, with beige carpeting and soft leather seats for twenty passengers. The third car contained forty upholstered reclining chairs and luxurious carpeting and curtains in shades of pearl gray. At the end was the window-wrapped solarium with chairs for twelve.

With the train under construction, Ralph Budd began searching for an appropriate name. Reading Chaucer's *Canterbury Tales* one evening, he came upon Zephyrus, the god of the west wind, and immediately called other Burlington officials to announce he had found a name. June Provines, a reporter for the Chicago *Tribune*, greeted the news with astonishment. She had never imagined, she said, that railroad presidents spent their evenings reading Chaucer.

The Zephyr rolled out of the plant on April 7, 1934, a mere nine and a half months after Budd had placed the order. Two days later it made a 24.8-mile trial run from Philadelphia to Perkiomen Junction, reaching a top speed

A crowd lines up to visit the Zephyr in Chicago in the summer of 1934. The train began its regular run, between Kansas City and Lincoln, Nebraska, the next November.

of 104 mph. At its formal dedication on April 18, broadcast nationwide over NBC radio from Philadelphia, Ralph Budd called the Zephyr a symbol of progress; Edward Budd referred to it simply as the "apple of my eye."

The first day after the dedication twenty-four thousand Philadelphians stood in line to visit the Zephyr. Over the next three weeks the Zephyr traveled to thirty Eastern cities, drawing crowds wherever it went. By the end of its first tour more than half a million people had walked through the new train.

But Ralph Budd wanted something more dramatic to introduce the Zephyr to Americans. In Chicago the Century of Progress Exposition was about to begin its second season, on May 26. Among the attractions was the "Wings of a Century" pageant, with scenes depicting the progress of American transportation from the Indian travois to the modern steam locomotive. Budd decided to have the Zephyr leave Denver at dawn, race nonstop to Chicago, and pull up on the pageant's stage at dusk for a grand finale that would officially reopen the exposition. Almost everyone else connected with the Zephyr, including Kettering and Hamilton, had misgivings. The train had made only short trips, yet Budd was proposing 1,015 miles nonstop at 100-mph speeds.

Stalled on the Nebraska prairie, it would be a national laughingstock.

Nonetheless, Budd ordered the Zephyr to Denver. It arrived at Union Station on Thursday, May 24, amid newspaper reports that "a silver train has flashed into the silver state." Again the crowds came, with fifty thousand touring the train in two days.

Requests to ride the Zephyr to Chicago poured in from celebrities, movie stars, and politicians across the country. But the eighty-five tickets (thirteen extra seats were set up in the baggage compartment) went to reporters and officials from the Burlington, General Motors, and the Budd company. The only other passenger was a burro named Zeph, a gift to the pageant from the Rocky Mountain *News* to represent early transportation in Colorado. When Budd was asked whether Zeph could ride the train, he replied: "Why not? One more jackass on this trip won't make any difference."

Early Friday evening the Zephyr went into the shops for final inspection. To their horror mechanics discovered a cracked motor armature bearing. When no replacement bearing could be found in Denver, calls went out to railroads across the country. After several frantic hours the Burlington got word that the Union Pacific had located a substitute bearing in Omaha. The Bur-

lington general manager there picked it up and boarded an airplane for Cheyenne, where a chartered airplane waited to whisk the bearing to Denver. At best it would arrive at about midnight, but installation could take hours.

That evening, with the Zephyr up on jacks, its nose pointed in the air, Budd went on NBC radio. If the Zephyr's race was to be canceled, now was the time. Instead, Budd told the nation, "Tomorrow at dawn we'll be on our way." He then invited everybody between Denver and Chicago to "come out and watch the Zephyr whiz by."

Mechanics worked through the night installing the substitute bearing. When dawn broke on Saturday, the Zephyr was ready to go, only one hour behind its original departure time. In the driver's compartment were the three men who would take two-hour turns at the controls: E. F. Weber, the Burlington superintendent of automotive equipment; J. S. Ford, an assistant master mechanic; and Ernie Kuehn, a Winton engineer. Three Burlington mechanics also rode in the cab.

To break in the new bearing, the Zephyr glided onto the plains at 50 miles per hour, with Kuehn, six feet tall and 230 pounds, sprawled facedown on the cab floor, ready to detect the first whiff of burning metal. Gradually the Zephyr began to gain speed, reaching 80 miles per hour.

It was still gathering speed when a door slammed on a wire, setting up a short circuit that burned out the engine starter cable. Smelling burning rubber, the driver turned off the engine and then could not restart it. As the Zephyr slowed to 40 miles per hour, everyone in the cab searched frantically for wire to splice the cable. At 15 mph Ralph Budd, ashen-faced, came out of his seat in the solarium and ran to the front, shouting, "Don't let her stop."

Another Electro-Motive engineer, Roy Baer, grabbed the ends of the wire and jammed them together. Electricity leaped across, burning Baer's hands, but he held on until the engine roared into life. The Zephyr had not stopped.

Now it opened up, racing across eastern Colorado at 90 miles per hour. It crossed Nebraska in four and a half hours and streaked through Iowa in three and a half hours. In one 19-mile stretch it cruised along at more than 100 miles per hour. Then it covered 3 miles at its top speed, 112.5 mph. It outdistanced the automobiles that tried to keep pace, and twice it even outdistanced airplanes.

More than a million people came out to see the Zephyr. In some towns the entire population was at the railroad track. Highways and roads were clogged with automobiles and trucks. Cars parked two deep lined the track for eight miles outside Galesburg, Illinois. Farmers stopped their tractors in the fields and tossed their hats in the air, cheering.

Every Burlington employee on the route took part in the Zephyr's run. Days before, section men had combed the track, making sure the rails were in good condition. The mechanical department had prepared detailed maps indicating the maximum speed at each section. Markers had gone up warning the drivers when to slow. Mail crane arms and water spouts had been wired down to keep them out of the way. Orders went out for other trains to wait in the sidings. Thousands of local policemen, Boy Scouts, and American Legion members stood guard at the 1,689 grade crossings.

Reporters riding the train dropped stories into eleven special chutes along the route, giving the nation frequent updates on the trip. At the exposition, news of the Zephyr's progress flashed across a large board while loudspeakers blared the Zephyr's location every thirty minutes.

At 4:55 P.M. the Zephyr roared through Princeton, Illinois, at 90 mph and passed the Aristocrat, which had left Denver twenty-four hours earlier. It dashed across the flat Illinois farmlands and into Chicago at 96 miles per hour, breaking the official tape at the Halsted Street Station at 7:09 P.M. Continuing along Illinois Central track to the exposition grounds at the lakefront, it pulled onto the two-hundred-foot-long stage at the amphitheater and stopped. The crowd went wild. Ten thousand spectators poured out of their seats and onto the stage, cheering and shouting, while boats on Lake Michigan blew their whistles and horns.

The Zephyr had set a host of records, including the world's record for the

*T*he train set a host of records, including the longest, fastest nonstop run ever.

In 1939 the Zephyr—renamed Pioneer Zephyr—passed its millionth mile.

longest and fastest nonstop railroad run. It had crossed 1,015.4 miles—one-third of the continent—in thirteen hours, four minutes, and fifty-eight seconds, at an average speed of 77.61 miles per hour. It had consumed 418 gallons of diesel fuel at four cents per gallon for a total cost of $16.72. The Aristocrat, on the other hand, used 85 tons of coal at $3 a ton, or $255.

That summer two million Americans toured the Zephyr as it traveled to 222 cities across the Midwest and West. Millions more watched it flash across the nation's movie screens as the star of the RKO film *The Silver Streak*. To Depression-weary Americans the train became a symbol of hope. As one passenger later remembered, the Zephyr "lifted our spirits. . . . it pointed the way

for better things to come."

On November 11, 1934, the Zephyr began its regular run between Kansas City and Lincoln. Tickets sold out days in advance for every trip. By month's end traffic on portions of the route had increased more than 100 percent over the previous November, and the Burlington ordered a fourth car. The next year General Motors replaced the diesel engine with another, slightly more refined one. The first engine went to the Smithsonian Institution.

Exceeding even the hopes of the four industrialists who had believed in it, the Zephyr did more than bring passengers back to the railroads. Its two-cycle diesel engine and lightweight metals revolutionized American railroading and put an end to the era of the steam locomotive. Before 1934 was out, eight major railroads ordered high-speed diesel-powered trains. In the mid-1940s diesel locomotives began outselling steam locomotives, and by the mid-1950s steam locomotives were no longer being manufactured in the United States. By 1961 the nation's 28,500 diesels were hauling twice the tonnage that 50,000 steam locomotives had carried in 1934, and at half the cost.

When other Zephyrs came on the Burlington roster, the first one received a new name: the Pioneer Zephyr. It worked almost every day for twenty-five years on Burlington routes, hauling more than one million passengers over 3,200,000 miles. When Americans again began deserting the railroads—this time for jetliners—it was still the last word in railroad transportation.

On May 26, 1959, the twenty-fifth anniversary of its historic race, the Pioneer Zephyr was retired. The following year it went to the Chicago Museum of Science and Industry. Named a National Historic Mechanical Engineering Landmark, it remains on permanent exhibit, still shiny and beautiful, still drawing the crowds, and still capable of racing a thousand miles from dawn to dusk, nonstop. ■

Margaret Coel became interested in the Zephyr while writing *Goin' Railroading: A Century on the Colorado High Iron* (Boulder, Colo.: Pruett Publishing, 1985).

STRUGGLING TO BECOME AN INVENTOR

by Dean J. Golembeski

Chester Carlson invented xerography by sheer dogged drive and methodical persistence

He is now recognized as a genius for inventing the process that makes the modern copier work, but Chester F. Carlson left a much different image in the minds of his college classmates. They remembered him as a very quiet student who didn't participate in many activities. They also recalled that he seemed to study harder than anyone else. In the words of his classmate Roland C. Hawes, of Monrovia, California, Carlson was "a little bit more of a plodder" than most students.

Carlson might have winced at those words, for he was tormented by his shortcomings, both academic and social. But Hawes meant it as a compliment. Only a stubborn, consummate plodder could have had the drive and persistence it took to overcome the frustrations and hardships Carlson faced. Fifty years ago last fall Chester Carlson demonstrated that it was possible to duplicate documents using a dry, nonphotographic process now known as xerography. He knew immediately that he had made a discovery of tremendous importance, but he had to wait more than twenty years, until 1960, before his invention was successfully applied and built the mighty Xerox Corporation.

Today we are addicted to copiers. We keep them in our offices, stores, schools, and libraries, and even in our homes. Roughly five million were in use in the United States at the end of 1987, and they churned out an estimated 497 billion copies, or 2,000 per American citizen. After the telephone, the copier is probably the most im-portant modern communications tool in use. But although almost every schoolchild learns about Alexander Graham Bell, almost nobody has ever heard of Chester Carlson.

He was an only child, born in 1906 in Seattle to Olof Adolph Carlson and his wife, Ellen. They were loving parents but were impoverished and infirm. Olof was an itinerant barber who was crippled by arthritis and tuberculosis; Ellen also suffered from tuberculosis, and their illnesses led them to move often in search of healthful climates. After their son was born, they moved from Washington to California, then to Arizona and Mexico and, by 1912, back to California, where they rented a farm in the small town of San Bernardino.

The many moves helped keep Carlson solitary. He was never able to forge lasting friendships and became shy and introverted. Even during his long stay in San Bernardino, circumstances

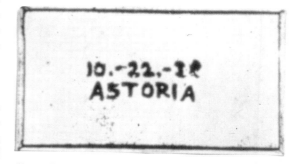

Above: The first xerographic copy (1938). Opposite: In 1963 Carlson re-created the experiment that produced it, exposing the inscribed slide and charged plate.

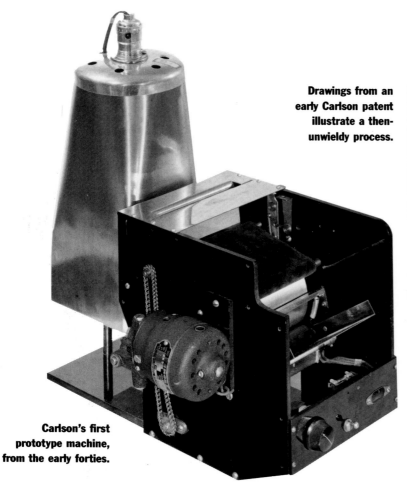

Carlson's first prototype machine, from the early forties.

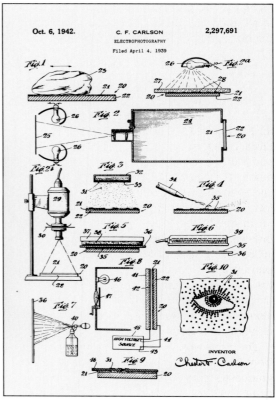

Drawings from an early Carlson patent illustrate a then-unwieldy process.

forced him to spend much of his time alone. "I used to pedal a broken-down bicycle to a country school," he later recalled. "It was hot and isolated, and for a time I was the only pupil. That made it terribly lonely."

When he was twelve, he began taking odd jobs after school and on weekends to support his parents. By the time he was thirteen, his father was bedridden, and within a year Chester had become the family's chief support. But he didn't quit school; instead, he rose at five each morning to wash store windows and sweep out a bank and newspaper offices.

Hard work became a trademark of Carlson's life. He always took on several jobs at a time, and he did remarkably well at most. His enjoyment of constant labor is summed up by an entry he wrote in his diary in 1928: "It has ceased to be interesting speculation with me and has become more and more an accepted fact that the most pleasure we get from life is sweating."

One of the jobs he took as a teen-ager was at a local print shop, where he did some work as a printer's devil in exchange for a small printing press that no one wanted. He used it to publish a little magazine for amateur chemists. "I don't think I printed more than two issues, and they weren't

much," he later said. "However, this experience did impress me with the difficulty of getting words into hard copy, and this, in turn, started me thinking about duplicating processes. I started a little inventor's notebook, and I would jot down ideas from time to time."

He never stopped. From then on Carlson always kept a small loose-leaf notebook in his pocket so he could record inventive ideas as well as keep personal reminders. He saved many of the books and planned at one time to use them in writing a history of Xerox.

His situation worsened when he was seventeen. His mother died, leaving the tall, thin, shy, good-looking youth alone to put himself through school and care for his ailing father. He went to work at a local cement plant. In 1925 he entered Riverside Junior College, where he enrolled in a work-study program that required him to spend alternate six-week periods working and attending school. He completed a three-year chemistry program as part of his curriculum.

At Riverside Carlson met a teacher who filled a need that his sick father couldn't: Howard H. Bliss, a professor of engineering, astronomy, and physics and the head of the work-study program. Bliss was young and athletic and had a passion for photography and outdoor activities. He had been teaching at Riverside for four years, and he recognized in Carlson his most brilliant student of all. Bliss became a companion and mentor to the busy and private Carlson.

He is the best teacher I have ever known," Carlson wrote in his college diary, which is now, along with most of his papers, part of the Chester F. Carlson Collection at the New York Public Library. The two spent countless hours together and built a bond that lasted until Carlson's death. They corresponded throughout their lives and even shared a hiking adventure through California's High Sierra after Carlson became successful in the 1960s. Their first trip together was a one-week vacation in Death Valley in December 1928, during which Bliss pursued his interest in photography, pressing Carlson into service as his assistant. Carlson reveled in Bliss's lectures on photography, literature, and the outdoors. He also developed a fondness for the solitary sports of hiking and trout fishing.

The professor, a tough critic, pushed Carlson from the start to raise his goals. When Carlson graduated from Riverside, in 1928, and was accepted at the California Institute of Technology as a third-year undergraduate majoring in physics, Bliss listed his weaknesses and told him how to improve. Carlson wrote in his diary: "Slowness in studying. Proposed medicine: assign myself a definite amount of time for studying each subject." Bliss noticed that Carlson appeared to lack self-confidence; Carlson wrote: "Pill: Put on a bold front, change tone of voice, call other fellows crazy once in a while. (Note: I feel self-confident, but perhaps I don't show it to others.)"

Carlson methodically developed a plan that he would follow at Caltech. He resolved to "cultivate acquaintance of faculty members," especially in the English department. He reasoned that he should join a campus organization, such as a theater group, that he must keep a financial record, and, perhaps most important, that he should "try to hold down a job for the first quarter or so." And he would make a review of his progress after the first term.

By his own measure, he failed miserably. In his end-of-semester evaluation, in December 1928, he scolded himself: He hadn't studied hard enough or played any tennis; his wardrobe, which embarrassed him, had become worse. His only real accomplishments had been getting a job and reading a few books.

Carlson's attempts to enforce self-improvement became a lifelong obsession. As an adult he would write long lists of his faults and their remedies. He kept them in the same notebooks he used for ideas for inventions. In 1958, for example, when he was fifty-two, he reminded himself in writing that he must pay attention to others, respect people's rights and feelings, stop meddling, control his talkativeness, and refuse unnecessary gifts. At the same time, he made notes about a new color photographic process.

His college classmate Roland Hawes called him "the hardest working person I ever knew." His classmates never knew that he was supporting his father, and Hawes now marvels at how much Carlson accomplished while in college. Jack B. Sturgess, another classmate, emphasizes that few people even knew Carlson: "He was an extreme introvert. He had very few personal friends. . . . He was devoted to one thing, and that was the study of physics."

Caltech was still a small school, only thirty-seven years old, but was in the midst of its rapid transformation from a small, local technical college to a top-notch national institution (see "Inventing Caltech," *Invention & Technology*, Spring 1986). In 1930, the year Carlson graduated, there were about six hundred graduate and undergraduate students, all men. Carlson avoided dances and other activities and sports. He lived at home and never became part of campus life.

During his first semester he toyed with the idea of quitting and heading east. He thought he might earn some money and then decide specifically what he wanted to do with his life. After a year he wrote: "Right now I am sorry I went to Caltech. I should have gone to Berkeley. True, the technical education here is probably better, but I am literally starved socially."

Like most college students, Carlson flirted with the possibilities of a number of occupations. He wanted to be a poet and jotted ideas for poems in his diary. He wanted to be a writer, an artist, a businessman, and finally an inventor. And he loathed his indecisiveness. "God, what a weakling I am," he wrote on January 12, 1929. "I can't concentrate, waste 10 minutes out of every 15 of an hour of study. I am awful at working with my hands. I can't even saw a board straight." Later on he wrote, "It humbles me to know that I am a prig." In April 1929 he resolved "to bend every effort to make my interests in others instead of my dull and stupid self."

He agonized about the choice of a career the whole time he was at Caltech. He asked in October 1928: "Is it necessary that I have a place. Yes, I think so, for I want some things that money alone will buy: home, travel, leisure. . . . I like science and invention, literature and home life.

He resolved to become a professional inventor before he was thirty.

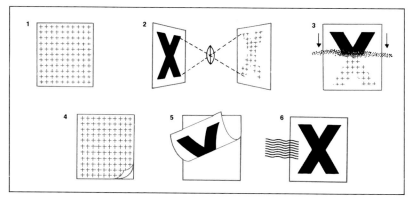

How xerography works: a plate with a positively charged photoconductive surface (1) records a pattern of light and dark projected on it (2). Negatively charged toner is attracted to the dark region (3). When positively charged paper is placed over the plate (4), it attracts the toner (5), which is then fixed to the paper by heat (6).

How will I pick the one which will bring money? Obviously, it is science and inventions. But how, teaching, industry or what? I have very little indication I would make a good teacher, or an inventor, and so my troubled mind continues."

Three months later, following his Death Valley trip with Bliss, he reflected: "Why does the problem of my future occupation bother me so much? I am continually wondering what kind of job I can hold down, what kind of work I will like and where I will find it." As the year wore on, he decided he would work best alone and in a field where he could be creative. He fancied that he could create a new vocation, "something new and never before attempted."

In the summer between his two years at Caltech, he went to work in a Los Angeles testing laboratory. During that time he decided the all-important question: He would be an inventor because an inventor "is always given a fair deal." He wrote, "I plan to break other business connections and go fully into a project of organizing a business for inventing, research on inventions and the buying and development commercially of patent interests on or before the age of 30."

He continued to work hard in his final year at Caltech, but he graduated without honors—that is, with less than a B-plus average. He also managed to end up fourteen hundred dollars in debt, even though he had spent far less than the average student. It was 1930, during the Depression. With methodical thoroughness, he sent out application letters to eighty-two companies. Two replied, both with rejections. Around the same time, his father died, and he headed to New York City. He landed a job there as a research engineer at Bell Telephone Laboratories, for thirty-five dollars a week. In 1931 he was transferred to Bell's patents department. In 1933 he was laid off, a victim of the Depression.

He managed to get another job, this time with a law firm specializing in patents. Less than a year later he resigned and took a job in the patents department of P. R. Mallory & Company, a maker of electrical components. The switch to Mallory turned out to be one of the most important moves in Carlson's life. He worked long hours comparing patent documents. Government regulations required copies of documents and drawings, and aside from photography, the only process for duplicating was by hand—typing texts and redrawing drawings and then examining them for errors. Carlson was nearsighted and starting to suffer from arthritis. He decided there had to be an easier way, and he set out to find it. He later recalled, "I recognized a very great need for a machine that could be right in an office where you could bring a document to it, push it in a slot and get a copy out."

He started by researching the available technical literature at the New York Public Library. He knew that such companies as Eastman Kodak were exploring photographic and wet-chemical duplicating methods; but he believed a dry-chemical process would be better, and if it worked, it would be his alone. He began exploring photoconductivity, the property certain materials have of undergoing a change in their electrical conductivity when exposed to light, and came upon the photoelectrical research of the Hungarian physicist Paul Selenyi. Selenyi had shown how electrostatically charged particles could be attracted to a surface in a predetermined pattern.

Unable to afford a laboratory, Carlson began experimenting with chemicals in the kitchen of his apartment in Queens, New York City. He soon filled his kitchen with jars of chemicals and began using his stove to cook up concoctions of them. He called the process he was seeking electrophotography. Simply put, he was experimenting with putting an electrostatic charge into a metal plate, which he would then expose to light. Depending on the intensity of the illumination, some areas of the plate would lose their charge. If the plate was then dusted with a powder, the powder would adhere to the areas that had retained their charge.

His experiments attracted attention around the building, for they often filled the halls with foul smells, including the rotten-egg stench of sulfur. One story has it that he met his first wife, Linda, during one of his experiments. She was the daughter of Carlson's landlady and came up to complain about the odors. She grew interested in his work and attracted to him. Carlson, for the first time in his life, fell in love. They were married in 1934.

Despite his marriage, his work, and his research, Carlson decided in 1936 that he needed a law degree, both to help him protect his research and to get him ahead in his job. Others in his department were earning more simply because they were attorneys. He enrolled at New York Law School in 1936, studying nights and weekends at the public library. He completed his law degree in 1939 and was admitted to the New York bar a year later.

Throughout the 1930s Carlson was consumed with himself and his work. He had no time for friends, recreation, or anything else outside his own interests. One early result was his first patent, issued on October 18, 1937. It covered the basic idea of electrophotography, and it granted Carlson broad rights since no one else was working in the field.

Carlson said later that he knew he had "a very big idea by the tail, but could I tame it?" Once he had the essential idea, his task was to put it into practice. First, at the insistence of his wife, he moved his work to a small room at the back of a beauty shop owned by her mother, in the Astoria section of Queens. Then he went out on a financial limb and hired an assistant, a German refugee physicist named Otto Kornei. Their research budget was ten dollars a month.

In their makeshift laboratory in Astoria, the two made the first successful experiment using electrophotography. It happened on October 22, 1938. Kornei rubbed a sulfur-coated zinc plate with a cotton cloth to create static electricity. They pressed the plate against a glass microscope slide with words written on it in ink and held the resulting sandwich up to a light; then Carlson removed the slide and dusted the plate with lycopodium powder, a yellowish moss spore; he pressed a piece of waxed paper against the plate, heated it, and peeled off the paper. When Carlson blew gently on the paper, there appeared on it a duplicate image bearing the words

he had written on the slide: "10-22-38 ASTORIA."

In near disbelief the pair repeated the experiment over and over. Carlson celebrated. Three years of intense work had finally paid off. Kornei was less impressed. The image was blurred, and he couldn't see where it would lead. He eventually left to take a job with International Business Machines, but Carlson never forgot him. In later years he rewarded Kornei with Xerox stock.

Carlson's jubilation over his achievement was short-lived. For more than five years he tinkered with the invention, building a small, simple copying machine in a wooden box. He tried to get a corporate sponsor to take an interest in it, but more than twenty companies, including RCA, General Electric, and IBM, rejected his machine. It was perhaps the most desperate time of his life.

"I did give up a few times and I tried to forget it. But I was so convinced it was important, I couldn't let it rest," he recalled later. "It was just hard to put over because the materials were so crude. It wasn't likely to excite a businessman." The primitive first copy made that day in Queens is now on display at the Smithsonian Institution.

Carlson was nearly broke and at his wits' end when his luck changed. The break came in 1944, when he mentioned his research to Dr. Russell W. Dayton, of the Battelle Memorial Institute, then a small research organization in Columbus, Ohio. Dayton had come to the P. R. Mallory offices to discuss other patents when Carlson

As he put it later, he had "a very big idea by the tail, but could I tame it?"

In today's Xerox 9400, a document inserted into a slot (1) is fed to a platen (2), where it is exposed via lamps and mirrors and through a lens (3) onto a photoreceptor belt (4). Magnetic rollers (5) brush the belt with toner, which clings to the image area. Copy paper from a tray (6) moves above the belt and picks up the toner (7). The image is fused to the paper between two rollers (8). A single copy emerges in a receiving tray (9); multiple copies are sent to a collator (10); or the paper is returned for printing on the other side (11). A central control console (12) and maintenance module (13) direct the operations.

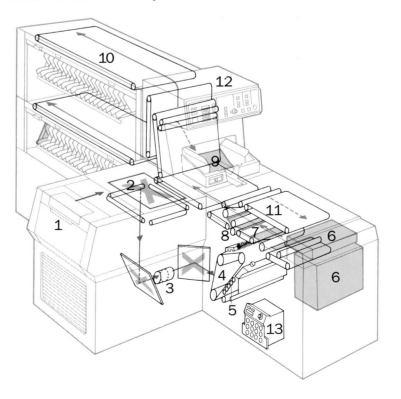

started talking about his own research. Instead of brushing Carlson off, Dayton listened. He had Battelle engineers study the device, and they concluded that, indeed, it might eventually take over some of the uses of carbon paper, mimeographs, photocopying, photo offset, and printing. After six months of discussions Carlson signed an agreement with Battelle. The nonprofit group agreed to spend three thousand dollars to research and develop Carlson's invention and to act as his agent to negotiate and grant licenses under his patents. Carlson would receive 40 percent of any profits.

Carlson jubilantly began spending all his spare time in Columbus, working on the invention. Once again his joy was premature. His wife, Linda, so often pushed aside by his work and subjected to his depressive moods, obtained a divorce in 1945. They had no children, no family life, and nothing to hold them together. Carlson had slid into a private world in which his work and his invention were everything.

Meanwhile, Battelle's research soon got too costly for the firm, so the company began seeking a corporate sponsor to underwrite its experimentation. It asked many of the nation's leading corporations for support and was rebuffed by all of them. Luckily, at the same time, the Haloid Company, a small manufacturer of photographic supplies in Rochester, New York, was looking for a new product to develop, and John Dessauer, head of research for Haloid, noticed an item about Carlson's invention in a technical magazine. Dessauer arranged a meeting between Haloid and Battelle officials. He was impressed when he saw Battelle's process at work, and so was his boss, Haloid's president, Joseph Wilson.

In late 1946, after months of negotiations, an agreement was reached giving Haloid a license to develop a copying machine based on Carlson's invention. Haloid had reported an income of only $101,000 in 1946, on sales of $6.7 million, and was making a tremendous gamble on Carlson's invention. The research involved would cost the company at least $25,000 a year. The gamble paid off; the little Haloid Company is now the Xerox Corporation.

As Haloid and Battelle struggled over the following lean years to refine Carlson's invention, they reworked their original agreement many times. Eventually Haloid became the exclusive licensee worldwide; Battelle and Carlson received royalties from Haloid and, later, stock.

One of the earliest concerns Haloid officials addressed was the need for a name. The word *electrophotography* did not present one. A Greek scholar came to their aid in 1947 with a new word, *xerography*, from *xeros* for "dry" and *graphos* for "writing" or "drawing." When the first copier was introduced, in 1949, it was given the name XeroX; the final *X* was later lowercased. Company officials admitted they had been influenced by the success of the name Kodak.

Haloid went to work developing an appealing box for Battelle's machine, did chemical research of its own, and verified results of experiments at Battelle. Haloid also provided direction by instituting a program that set specific research goals and schedules for scientists both at Battelle and at Haloid. Battelle scientists had already refined many elements of the dry-copy process, including the method for fusing images to paper. One key discovery was that selenium was far preferable to the sulfur used by Carlson for the photoconductive process.

On October 22, 1948, ten years to the day after

Carlson's first successful experiment, Battelle and Haloid finally revealed to the world the process they had developed. The announcement was made at a meeting of the Optical Society of America, in Detroit. The consensus among the audience was that the technology was interesting but had no future.

In 1949 Haloid marketed its first machine using xerography. The XeroX Model A—popularly known as the "ox box"—was crude and primitive, and it used a flat plate rather than the drum used in later machines. It required fourteen different manual operations and worked only if every step was followed exactly. The machines were uniformly rejected as too complicated. Haloid officials were stunned. However, the machine did achieve some success as a device for making masters for offset printing.

In 1955, Haloid introduced the Copyflo, the first completely automated copier, which produced enlarged prints from microfilm on a continuous roll. It was the first machine to use a drum as a photoconductive element instead of a flat plate. Its modest success prompted the company to change its name to Haloid Xerox in 1958.

Carlson remained involved in the work, making frequent trips to Columbus and Rochester to keep up with developments. He had remarried in 1946, and in 1954 he and his second wife, Dorris, moved from New York to the Rochester suburb of Pittsford to be closer to Haloid. Though he became an unofficial adviser to Haloid, he was never hired by the company. He attended meetings, looked over the shoulders of those who built the equipment, made occasional key suggestions, and worked on patents.

He became extremely concerned about his health during this time. His heart was bad, his cholesterol level was high, and his arthritis had worsened. The pain he suffered showed in his tired-looking appearance. He was just over six feet tall and weighed 185 pounds; he had a full face with wire-rim glasses and a usually unkempt crop of hair.

*I*n 1960, after investing sixty million dollars, Haloid Xerox introduced its first genuinely successful office copier, the 914. The machine was the size of a freezer and weighed six hundred pounds, but it could be operated with the push of a button. Its name derived from the fact that it made copies nine by fourteen inches. Dozens of difficult technical problems had had to be solved by Haloid's researchers. For instance, tiny air nozzles were developed to pull individual sheets of blank paper into the machine without prematurely charging them with static; a consistent, dependable toner (powdered ink) was developed in a Rochester garage; a rotating brush of Australian rabbit fur was painstakingly designed to remove waste toner from inside the machine after each copy was made. If xerography itself had one inventor, the 914 had many.

Haloid decided not to sell the machines but to lease them, for as little as ninety-five dollars a month. It built them with interchangeable parts designed to simplify repair and put in place a large, trained sales-and-service force. The 914 made millionaires out of many who invested in the company, which became the Xerox Corporation in 1961. The company's revenues leaped from thirty-two million dollars in 1959 to sixty million in 1961 to five hundred million in 1966.

Carlson was, of course, among those who found themselves fabulously rich after 1960. Right up until then he had struggled along nearly penniless on royalties from his invention, and he had poured all he could back into Battelle's and Haloid's research. He had even borrowed money from relatives to retain the option that provided him 40 percent of Battelle's royalties from xerography. In the 1960s his wealth reached an estimated one hundred and fifty million dollars, and in idealistic but methodical fashion, he set out to share it. He spent the rest of his life giving away an estimated one hundred million dollars to various research projects and charities. He built up a huge correspondence with hundreds of people who asked him for money. Most of his donations were made anonymously. Caltech built a research laboratory with funds he provided.

Carlson also renewed an old interest in religion, which he had first displayed in college. He gave financial support to groups investigating parapsychology or studying Far Eastern religions, and spiritual subjects became a kind of obsession for him; but as much as in his younger days, he spent his last years pushing himself hard in many directions at once.

He died of a heart attack on September 19, 1968, in New York City. He had attended a conference early in the day and had several hours of spare time before a scheduled meeting with his wife that night. He elected to spend some of his free time watching a movie, and his body was found at the theater by an usher. After spending so much of his life as a loner, Chester Carlson met his death very much alone. ★

Dean J. Golembeski is a freelance writer living in Torrington, Connecticut.

Xerography had one inventor; the office copier that it spawned had many.

HOW VON NEUMANN SHOWED THE WAY

by T. A. Heppenheimer

Before there could be hardware or software, there had to be a vision of exactly how computers would work. A handful of brilliant mathematicians, chief among them John Von Neumann, saw the future.

There were ten people in the party, and they were about to descend into the Grand Canyon. The guide wore a cowboy hat and leather chaps; a coil of rope hung from his saddle. Most of the others were dressed for a day outdoors, wearing hats, loose-fitting shirts, and the like. At the rear of the group was John Von Neumann—hatless and in the formal suit and tie of a banker. Moreover, while everyone else sat on a mule facing right, his faced left.

Von Neumann had been following his own rules for years. He owned a photographic memory that held the complete texts of works of literature and one of the world's largest collections of off-color limericks. Yet he would phone home to ask his wife to help him remember an appointment. He loved to throw parties—and sometimes would steal away to work in his office while his guests remained downstairs. Among his friends he was nearly as well known for his traffic accidents as for his accomplishments in mathematics. A strong supporter of the military, he was fond of attending nuclear-weapons tests. He died of cancer at the age of fifty-three.

Through it all, he was one of the century's most creative and productive mathematicians, lifting his intellectual scepter across a host of technical fields. Mostly he worked with pencil and paper, but in the years after 1945, for the first time in his life, he set him-self the task of managing the design and construction of a piece of equipment. This was the Institute for Advanced Study computer, and it set the pattern for subsequent computers as we know them today.

What distinguished this IAS machine was programmability. It embodied Von Neumann's insistence that computers must not be built as glorified adding machines, with all their operations specified in advance. Rather, he declared, they should be built as general-purpose logic machines, built to execute programs of wide variety. Such machines would be highly flexible, readily shifted from one task to another. They could react intelligently to the results of their calculations, could choose among alternatives, and could even play checkers or chess.

This represented something unheard of: a machine with built-in intelligence, able to operate on internal instructions. Before, even the most complex mechanisms had always been controlled from the outside, as by setting dials or knobs. Von Neumann did not invent the computer, but what he introduced was equally significant: computing by use of computer programs, the way we do it today.

The roots of this invention lay not in electronics but in the higher reaches of mathematics, in a problem that tantalized specialists in mathematical logic during this century's early decades: the challenge of establishing basic foundations for math. These would take the form of an explicit set of definitions and axioms, or fundamental statements, from which all known results might be derived.

Everyone expected that such foundations could be constructed if people were only clever enough. David Hilbert of Göttingen University, widely regarded as the world's leading mathematician, summarized this viewpoint in a 1900 address: "Every mathematical problem can be solved. We are all convinced of that. After all, one of the things that attracts us most when we apply ourselves to a mathematical problem is precisely that within us we always hear the call: here is the problem, search for the solution; you can find it by pure thought, for in mathematics there is no *ignorabimus* [we will not know]."

In fact, however, a powerful *ignorabimus* lay at the center of the problem of mathematical foundations. The man who demonstrated this was Kurt Goedel, a logician at the University of Vienna. He was a smallish man with an earnest expression and a thick pair of glasses; he appeared even smaller than he was because of his reluctance to eat. Psychological depressions and other illnesses dogged him throughout much of his life, made more serious at times by his distrust of doctors. In contrast with the gregarious and hearty Von Neumann, Goedel was solitary in his habits, but he did form a few close relationships. One was his lifelong marriage to Adele Nimbursky, a former cab-

aret dancer. Another was a warm friendship with Albert Einstein.

In two epochal papers, published in 1931, when he was twenty-five, Goedel showed that no foundations could be constructed. More particularly, he showed that if anyone tried to set forth such foundations, it would be possible to devise mathematical statements that were "formally undecidable"—incapable of being proved or disproved using the proposed foundations. Anil Nerode of Cornell University describes this conclusion as "the paper that everyone read, because it was the most signal paper in logic in two thousand years."

In particular, this work offered two major results for the eventual development of computer science. To prove his theorems, Goedel introduced a notation whereby statements in mathematical logic were encoded as numbers. Every such statement could be expressed as an integer, usually a very large one, and every integer corresponded to a statement in logic. This introduced a concept that would be key to the later advent of computer programming: that not only numerical data but also logic statements—and by extension, programming instructions—could be expressed in a common notation. Further, Goedel's work showed that this notational commonality could give results of the deepest significance in mathematics.

Among the mathematicians who soon took up the study of these matters was Alan Turing, of Cambridge University. Turing was a vigorous man, fond of running and cycling, and sometimes eccentric. Issued a gas mask, he wore it to prevent hay fever. Fearing that British currency would be worthless in World War II, he withdrew his savings and purchased two ingots of silver, buried them in his yard—and then failed to draw a suitable treasure map that would permit him to find them. And when his bicycle developed

Von Neumann and his wife, Klári, in front of their Princeton, New Jersey, home, 1954.

the habit of having its chain come loose, he refused to take it in for repairs. Instead he trained himself to estimate when this was about to happen so he could make timely preventive fixes by himself.

Turing was a twenty-five-year-old undergraduate when he made his major contribution to computer science. It came in a 1937 paper, "On Computable Numbers," in which he specifically dealt with an imaginary version of the computer. This idealized machine was to follow coded instructions, equivalent to computer programs. It was to deal with a long paper tape that would be marked off in squares, each square either black or white and thus representing one bit of information. On this tape, in response to the coded commands, the machine would execute a highly limited set of operations: reading, erasing, or marking a particular square and moving the tape.

Analyzing this idealized computer, Turing proved that it offered properties closely related to Goedel's concept of formal undecidability. What was important for computer science, however, was another realization: that with sufficiently lengthy coded instructions this simple machine would be able to carry out any computation that could be executed in a finite number of steps. Here, in its essential form, was the concept of a general-purpose programmable computer.

The basic idea of a calculating machine was not new. The first crude adding machines dated to the seventeenth century. In the nineteenth century Britain's Charles Babbage, assisted by Lady Ada Lovelace, had struggled to invent an "Analytical Engine" that was really a crude mechanical computer. What was new and pathbreaking in Turing's work was that for the first time he gave a clear concept of what a computer should be: a machine that carries out a few simple operations under the direction of a program that can be as intricate as one may wish.

These developments were very interesting to John Von Neumann. As a student in Germany (he was born in Hungary in 1903), he had worked closely with Hilbert himself, plunging deeply into the search for mathematical foundations. He had shared Hilbert's belief that such foundations could in fact be constructed, had written a paper that contributed some mathematical bricks to the intellectual masonry — and was surprised and chagrined by Goedel's proofs. He had not thought that formal undecidability might exist, and he came away with the feeling that Goedel had scooped him.

He had plenty of reasons to feel confident, however. The son of a Budapest banker who had received a minor title of nobility, the source of his "Von," he had shown himself very early to be a *Wunderkind*, dividing eight-digit numbers in his head at age six and talking with his father in ancient Greek. By age eight he was doing calculus and demonstrating a photographic memory: he would read a page of the Budapest phone directory and recite it back with his eyes closed. His father's wealth made it easy for him to attend the University of Budapest, from which he traveled widely: to the University of Berlin, to Zurich and its equally famous university, and to Göttingen, the world's center of mathematics. At age twenty-two he received his Ph.D. Nor did he keep his genius to himself; his daughter Marina, born in 1935, would rise to become a leading economist in the United States.

Von Neumann had made his reputation during the 1920s, establishing himself as clearly one of the world's outstanding mathematicians. Particularly significant was his work in developing a rigorous mathematical basis for quantum mechanics. That brought him an invitation to Princeton University, which he joined in 1930, when he was twenty-six. "He was so young," says a colleague

J. Presper Eckert, Jr. (foreground), and John W. Mauchly (center) work at their room-size computer, ENIAC, 1946.

You didn't program ENIAC; you laboriously set it up, using patch cords.
Von Neumann joined the group to figure out a better way.

Mauchly at ENIAC's "computing table"—a wall of switches—with an abacus in one hand.

from around that time, "that most people who saw him in the halls mistook him for a graduate student." Then in 1936 Turing came to Princeton to do his graduate work; he was twenty-four. Von Neumann, who had moved to the Institute for Advanced Study in 1933, was quite interested in Turing's work and offered him a position as his assistant after he received his doctorate, but Turing chose to return to Cambridge.

Meanwhile, Von Neumann was doing much more than reading his colleagues' papers. During the early 1940s he began to work extensively on problems of fluid flow. These problems were widely regarded as nightmares, marked by tangles of impenetrable equations. To Von Neumann that meant they were interesting; understanding them could lead to such consequences as accurate weather prediction, and because such problems posed intractable difficulties, they were worthy of his attention.

Then came the war and the Manhattan Project. Von Neumann's expertise in fluid flow now took on the highest

national importance. As the work at Los Alamos advanced, he became responsible for solving a problem that was essential to building the plutonium bomb. This was to understand the intricate physical processes by which a thick layer of high-explosive charges, surrounding a spherical core of plutonium, could detonate to produce an imploding shock wave that would compress the core and initiate the nuclear explosion.

As his colleague George Kistiakowsky later wrote, high explosives had been "looked upon as blind destructive agents rather than precision instruments." In the plutonium bomb, however, it would be essential to predict with some accuracy the behavior of the shock waves that would converge on the core. Even Von Neumann's brilliance was inadequate for this. He had hoped that ingenuity and insight would enable him to simplify the pertinent equations to a form both solvable and sufficiently accurate. His collaborator Stanislaw Ulam insisted that it would

be necessary to face their full complexity and calculate them, in an age when there were no computers, using methods that would later be programmed to run on computers. Fortunately, the Los Alamos lab was due to receive a shipment of IBM calculating machines. Stanley Frankel, another Los Alamos man, set up a lengthy sequence of steps that these machines could carry out, with Army enlistees running them. It amounted to a very slow computer with human beings rather than electronic devices as the active elements, but it worked. Von Neumann got the solutions he needed, and he proceeded to design the high-explosive charges for Fat Man, the bomb dropped on Nagasaki.

Meanwhile, at the University of Pennsylvania, another effort as secret as the Manhattan Project was under way: the construction of the first electronic computer. This was ENIAC (Electronic Numerical Integrator and Computer), an Army-sponsored project intended for use in calculating the trajectories of artillery shells. Its employment of vacuum tubes rather than people as active elements represented a decided advance, but while the potential value of such tubes for high-speed computing was widely appreciated, the tubes of the day were not particularly reliable. That did not matter when only a few were needed, as in radar or radio, but it would matter greatly in a computer, where a single failed tube could vitiate a lengthy calculation. (Because of this, Harvard's Howard Aiken had gone to work on a computer that would use the electromechanical switches of telephone circuitry. They were far slower than vacuum tubes, but still much faster than human beings, and they were reliable.)

The ENIAC project leaders, John W. Mauchly and J. Presper Eckert, Jr., solved the reliability problem in a simple way. They were working with tubes whose manufacturers had guaranteed a service life of twenty-five hundred hours. With 17,468 tubes in ENIAC, that meant one could be expected to fail, on the average, every eight minutes—and with major computations requiring weeks of operation, this was quite unacceptable. Eckert, however, simply "unloaded" the tubes, arranging it so that they would handle no more than one-half of their rated voltage and one-fourth of their rated current. This reduced the failure rate from one every eight minutes to about one every two days, which was sufficient for practical operation.

The Army's representative on the project was Lt. Herman H. Goldstine, who had taught mathematics at the University of Michigan. He was working out of the Aberdeen Proving Grounds in Maryland, where Von Neumann was a consultant. One day in August 1944 he saw Von Neumann waiting for a train. "I had never met this great mathematician," Goldstine recalled. "It was therefore with considerable temerity that I approached this world-famous figure, introduced myself, and started talking. Fortunately for me Von Neumann was a warm, friendly person who did his best to make people feel relaxed in his presence. The conversation soon turned to my work. When it became clear to Von Neumann that I was concerned with the development of an electronic computer capable of 333 multiplications per second, the whole atmosphere changed from one of relaxed good humor to one more like the oral examination for a doctor's degree in mathematics."

ENIAC was a large air-conditioned room whose walls were covered with cabinets containing electronic circuitry—three thousand cubic feet of it. It weighed thirty tons and drew 174 kilowatts of power. Its computational speed and capability would fail to match the hand-held programmable calculators of the mid-1970s, but even so, it was such an advance over all previous attempts at automatic computation as to stand in a class by itself. Still, it was not without its faults, as its

Eckert stands at a control panel. ENIAC would be outperformed by a 1970s pocket calculator.

builders were well aware. Its main memory (random-access memory) could hold only a thousand bits of information—the equivalent of about three lines of text. And it was completely lacking in any arrangements for computer programming.

You did not program ENIAC; rather, you set it up, like many other complex systems. Although it was a general-purpose computer, able to solve any problem, it relied on physical interconnections. You prepared for a particular problem by running patch cords between jacks and other plugs, with cabling up to eighty feet long. The task could take two days or longer. In a 1943 report the builders admitted that "no attempt has been made to make provision for setting up a problem automatically," adding that "it is anticipated that the ENIAC will be used primarily for problems of a type in which one setup will be used many times before another problem is placed on the machine."

By the summer of 1944, however, Eckert, Mauchly, and their colleagues were already beginning to think seri-

ously about ENIAC's successor. This would have the name EDVAC (Electronic Discrete Variable Automatic Computer). As early as January of that year Eckert had described a computer in which an "important feature" was that "operating instructions and function tables would be stored in exactly the same sort of memory device as that used for numbers." Eckert was also inventing an appropriate memory device: a "delay line," or long tube filled with mercury in which bits of data would take the form of pressure pulses traversing the tube at high speed. And in October 1944, at Goldstine's urging, the Army awarded a $105,600 contract for work on the EDVAC concept.

Into this stimulating environment stepped Von Neumann. He joined the ENIAC group as a consultant, with special interest in ideas for EDVAC. He helped secure the EDVAC contract and spent long hours in discussions with Mauchly and Eckert. "He was really racing far ahead and speculating as to how you build better computers, because that's what we were talking to him about," Mauchly later said. "We

Von Neumann's "Report on the EDVAC" envisioned a computer using programs as the brain uses memory. Soon he was building one.

EDVAC and three of the men who built it, at the University of Pennsylvania in the late 1940s.

said we don't want to build another of these things [ENIACs]. We've got much better solutions in many ways."

Von Neumann's particular strength was the logical structure of a computer, the details of its logic operations. His leadership made the EDVAC discussions more systematic. Before his arrival Eckert and Mauchly had relied mostly on informal conversations; with Von Neumann there were regular staff meetings with recorded minutes. As Goldstine reported to his boss, Von Neumann was "devoting enormous amounts of his prodigious energy to working out the logical controls of the machine. He also has been very much interested in helping design circuits for the machine."

In late June 1945, working at Los Alamos, Von Neumann completed a 101-page document titled "First Draft of a Report on the EDVAC." In his clear and penetrating way, he set forth an overview of the design of a digital computer that would feature stored-program operation. It had much more than circuitry and logic; it reflect-

ed Von Neumann's broad interests by drawing on the work of Warren McCulloch, a neurophysiologist who in 1943 had published a description of the functioning of the human brain. Von Neumann boldly drew comparisons between his electronic circuits and the brain's neurons, emphasizing that just as the brain relies on its memory, so the computer would depend on its programs. Goldstine soon was distributing copies to interested scientists. In time the "First Draft" would become one of the most influential papers in computer science.

Goldstine circulated the draft with only Von Neumann's name on the title page. In a later patent dispute, Von Neumann declined to share credit for his ideas with Mauchly, Eckert, or anyone else. So the "First Draft" spawned the legend that Von Neumann invented the stored-program computer. He did not, though he made contributions of great importance. But by writing the "First Draft," and subsequent reports, he gave a clear direction to the field. The prestige of his name ensured that he would be followed. "The new ideas

were too revolutionary for some. . . ," said the British computer expert Maurice Wilkes. "Powerful voices were being raised to say that . . . to mix instructions and numbers in the same memory was to go against nature." Von Neumann stilled such doubts.

As 1945 proceeded, he became convinced that he should not merely write about stored-program computers but should take the lead in another way: by building one. Raising money for such a project would be no problem; he knew his way around Washington. The problem was that his home base was, and had been since 1933, the Institute for Advanced Study, in Princeton, New Jersey. Founded by the department-store magnate Louis Bamberger and his sister, Carrie Fuld, it was a center for pure contemplation and thought, a place where Einstein and Goedel would feel at home and spend much of their careers. To propose building a computer at IAS was like offering to install a radar facility in St. Peter's Basilica.

Von Neumann overcame his colleagues' objections by playing the IAS against two other institutions that wanted him, the University of Chicago and the Massachusetts Institute of Technology. At MIT Norbert Wiener, a colleague from Von Neumann's Göttingen days and himself a pioneer in computing, offered Von Neumann the chairmanship of the mathematics department, emphasizing that he would be free to work on his "favorite projects." Chicago offered to set up an Institute of Applied Mathematics with Von Neumann as its head. Faced with such offers and wanting to keep Von Neumann as one of their own, his IAS colleagues gave in and granted permission, consoling themselves with the thought that the new computer might after all be useful in research.

Then the ENIAC group broke up. The source of this was a new director of research at the University of Pennsylvania, where the computer had been built, Irven Travis. Travis had spent his war in the Navy and proposed to run a tight ship now that he was back in the civilian world. He soon was quarreling with Eckert and Mauchly over the issue of patents. The two ENIAC inventors saw great commercial prospects in computers and had a letter from the university president that agreed they could hold patents on ENIAC. Travis, however, insisted that they must sign patent releases. He made no bones about it; in one meeting with Mauchly he stated, "If you want to continue to work here at the university, you must sign these agreements." Mauchly and Eckert refused and were soon out on their own as independent entrepreneurs.

By the summer of 1946, then, three groups were seeking to build a stored-program computer along the lines of the "First Draft." Eckert and Mauchly had by far the most experience in this area, but were out in the cold with little money, few contacts, and slight business experience. The remnants of the ENIAC group, at the University of Pennsylvania, had few good people but were committed by contract to build an EDVAC, and build it they would, however slowly. Von Neumann had the overall vision, the charismatic reputation, the genius, and the acquiescence of the IAS. What he lacked was experience in project management.

Of these deficiencies, Von Neumann's was the most easily remedied. He had technical support from RCA, which had built a lab in Princeton. He had Herman Goldstine, who left the Army to join him. And at Norbert Wiener's recommendation he hired Wiener's wartime assistant, Julian Bigelow, who had worked on radar-guided fire control of antiaircraft guns and who knew how to build electronic systems of a very demanding character.

The computer was to be built in the boiler room of Fuld Hall, the main building at the IAS. As Bigelow describes the work, "Von Neumann would put half-finished ideas on the blackboard and Goldstine would take them back

Eckert plays at the controls of UNIVAC, the first commercially successful computer, in 1951.

down and digest them and make them into something for the machine. On the other hand, Von Neumann often had only the foggiest ideas about how we should achieve something technically. He would discuss things with me and leave them completely wide open, and I would think them over and come back with an experimental circuit, and then my group would test it out."

When completed—in a building of its own, well across the IAS campus— the computer had only twenty-three hundred vacuum tubes, considerably fewer than ENIAC's almost eighteen thousand. It was fully automatic, digital, and general-purpose, but like other programmable computers of its generation, it was built years in advance of programming languages such as Fortran or Pascal. Its commands instead were written directly in machine language, long strings of ones and zeros. An expression such as "A + B," for instance, might be rendered as something like 01101101 10110110 01110011; a significant program would feature many pages written in such notation. In Bigelow's words, there were "none

of the tricks that we now have. This was a case where Von Neumann was so clever technically that he had no problem with it. And he couldn't imagine anyone else working with a computer who couldn't program in machine code."

How significant was this IAS computer? The science historian Joel Shurkin, who has sought to assess fairly the claims of various inventors as to priority, writes that "Von Neumann's technical contributions are manifest and beyond controversy. The machine he designed would be faster than anything else. . . . While all the other computer makers were generally heading in the same direction, Von Neumann's genius clarified and described the paths better than anyone else in the world could. Moreover, many of the developments in programming and in machine architecture at the institute profoundly influenced future computer development. . . . While others were using crude digital instructions for their machines, Von Neumann and his team were developing instructions (what scientists call codes) that would last,

All the later technical advances would merely offer better ways to implement the basic concept that Von Neumann had described.

with modification, through most of the computer age."

The machine received its baptism with the nation again at war, in Korea, and with the hydrogen bomb now a matter of highest priority. Von Neumann, who had maintained his leadership in nuclear-weapons work, arranged to run a problem dealing with H-bomb physics. It would be the most extensive computation ever carried out. "It was computed in the summer of 1950," says Bigelow, ". . . while the machine had clip leads on it. We had engineers there to keep it running and it ran for sixty days, day and night, with very few errors. It did a nice job."

The way was open, then, for the computer to sweep all before it. There would be substantial technical advances: programming languages beginning in the mid-1950s, then transistors, integrated circuits, and microprocessors. But these would merely offer better ways to implement the basic concept—the stored-program computer—that Von Neumann had described in his 1945 "First Draft."

As if computation carried with it some dreadful incubus, a number of its pioneers would die amid tragedy. Alan Turing was the first, in 1954, at age forty-one. Convicted in England of soliciting sexual favors from a teen-age boy, he was given a choice of prison or hormone treatments. He chose the hormones and soon found his breasts growing. Driven to despair, he made up a batch of cyanide in a home laboratory and died an apparent suicide.

For Von Neumann it was even worse. In the summer of 1955 he was diagnosed with bone cancer, which soon brought on excruciating pain. In the words of his friend Edward Teller, "I think that Von Neumann suffered more when his mind would no longer function than I have ever seen any human being suffer." Toward the end there was panic and uncontrolled terror. Early in 1957 he too was gone.

For Kurt Goedel it was his own per-

A technician with a UNIVAC in 1955: by now the computer was sweeping all before it.

sonal demons that would drive him to death. In an epic escape from Nazi-occupied Austria, he and his wife had crossed the Soviet Union and then the Pacific to reach the United States. From 1940 to 1976 he was himself a member of the IAS. The author Edward Regis describes him, in his last years, as "a cadaverous old man shuffling past alone, dressed in his black coat and winter hat." After his wife underwent surgery and was placed in a nursing home, in 1977, Goedel refused to take any food. He starved himself to death. When he died early the next year, the death certificate of this great logician stated that the cause was "malnutrition and inanition caused by personality disturbance."

John Mauchly's later years were racked by deep bitterness. He was bitter at Von Neumann for not giving him credit as a co-inventor of the stored-program computer and at Goldstine for being one of Von Neumann's most effective supporters. Mauchly, along with Eckert, had struggled through lean years but then won success by building UNIVAC, the first commercially successful computer. The firm of Remington Rand brought them in—

and eventually the roof fell in. In a major lawsuit their ENIAC patent was invalidated, with the judge ruling that they were not even the true inventors of the electronic computer. "Lawyers keep making money," said Mauchly toward the end. "We've got down to the point where maybe we can buy some hot dogs with our Social Security." In 1980 he died from a disfiguring genetic disease.

Nor were the pioneering institutions spared, though for them the incubus brought ill-considered abandonment of the computer field rather than unpleasant death. The University of Pennsylvania never recovered from the effects of Irven Travis's decisions, which cost that school its best computer people. The computer group did manage to build EDVAC, or at least enough of it to satisfy the Army, but it amounted to a last try by this group and led to no new projects. And after Von Neumann died, the IAS abandoned computer science altogether, shipping his computer to the Smithsonian.

The room where it was built, writes Regis, "is not treated as a historical site. No plaque or bust commemorates the birth of the stored program computer within. The room, at the end of a dark and lonely hallway, today houses the Institute's stationery supplies, and boxes of file folders, pads of paper, and inter-departmental mail envelopes reach almost to the ceiling."

Yet elsewhere at the IAS, and around the world, are today's computers, which still follow the directions Von Neumann set forth in his "First Draft" and subsequent writings and that he demonstrated in his project at the IAS. These computers, rather than plaques or busts cast in bronze, are among the true monuments to the cheerful and highly creative man who was John Von Neumann. ★

T. A. Heppenheimer writes frequently on science. His most recent book is *The Coming Quake: Science and Trembling on the California Earthquake Frontier* (Times Books, 1988).

The Patriarch of Pong

Remember Pong? In 1972 it became the first successful video-arcade game. That same year Magnavox released Odyssey, the first home game, giving people new ways to stimulate their minds with a television set. Thus the video game is generally thought of as a creation of the 1970s. In reality, though, it was invented in 1958, in a laboratory in then-rural Upton, New York, by a man named William Higinbotham.

Higinbotham was in charge of instrumentation design at Brookhaven National Laboratory (BNL), a government-supported nuclear-research facility. Although BNL concentrated on peaceful uses of the atom, as it still does, in those Cold War times area residents were concerned that they would one day be blown out of their potato fields by a huge atomic explosion. To assure people that they were in no danger, and that their crops would not mutate, the laboratory ran tours to show how useful, important, and safe its research was.

The displays on these tours were usually simple groups of photographs or static displays of equipment, informative but rather dry. Higinbotham wanted to liven things up. His department had a small analog computer that, with an oscilloscope and a few capacitors, potentiometers, and other common household items, could display the trajectories of missiles or bullets—or the path of a bouncing ball. This gave Higinbotham an idea.

He envisioned a tennis game, with the court displayed on the oscilloscope's screen. For a man who had helped develop the first radar systems and designed timing devices for the Manhattan Project's atomic bomb, it was a simple matter to plan the necessary circuitry, and within a couple of days the game was finished.

The court and net were displayed in rapid alternation with the ball motion on the oscilloscope screen. The circuits that created them used conventional vacuum tubes and relays, and the time-sharing circuit contained some of the transistors that were then coming into use. A simple resistor simulated wind drag. Players hit the ball by pushing a button, and by turning a knob they could adjust the angle of return. An unwise setting would send the ball crashing into the net.

The game was the hit of visitors' days for the next two years. "People would stand on line for hours to play it," recalls one scientist. A later ver-

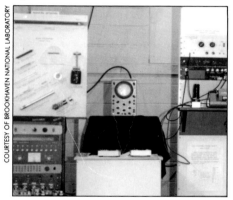
The very first video game, at center, in 1958.

sion allowed aspiring astronauts to play on the Moon or Jupiter, with gravity set appropriately. But eventually the apparatus was dismantled, and through the sixties video games were but a dim cathode-ray tube glowing faintly in the distance.

Why didn't Higinbotham patent his invention? In his words, "I considered the whole idea so obvious that it never occurred to me to think about a patent." If he had, it probably wouldn't have seemed worthwhile. In an age of Hula-Hoops and Fabian, who knew how long the games would stay popular? Anyway, Higinbotham's job was designing things like radiation detectors. The tennis game was just a trifle.

Besides, he was an employee of the U.S. government. If he had taken out a patent, Uncle Sam would have owned it. Then anyone wanting to make a new game would need a federal license. While this would certainly help reduce today's budget deficit, it's hard to say whether new taxes or new video games would be a greater threat to the Republic.

Would it have been feasible? Cheap home games would have to wait for the microprocessor age, of course, but how about a pinball-machine-size game costing a few hundred dollars? "I believe that my game or a TV modification could have been produced in that price range in 1960," Higinbotham says. Of course, we'll never know.

In looking at today's video games, with their themes of destruction and cartoonish explosions, Higinbotham might feel a strange ambivalence. Back in his Manhattan Project days, he witnessed the first test detonation at Los Alamos. What he saw made him determined to reduce the awesome threat that nuclear weapons posed to the world. Since then he has lobbied tirelessly for arms control and nonproliferation. In the late 1960s he was one of the founders of Brookhaven's nuclear-safeguards group, which develops ways to ensure the security of nuclear materials and to verify arms-control agreements. Today Brookhaven's group is among the world's foremost, and Higinbotham, now in his eighties, still acts as a consultant (when he isn't testifying in video-game patent suits).

About eight years ago Higinbotham's pioneering role was revealed in *Creative Computing* (whose editor, David Ahl, had seen the game as a youth touring the laboratory). Since then he has been known as the father of the video game. It's nice to be the patriarch of Pong. But if current trends continue and his scientific efforts end up leading to a peaceful world, Willy Higinbotham will have accomplished something much greater. ★

SIDEWINDER

by Ron Westrum and Howard A. Wilcox

There was never supposed to be a Sidewinder missile. The Navy didn't ask for it; the Air Force didn't want it. Yet a small, dedicated team of Navy scientists and engineers at a desert laboratory produced it against all odds. Bill McLean and his coworkers succeeded where larger teams with much more money and support failed, in developing a simple, inexpensive, immensely successful air weapon, and in so doing they showed how technical creativity can soar in the right environment.

Thirty-three years after it entered service, the Sidewinder heat-seeking air-to-air missile remains one of our nation's most reliable and economical weapons. It represents one man's vision; that vision was nurtured and brought to reality in an unusual government-research environment especially designed to foster creativity—the Naval Ordnance Test Station, at China Lake, in the Mojave Desert 150 miles northeast of Los Angeles. The man was William Burdette McLean.

McLean, born in 1914, was drawn to mechanical things at an early age. His father, a Protestant clergyman, believed in self-reliance and practical skills; his mother taught him to knit, crochet, and use a sewing machine before he entered kindergar-

ten. As a boy McLean built surfboards, canoes, rafts, and his own photographic enlarger, and when he was eleven he helped his family build a new house. A quiet, serious young man, he was good at science and mathematics in high school and poor at English and history. His technical abilities got him admitted to Caltech, where he took three degrees in physics, finishing with a doctorate in 1939. One professor, Charles Lauritsen, observed that McLean sometimes seemed more interest-

ed in the laboratory equipment than in the measurements it produced.

World War II brought McLean to the National Bureau of Standards (NBS), where his mechanical abilities were quickly recognized, and he became head of the Mechanical Design Section of the Ordnance Division, designing the arming devices for proximity fuzes. These were complicated and dangerous devices; a fuze absolutely must function when it gets to the target and not at any other time. Achieving designs that could be safely and reliably manufactured was an awesome challenge. He also worked, while at NBS, on a guidance system for the Bat missile, a large glide bomb. Jacob Rabinow, an inventor who worked

under him at NBS and now holds 225 U.S. patents, remembers McLean as the "best engineer I have ever known."

At war's end McLean went to the Naval Ordnance Test Station (NOTS) on a visit that he expected to last two months. He stayed there for twenty-three years. In 1954 he was named technical director, assuming a major role in shaping programs and policies at what had become one of the Navy's most important laboratories. NOTS—today the Nav-

How a small and independent Navy research team built a simple, inexpensive guided missile that is still indispensable more than thirty years later

al Weapons Center—was a product of lessons learned during the war about what science and technology could accomplish given sufficient leadership, money, and staff. It was set up in 1943 as a "unique experiment in civilian-military partnership," to be run by the military under naval commanding officers but with civilian technical directors supervising the technical work. NOTS was to be a "full-spectrum" laboratory, with all the personnel and equipment needed to take ideas from the first rough sketch through full development and even initial production.

At thirty-one McLean was already recognized as a technical leader. His quiet demeanor and half-smile accompanied a lightning mind.

He was not charismatic, but he had a presence that commanded both attention and respect. As head of NOTS's Aviation Ordnance Division, in 1946, he found himself working on aiming systems for air-to-air rockets. His analysis of these systems required consideration of many factors, including altitude, speed, and maneuvering acceleration for both planes. This work convinced him that the most precise possible aiming system for an unguided weapon could never enable it to destroy an unpredictably accelerating target. The weapon would have to be able to guide itself after being fired. Radar systems in those days were quite bulky—too large, McLean felt, to fit into the nose of an air-to-air rocket. But infrared detectors able to sense the heat emissions of aircraft targets were about the size of a dime. So he concluded that a guidance unit sensitive to infrared radiation might be compact enough to do the job.

The small but growing guided-missile community had arrived at a different conclusion. Infrared was thought useless for air-to-air missiles because it wouldn't work through clouds; only an all-weather missile was considered worth pursuing. Since radar homing *would* work through clouds, both the Navy and the Air Force wrote requirements specifying all-weather missiles.

McLean had come to distrust requirements during his stay at the National Bureau of Standards. These official guidelines for new technology to be produced often asked for the impossible. Worse, they sometimes

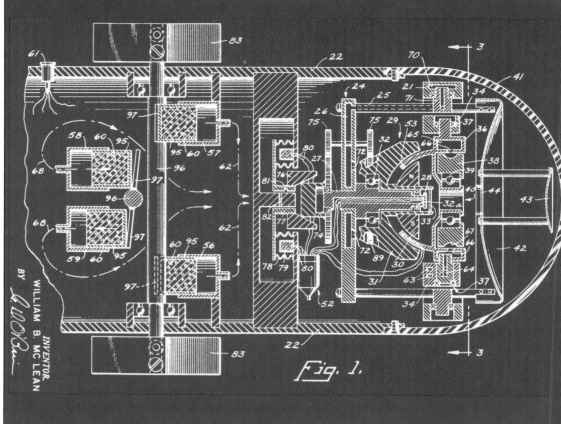

failed to ask for what was feasible and wise. McLean felt that requirements were best written after a device was developed, so instead of thinking in terms of a requirement, he concentrated on the actual needs of a combat pilot.

He began to survey the guided-missile scene and found that indeed, many people expected the all-weather missiles to be unsatisfactory. The radar missiles under development were called pilotless interceptors; they were small airplanes flown by robotic mechanisms instead of pilots. They were going to be bulky, complicated, expensive, likely to break down, and hard to store and maintain aboard ships at sea. McLean decided that a successful missile must address all these faults. He set to work to create a simple, cheap, easy-to-ready, easy-to-use missile.

To begin with, he concluded that infrared would be good enough. He knew that most bomber attacks would be flown at above twenty thousand feet, where rain is rare and clouds are few. Indeed, almost no military missions of any kind were flown through clouds or fog. And a guidance system that worked 90 percent of the time would be far better than a radar system that was too complicated ever to work reliably and too expensive to be produced in quantity.

In 1947 he began to evolve a heat-homing guidance system. The key idea was a spinning and hence gyroscopically stabilized magnet that

would reflect the emissions from a heat source onto a sensitive photocell. When the source moved off the axis of the gyro, the photocell would generate a signal in a coil surrounding the magnet, forcing it to turn its axis toward the moving heat source. This meant it could continuously track a distant aircraft target. A servomechanism (a feedback device for automatic control) could use the same signal to make the system's control fins accelerate the missile toward the target.

In 1949 McLean submitted a proposal to NOTS management for the development of a "heat-homing rocket." The last word is significant: McLean thought of the missile not as an unmanned aircraft but as a piece of ordnance, a *rocket*. Aircraft are

carefully and continually maintained for repeated use; ordnance is simply stored and then fired. If a missile were to be treated as ordnance, it would have to be extremely simple and sturdy. McLean also felt it should cost only a few hundred dollars. Others at the time expected guided missiles to cost hundreds of thousands of dollars apiece.

McLean began testing his concept. His team started small—since there was no Navy requirement for a heat-homing rocket, there was no major funding. But McLean preferred a small team. For the first two years, he relied on internal NOTS discretionary funds plus Navy money for fuze development. The effort became "Local Fuze Project 602," with the rationale that the seeker head was

actually a fuze attempting to get the missile closer to the target before detonation. Later the project became "Feasibility Study 567"—another obfuscation.

Navy funds for guided missiles were being pruned, and NOTS had just failed to produce an authorized missile, the NOTS AAM (air-to-air missile). Meanwhile the Navy's Bureau of Aeronautics was developing the Sparrow missile and made it known that all guided missiles should be under its direction, as aircraft with robot pilots. It looked as if McLean had begun his project at a bad time and in the wrong place. But he was able to get volunteer help from many of NOTS's scientists and technicians. His rocket began to take shape.

He set his sights carefully. He aimed at simplicity not only for manufacture but also for shipboard assembly and use in combat. He felt that a good servomechanism for steering would be crucial —with the right servo "you could fly a barn door"—so the wings and control fins could even be rectangular. This reasoning nearly drove his aerodynamicist, Lee Jagiello, to distraction. The first model of Sidewinder did in fact have rectangular fins and wings, and they flew fairly well. But eventually Jagiello prevailed, and the final version had swept-back leading edges on its wings and fins.

The problem of preventing the rocket from rolling too rapidly was solved by a technician named Sidney Crockett. He suggested that solid gyroscope wheels be mounted on flaps on each of the four rear wings. These "rollerons" had notches cut into their outer rims so that the airstream flowing past the missile would make them rotate; should the missile start to roll, the rollerons would automatically respond by forcing the flaps out into the airstream to oppose the roll.

Another key element was the infrared seeker. McLean, wanting to leave options open whenever possible, encouraged parallel work on five different seeker arrangements, labeled *A* through *E*. The *A* seeker won out in the end because it had a gyroscope that functioned independently of the missile's roll. The gyroscope kept track of the motion of the target, and the

This emblem appeared on the cover of McLean's 1949 "heat-homing rocket" proposal.

fins then turned the missile to move it toward a collision course. The missile avoided a lot of additional circuitry by never worrying about where it itself was; it kept track only of how the target was moving, and it used what was called proportional navigation to reach the target.

Another remarkable innovation was the Sidewinder's torque-balance servo. Because air density diminishes as altitude increases, a steering system can't work by simply commanding the fins to turn a given angle for a given turn; that would produce a sharper turn both at higher speeds and at lower altitudes. McLean's servo solved this complicated problem by generating a torque on the fin. At high speeds or low altitudes the torque would turn the fin a relatively small angle; at low speeds or high altitudes the commanded torque would turn it much farther. This "torque-balance" system automatically compensated for differences in speed and altitude. It enabled McLean's team to boast that "our missile is independent of aerodynamics."

Even though the functions the missile performed were complex, its hardware—seven vacuum tubes and about two dozen moving parts—

made it about as complicated as a portable radio combined with a washing machine. Since top-of-the-line radio monitoring equipment was expensive and fragile, much of the telemetry on the missile had to be done with kits made for electronics amateurs. An engineer named Rod McClung taught a group of women at NOTS to build the Heathkits; after they were skilled at that, he had them assemble seeker heads.

As the design progressed, more money was required, and groups from various Washington agencies started showing up to see how the project was coming along. The team developed a series of strategies for briefing and impressing such groups. One particularly successful ploy was to mount the seeker from the missile head on the antenna of a surplus radar van, wired so that the seeker's output could be used to point the radar antenna. The whole system would then be made to follow an aircraft flying overhead or a distant person holding a lighted cigarette. This proved an endless source of fascination and a valuable tool for converting reluctant bureaucrats and ad-

mirals. Another trick was to demonstrate the rollerons, which were both ingenious and easy to understand. But the team was kept on its toes trying to predict just what objections the next group of visitors might bring with them.

In 1951 Adm. William S. ("Deak") Parsons, deputy chief of the Bureau of Ordnance, visited NOTS; McLean briefed Parsons on his progress to date, and Parsons acted decisively. "We will pursue this weapon system," he announced, and he decreed that the project would be directed primarily from within NOTS rather than from Washington. Shortly thereafter, NOTS received the first installment of three million dollars in funding. The missile had already been

The Navy was requiring radar-homing missiles; McLean decided infrared would do much better.

designated Sidewinder, a name suggested by McLean's colleague Gilbert Plain, who knew that the sidewinder snake senses its prey by detecting its heat emissions. The project, already well along, was now also official.

To get the job done, each part of the missile had to be designed almost simultaneously. A number of small groups set to work, some with help from outside contractors. McLean devoted himself mainly to designing the servo system, but other components presented serious problems as well. The

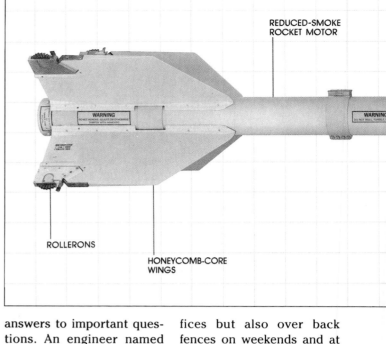

REDUCED-SMOKE ROCKET MOTOR

WARNING

WARNING

ROLLERONS

HONEYCOMB-CORE WINGS

energy to operate the servo and electronics was to be supplied not by batteries but by the hot gas from a small grain of chemical fuel. Getting the fuel to burn properly proved an especially difficult job.

Another focus of attention was the canard fins, which turned the missile in flight. McLean put those control surfaces up front so that the missile could be easily taken apart for shipboard storage. If they had been in the rear, as was common with missiles at the time, electrical connectors would have been needed to link them to the seeker. That would have made assembly more difficult. Also, McLean distrusted connectors because they often became worn out from repeated use. By putting seeker and fins in one package, he avoided the problem.

As the airframe and the seeker were completed, they were tested first separately and then together. Ground firings were followed by air firings, then by air firings against drones and target rockets, and finally by air firings with live warheads against drones. The first Sidewinder test pilot was a young Navy lieutenant, Walter A. ("Wally") Schirra, who later became world-famous as a moon-mission astronaut.

Late hours at little or no extra pay became common for everyone on the project. Howard A. Wilcox, a member of the Sidewinder design team as well as coauthor of this article, remembers returning to NOTS's Michelson Laboratory almost every evening in the early fifties.

He would invariably see a small knot of cars in the parking lot—the cars of the Sidewinder group. The laboratory lights were always on, and the doors always open, and McLean himself was usually among those at work, often staying until 2:00 A.M. Sometimes a group found itself out on the rocket ranges in the middle of the night. People were willing to search on their hands and knees in the dark for pieces of rockets when they knew that Bill McLean was searching on his hands and knees right alongside them.

The physicist Warren Legler recalls work proceeding "not day to day but hour by hour." McLean disapproved of delay, and a suggestion from him was usually taken as an indication of a need. "What happened with that component we were talking about yesterday?" he might ask; people felt decidedly uncomfortable when they couldn't answer such a question.

McLean encouraged the development of instrumentation that could give quick answers to important questions. An engineer named Bob Hummer put together a device that provided an easily read photograph of twenty-four channels of radioed information about what went on in the missile while in flight. The "Hummergram" was far from state-of-the-art, but it made data available less than an hour after a test flight. Sometimes a new missile component was designed and built in one day and its performance was checked by Hummergram the next.

McLean kept the group so focused on its objectives that discussion of the Sidewinder took place not only in the laboratories and offices but also over back fences on weekends and at cocktail parties, where one might see a few people with McLean in a corner talking rocket motors. The isolation of the Mojave Desert provided unusual freedom from distractions, and the base became an intellectual pressure cooker.

There was a sense of excitement born of working on a project that everyone felt was important and obviously a good idea, and McLean was always ready to listen to anyone's ideas and see them tried out. He firmly believed that test results, not argument or calculation, should be the ultimate arbiter. As one physicist later put it, "You could do anything you were big enough to do."

Some members of the group nervously compared themselves with much bigger operations at work on other missiles—Lee Jagiello once asked, "How can we compete? Over at Hughes they have hundreds of aerodynamicists working on the Falcon. Here we have only one. How can we possibly hope to accomplish anything?" Howard Wilcox replied, "All those people will

Technicians inspect an early, square-finned Sidewinder airframe, circa 1952. Sidney Crockett, middle, later devised the missile's rollerons.

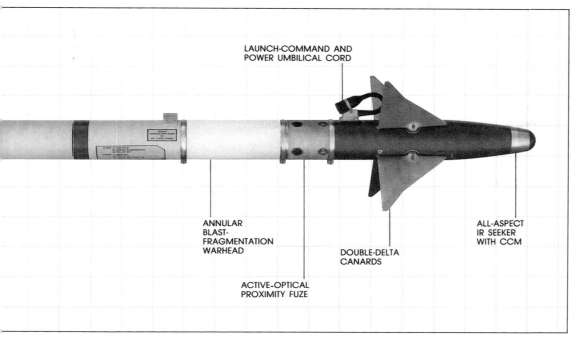

LAUNCH-COMMAND AND
POWER UMBILICAL CORD

ANNULAR
BLAST-
FRAGMENTATION
WARHEAD

ACTIVE-OPTICAL
PROXIMITY FUZE

DOUBLE-DELTA
CANARDS

ALL-ASPECT
IR SEEKER
WITH CCM

just get in one another's way. Besides, we have a secret weapon: Bill McLean."

The team's faith in McLean was crucial, for the problems were constant. The seeker gyroscope began to wobble when the signal got too strong, until a damper was designed for it. The tiny infrared detector behaved strangely under some conditions. The gas grain burned properly on the bench but not in flight. For a while vibration from an unknown source—it turned out to be unbalanced rollerons—overwhelmed the tracking signal. One after another such hurdles appeared and were overcome.

By 1953 more than two hundred people at NOTS were involved in the project, along with a like number at other government laboratories and industrial contractors. Flexibility was vanishing, and the design was becoming stabilized. But the missile still couldn't be gotten to work. By September there had been more than a dozen unsuccessful shots. People began to worry that time was running out. Wilcox ordered careful preparation of two identical missiles. One of them was fired,

and a Hummergram revealed that it had suddenly lost its target signal when the rocket motor burned out. This suggested that the gyroscope cager's retaining pins had broken during acceleration, allowing the gyro to recage. So the second round was fitted with new, stronger retaining pins. It was fired on September 11, 1953, and passed within six inches of a target drone, and Howard Wilcox declared it a virtual hit in a telegram to the Bureau of Ordnance, in Washington.

E motions ran high both East and West that night. McLean and his wife threw an impromptu beer blast to celebrate. At 2:00 A.M. a call was placed from McLean's home to Adm. P. D. Stroop, former NOTS commanding officer—everyone felt he would want to be among the first to hear the good news. But in the hullabaloo he couldn't make out what had happened. He demanded to speak to someone dependable: "Get Polly Nicol. She's got a lot of sense; she'll tell me what's going on." He was

told: "I can't. She's up on the roof."

Further shots hit drones. One particularly persuasive photograph, used with effect in Washington, showed an old QB-17 bomber-drone going down in flames after a direct hit. Some "experts" had said the Sidewinder's proportional-navigation homing system would create instability near the end of the missile's flight. They were proved wrong. Five-inch-diameter rockets were designed as targets and were usually hit. Small thermite heat sources were mounted on drones' wing tips; they were usually knocked off with no further damage to the expensive drones. Wilcox estimated the average miss distance of the Sidewinder, against a point target, as an inch or two.

The Sidewinder team now knew it had a working missile, so plans had to be made to engineer it for use in the fleet. Every effort was made to make its assembly and storage as simple as possible. The missiles became

so easy to put together that eventually two seamen could assemble them at the rate of one per minute.

Meanwhile the Air Force remained essentially unaware of the Sidewinder. Howard Wilcox, by now head of the project, knew that the Air Force needed the missiles even more than the Navy did, to defend the continental United States against attack by enemy bombers. He tried unsuccessfully to convince the Air Force of the importance of the new missile and finally gave up. Then one day he got a 6:00 A.M. phone call from McLean, who wanted him to join a breakfast meeting three hours hence with Professor Charles Lauritsen of Caltech and Assistant Secretary of the Air Force Trevor Gard-

Seeking maximum simplicity, McLean even suggested rectangular wings and fins.

ner. As the four ate breakfast, in Pasadena, McLean and Wilcox presented the case for the Sidewinder. After two hours of hard listening and pointed questions, Gardner was persuaded. He said he would commission an Air Force study and be sure to tell the analysts what conclusion was needed. But there would have to be a "shoot-off" between the Sidewinder and the Air Force's Falcon missile.

Within a few months the study duly appeared, bearing the promised conclusion that the Air Force needed the Sidewinder and that first it must be tested against drone targets. The shoot-off would take place at Holloman Air Force base, in New Mexico.

On June 12, 1955, the Sidewinder group arrived at Holloman with two jet fighters, a transport plane, and a telemetry truck. Four Sidewinder rounds had been mounted on the two jets. Air Force eyebrows were raised when the Sidewinders were readied for action in four hours and left on the planes overnight, a procedure that would have been unthinkable with the delicate Falcons. Eyebrows lifted even higher when the visitors requested only a flashlight and a small multimeter for test equipment. The Air Force colonel in charge took the group to see the Falcon test equipment: a battery of dials, gauges, and meters along a wall forty feet long. The Falcons, each loaded with dozens of radio tubes, moved along on a trolley in front of the equipment and were checked at a series of stations. The extent of the equipment suggested that the Falcon might be a very temperamental missile. It was.

When the first Sidewinder was fired it went straight up the exhaust pipe of the drone, blowing it apart even though the missile didn't carry a warhead. There was cheering from the crowd. The Air Force then announced that the next Sidewinder must fly in downward and track a drone against the infrared glare of the hot desert sand. The Sidewinder again destroyed the drone. The pilot, Lt. Glenn Tierney, was so exultant that he pulled a diving vic-

An F-16 ground crew handles a Sidewinder at MacDill Air Force Base near Tampa, Florida, October 1988.

tory roll that broke the sound barrier. Since sonic booms were against military regulations, he and the project engineer were officially cautioned. But the point had been made.

However, Air Force officials remained reluctant. They wanted to see the Sidewinder prove itself at above fifty thousand feet. No drones could operate that high, so NOTS said it would use rockets for targets. Air Force eyebrows rose again at the confidence this showed, but the tests were

scheduled. Six rockets were fired from planes, and the planes then fired Sidewinders at them from fifty thousand feet. When the pilots returned, they reported success; all the missiles had homed on the rockets. So the Air Force finally accepted the Sidewinder.

Ironically, when photographic data became available several months later, it turned out that all the shots had gone astray. The missiles had been fired with their rollerons removed, making them unstable at high

altitude. But by then the Air Force had already written and issued formal requirements for the Sidewinder missile system.

On the first working day of 1956, the Sidewinder was released for naval fleet use; it had its first use in combat two years later, after NOTS implemented a crash program to provide Sidewinders to the Chinese Nationalist Air Force, of Taiwan. On September 24, 1958, a squadron of Nationalist F-86D Sabre jets attacked a much larger contingent of Communist Chinese MIGs. The Communist pilots, surprised by the new weapon, found themselves being hunted down. The Sidewinders accounted for four kills. The Cummunists were so impressed that they declined all further aerial engagements with the Nationalists.

In Vietnam the Sidewinder and other air-to-air missiles did badly at first, thanks to faulty manufacturing, shipping, and training. Eventually, however, Sidewinder emerged as the missile of choice among combat pilots. It has been claimed that the AIM-9H Sidewinder had a success rate of more than 80 percent in Vietnam, much higher than any other air-to-air missile. In the 1980s, when AIM-9L Sidewinders were used by the British over the Falklands, they achieved a single-shot kill probability of 82 percent. In both 1981 and 1989 Libyan fighters attacking American planes over the Mediterranean were shot down with Navy Sidewinder missiles.

Other nations have developed their own versions of the Sidewinder. Using the same principles and sometimes virtually the same design, several hundred thousand U.S. and foreign copies of the Sideminder have been produced, by far the most of any air-to-air missile. Later models are more sophisticated and more expensive, with longer rangers and finer-tuned tracking, and costs have escalated. Still, compared with the cost of its targets, Sidewinder is a bargain. Indeed, it is today the least costly U.S. air-to-air

missile, with a price in the mid-tens of thousands of dollars apiece while other missiles range into six or even seven figures. And by all accounts it remains the best.

The Sidewinder's simplicity has given it amazing flexibility over the years. It can be mounted on virtually any airplane, and although it was designed as an air-to-air missile, it has spawned ground-to-air versions (Chapparral) and air-to-ground versions (Focus). It has even been adapted for ships (Sea Chaparral) too small to handle larger anti-aircraft missiles. Because the missile is self-contained, very little apparatus has to be mounted on its launching platform. The Red-Eye and Stinger missiles are both close relatives. McLean's emphasis on simplicity has paid off richly.

In 1954, when he was elevated to the post of NOTS technical director, McLean stopped managing the Sidewinder project, leaving it to his number-two man, Howard Wilcox. McLean's attention then turned elsewhere. He became involved in the development of space reconnaissance and weapons systems. In 1958 NOTS launched six satellites that used orientation systems devised and patented by McLean. Similiar systems have since been used by many other satellites.

As a result of his missile and satellite work, McLean came to believe that in the future no ship on the sea surface would be safe from missiles—surface ships were too visible and too slow and

couldn't hide by submerging. He began working on the Moray two-person submarine, on "mother" submarines, and on other submersibles. In 1967 the became director of the Naval Undersea Center (now the Naval Ocean Systems Center), in San Diego.

As he diverged into these larger naval- and space-warfare areas, McLean's ideas met more resistance. The Sidewinder had meant to switch from radar to infrared, but it was still a guided missile and fitted into the scheme of things; its buyers were simply choosing one missile over another. In suggesting new naval or space tactics, McLean was a technical man invading the province of admirals. His position was not helped by his bluntness about how vulnerable favored systems, such as giant aircraft carriers, might be. With regret he watched his influence wane and the system of official requirements he had fought become even more strict. He complained, shortly before his death in 1976, that innovation had been easier in the old days at NOTS.

Sidewinder and other projects like it could have been a warning that the military development and procurement system was becoming too rigid and bureaucratic. But the kind of creative budgeting that gave birth to the Sidewinder might now land its practitioners in jail. Less discretion is allowed at military laboratories, and intrusive "micromanagement" of government projects has thrived. As bureaucratic con-

trols have multiplied, successes have grown fewer.

What should have been learned is that a system's success simply cannot be calculated in advance. McLean felt that a specification should never be written for an experimental system but only for production in quantity. And while experimenters must keep the needs of their clients in mind, they must also be free to follow their instincts and findings. The instincts of managers lead toward prediction and control, but creativity must be encouraged and cultivated. The Sidewinder was the result of cultivation. Today, when so many new weapons work badly and cost too much, it is worth remembering how NOTS supported

In a crucial test for the Air Force, the missile went straight up its target's exhaust pipe.

Bill McLean and his band of inventors. ★

Ron Westrum is professor of sociology and interdisciplinary technology at Eastern Michigan University and is editor of *Social Psychology of Science Newsletter* and co-author of *Complex Organizations: Growth, Struggle, and Change*. Howard A. Wilcox became chief of the Sidewinder team, served as deputy director of defense research and engineering in the Pentagon, and has been technical director of research and engineering for General Motors.

BAR CODES SWEEP THE WORLD

■ **by Tony Seideman**

Supermarkets are a perilous business. They must stock thousands of products in scores of brands and sizes to sell at painfully small markups. Keeping close track of them all, and maintaining inventories neither too large nor too small, is critical. Yet for most of this century, as stores got bigger and the profusion on their shelves multiplied, the only way to find out what was on hand was by shutting the place down and counting every can, bag, and parcel. This expensive and cumbersome job was usually done no more than once a month. Store managers had to base most of their decisions on hunches or crude estimates.

Long before bar codes and scanners were actually invented, grocers knew they desperately needed something like them. Punch cards, first developed for the 1890 U.S. Census, seemed to offer some early hope. In 1932 a business student named Wallace Flint wrote a master's thesis in which he envisioned a supermarket where customers would perforate cards to mark their selections; at the checkout counter they would insert them into a reader, which would activate machinery to bring the purchases to them on conveyor belts. Store management would have a record of what was being bought.

The problem was, of course, that the card-reading equipment of the day was bulky, utterly unwieldy, and hopelessly expensive. Even if the country had not been in the middle of the Great Depression, Flint's scheme would have been unrealistic for all but the most distant future. Still, it foreshadowed what was to come.

The first step toward today's bar codes came in 1948, when Bernard Silver, a graduate student, overheard a conversation in the halls of Philadelphia's Drexel Institute of Technology. The president of a food chain was pleading with one of the deans to undertake research on capturing product information automatically at checkout. The dean turned down the request, but Bob Silver mentioned the conversation to his friend Norman Joseph Woodland, a twenty-seven-year-old graduate student

and teacher at Drexel. The problem fascinated Woodland.

His first idea was to use patterns of ink that would glow under ultraviolet light, and the two men built a device to test the concept. It worked, but they encountered problems ranging from ink instability to printing costs. Nonetheless, Woodland was convinced he had a workable idea. He took some stock-market earnings, quit Drexel, and moved to his grandfather's Florida apartment to seek solutions. After several months of work he came up with the linear bar code, using elements from two established technologies: movie soundtracks and Morse code.

Woodland, now retired, remembers that after starting with Morse code, "I just extended the dots and dashes downwards and made narrow lines and wide lines out of them." To read the data, he made use of Lee de Forest's movie sound system from the 1920s. De Forest had printed a pattern with varying degrees of transparency on the edge of the film, then shone a light through it as the picture ran. A sensitive tube on the other side translated the shifts in brightness into electric waveforms, which were in turn converted to sound by loudspeakers. Woodland planned to adapt this system by reflecting light off his wide and narrow lines and using a similar tube to interpret the results.

Woodland took his idea back to Drexel, where he began putting together a patent application. He decided to replace his wide and narrow vertical lines with concentric circles, so that they could be scanned from any direction. This became known as the bull's-eye code. Meanwhile, Silver investigated what form the codes should ultimately take. The two filed a patent application on October 20, 1949.

In 1951 Woodland got a job at IBM, where he hoped his scheme would flourish. The following year he and Silver set out to build the first actual bar-code read-

Today's ubiquitous bar codes are the result of almost half a century of planning, preparation, and just plain waiting

er—in the living room of Woodland's house in Binghamton, New York. The device was the size of a desk and had to be wrapped in black oilcloth to keep out ambient light. It relied on two key elements: a five-hundred-watt incandescent bulb as the light source and an RCA 935 photomultiplier tube, designed for movie sound systems, as the reader.

Woodland hooked the 935 tube up to an oscilloscope. Then he moved a piece of paper marked with lines across a thin beam emanating from the light source. The reflected beam was aimed at the tube. At one point the heat from the powerful bulb set the paper smoldering. Nonetheless, Woodland got what he wanted. As the paper moved, the signal on the oscilloscope jumped. He and Silver had created a device that could electronically read printed material.

It was not immediately clear how to transform this crude electronic response into a useful form. The primitive computers of the day were cumbersome to operate, could only perform simple calculations, and in any case were the size of a typical frozen-food section. The idea of installing thousands of them in supermarkets from coast to coast would have been pure fantasy. Yet without a cheap and convenient way to record data from Woodland and Silver's codes, their idea would be no more than a curiosity.

The first prototype, built in a living room in 1952, used a 500-watt light bulb and had to be shielded beneath black oilcloth.

Then there was that five-hundred-watt bulb. It created an enormous amount of light, only a tiny fraction of which was read by the 935 tube. The rest was released as expensive, uncomfortable waste heat. "That bulb was an awful thing to look at," Woodland recalls. "It could cause eye damage." The inventors needed a source that could focus a large amount of light into a small space. Today that sounds like a prescription for a laser, but in 1952 lasers did not exist. In retrospect, bar codes were clearly a technology whose time had nowhere near come.

But Woodland and Silver, sensing the potential, pressed on. In October 1952 their patent was granted. Woodland stayed with IBM and in the late 1950s persuaded the company to hire a consultant to evaluate bar codes. The consultant agreed that they had great possibilities but said they would require technology that lay at least five years off. By now almost half the seventeen-year life of Woodland and Silver's patent had expired.

IBM offered a couple of times to buy the patent, but for much less than the inventors thought it was worth. In 1962 Philco met their price, and they sold. (The following year Silver died at age thirty-eight.) Philco later sold the patent to RCA. In 1971 RCA would jolt several industries into action; before then, the next advances in information handling would come out of the railroad industry.

Freight cars are nomads, wandering all across the country and often being lent from one line to another. Keeping track of them is one of the most complex tasks the railroad industry faces, and in the early 1960s it attracted the attention of David J. Collins. Collins got his master's degree from MIT in 1959 and immediately went to work for the Sylvania Corporation, which was trying to find military applications for a computer it had built. During his undergraduate days Collins had worked for the Pennsylvania Railroad, and he knew that the railroads needed a way to identify cars automatically and then to handle the information gathered. Sylvania's computer could do the latter; all Collins needed was a means to retrieve the former. Some sort of coded label seemed to be the easiest and cheapest approach.

Strictly speaking, the labels Collins came up with were not bar codes. Instead of relying on black bars or rings, they used groups of orange and blue stripes made of a reflective material, which could be arranged to represent the digits 0 through 9. Each car was given a four-digit number to identify the railroad that owned it and a six-digit number to identify the car itself. When cars went into a yard, readers would flash a beam of colored light onto the codes and interpret the reflections. The Boston & Maine conducted the first test of the system on its gravel cars in 1961. By 1967 most of the kinks had been worked out, and a nationwide standard for a coding system was adopted. All that remained was for railroads to buy and install the equipment.

Collins foresaw applications for automatic coding far beyond the railroads, and in 1967 he pitched the idea to his bosses at Sylvania. "I said what we'd like to do now is develop the little black-and-white-line equivalent for conveyor control and for everything else that moves," he remembers. In a classic case of corporate short-sightedness, the company refused to fund him. "They said, 'We don't want to invest further. We've got this big market, and let's go and make money out of it.'" Collins quit and cofounded Computer Identics Corporation.

Sylvania never even saw profits from serving the railroad industry. Carriers started installing scanners in 1970, and the system worked as expected, but it was simply too expensive. Although computers had been getting a lot smaller, faster, and cheaper, they still cost too much to be economical in the quantities required. The recession of the mid-1970s killed the system as a flurry of railroad bankruptcies gutted industry budgets. Sylvania was left with a white elephant.

Meanwhile, Computer Identics prospered. Its system used lasers, which in

the late 1960s were just becoming affordable. A milliwatt helium-neon laser beam could easily match the job done by Woodland's unwieldy five-hundred-watt bulb. A thin stripe moving over a bar code would be absorbed by the black stripes and reflected by the white ones, giving scanner sensors a clear on/off signal. Lasers could read bar codes anywhere from three inches to several feet away, and they could sweep back and forth like a searchlight hundreds of times a second, giving the reader many looks at a single code from many different angles. That would prove to be a great help in deciphering scratched or torn labels.

Developing a workable, standardized bar-code system turned out to be the grocery industry's Manhattan Project.

In the spring of 1969 Computer Identics quietly installed its first two systems—probably the first true bar-code systems anywhere. One went into a General Motors plant in Pontiac, Michigan, where it was used to monitor the production and distribution of automobile axle units. The other went into a distribution facility run by the General Trading Company in Carlsbad, New Jersey, to help direct shipments to the proper loading-bay doors. At this point the components were still being built by hand; Collins made the enclosures for the scanners by turning a wastebasket upside down and molding fiberglass around it. Both systems relied on extremely simple bar codes bearing only two digits' worth of information. But that was all they needed; the Pontiac plant made only eighteen

types of axle, and the General Trading facility had fewer than a hundred doors.

Computer Identics's triumph proved the potential for bar codes in industrial settings, but it was the grocery industry that would once again provide the impetus to push the technology forward. In the early 1970s the industry set out to propel to full commercial maturity the technology that Woodland and Silver had dreamed up and Computer Identics had proved feasible.

Already RCA was moving to assist the industry. RCA executives had attended a 1966 grocery-industry meeting where bar-code development had been urged, and they smelled new business. A special group went to work at an RCA laboratory in Princeton, New Jersey, and the Kroger grocery chain volunteered itself as a guinea pig. Then, in mid-1970, an industry consortium established an ad hoc committee to look into bar codes. The committee set guidelines for bar-code development and created a symbol-selection subcommittee to help standardize the approach.

This would be the grocery industry's Manhattan Project, and Alan Haberman, who headed the subcommittee as president of First National Stores, recalls proudly, "We showed that it could be done on a massive scale, that cooperation without antitrust implications was possible for the common good, and that business didn't need the government to shove it in the right direction."

At the heart of the guidelines were a few basic principles. To make life easier for the cashier, not harder, bar codes would have to be readable from almost any angle and at a wide range of distances. Because they would be reproduced by the millions, the labels would have to be cheap and easy to print. And to be affordable, automated checkout systems would have to pay for themselves in two and a half years. This last goal turned out to be quite plausible; a 1970 study by McKinsey & Company predicted that the industry would save $150 million a year by adopting the systems.

"It turns out there were massive savings that we called hard savings—out-of-pocket savings in labor and other areas," Haberman says. "And there were gigantic savings available in the use of the information and the ability to deal with it more easily than we had before, but we never quantified that." Hard, quantifiable savings were what would draw retailers. These included checking out items at twice the speed of cashiers using traditional equipment, which would mean shorter lines without staff increases.

Still, while early bar-code systems would automate the checkout, they would not be useful for monitoring inventory, because at first too few items would come labeled with codes. Savings from using the collected information, instead of simply from cutting labor costs, would have to wait until most items bore codes. After that happened, management at every level would have to transform the way it operated.

In the spring of 1971 RCA demonstrated a bull's-eye bar-code system at a grocery-industry meeting. Visitors got a round piece of tin; if the code on top contained the right number, they won a prize. IBM executives at that meeting noticed the crowds RCA was drawing and worried that they were losing out on a huge potential market. Then Alec Jablonover, a marketing specialist at IBM, remembered that his company had the bar code's inventor on staff. Soon Woodland—whose patent had expired in 1969—was transferred to IBM's facilities in North Carolina, where he played a prominent role in developing the most popular and important version of the technology: the Universal Product Code (UPC).

RCA continued to push its bull's-eye code. In July 1972 it began an eighteen-month test in a Kroger store in Cincinnati. It turned out that printing problems and scanning difficulties limited the bull's-eye's usefulness. Printing presses sometimes smear ink in the direction the paper is running. When this happened to bull's-eye symbols, they did not scan properly. With the UPC, on the other hand, any extra ink simply flows out the top or bottom and no information is lost.

For a time such exotica as starburst-

shaped codes and computer-readable optical characters were considered, but eventually the technically elegant IBM-born UPC won the battle to be chosen by the industry. No event in the history of modern logistics was more important. The adoption of the Universal Product Code, on April 3, 1973, transformed bar codes from a technological curiosity into a business juggernaut.

Before the UPC, various systems had begun to come into use around the world in stores, libraries, factories, and the like, each with its own proprietary code. Afterward any bar code on any product could be read and understood in every suitably equipped store in the country. Standardization made it worth the expense for manufacturers to put the symbol on their packages and for printers to develop the new types of ink, plates, and other technology to reproduce the code with the exact tolerances it requires.

Budgets for the bar-code revolution were on a scale to make the Pentagon blanch. Each of the nation's tens of thousands of grocery outlets would have to spend at least $200,000 on new equipment. Chains would have to install new data-processing centers and retrain their employees. Manufacturers would potentially spend $200 million a year on the labels. Yet tests showed that the system would

Budgets were on a scale to make the Pentagon blanch. Each store would have to spend $200,000 on new equipment.

pay for itself in a few years.

Standardization of the code meant the need for a standardized system of numbers to go on it. "Before we had bar codes, every company had its own way of designating its products," Haberman says. Some used letters, some used numbers, some used both, and a few had no codes at all. When the UPC took over, these companies had to give up their individual methods and register with a new Uniform Code Council (UCC).

The code is split into two halves of six digits each. The first one is always zero, except for products like meat and produce that have variable weight, and a few other special types of items. The next five are the manufacturer's code; the next five are the product code; and the last is a "check digit" used to verify that the preceding digits have been scanned properly. Hidden cues in the structure of the code tell the scanner which end is which, so it can be scanned in any direction. Manufacturers register with the UCC to get an identifier code for their company, then register each of their products. Thus each package that passes over a checkout stand has its own unique identification number.

Two technological developments of the 1960s finally made scanners simple and affordable enough. Cheap lasers were one. The other was integrated circuits. When Woodland and Silver first came up with their idea, they would have needed a wall full of switches and relays to handle the information a scanner picked up; now it's all done by a microchip.

On June 26, 1974, all the tests were done,

all the proposals were complete, all the standards were set, and at a Marsh supermarket in Troy, Ohio, a single pack of chewing gum became the first retail product sold with the help of a scanner. Decades of schemes and billions of dollars in investment now became a practical reality. The use of scanners grew slowly at first. A minimum of 85 percent of all products would have to carry the codes before the system could pay off, and when suppliers reached that level, in the late 1970s, sales of the systems started to take off. In 1978 less than one percent of grocery stores nationwide had scanners. By mid-1981 the figure was 10 percent, three years later it was 33 percent, and today more than 60 percent are so equipped.

Meanwhile, the technology has been creeping into other industries and organizations. Researchers have mounted tiny bar codes on bees to track the insects' mating habits. The U.S. Army uses two-foot-long bar codes to label fifty-foot boats in storage at West Point. Hospital patients wear bar-code ID bracelets. The codes appear on truck parts, business documents, shipping cartons, marathon runners, and even logs in lumberyards. Federal Express, the package-shipping giant, is probably the world's biggest single user of the technology; its shipping labels bear a code called Codabar. Along the way refinements of the basic UPC have been developed, including the European Article Number-

ing system (EAN), developed by Joe Woodland, which has an extra pair of digits and is on its way to becoming the world's most widely used system. Other codes, which are given such fanciful names as Code 39, Code 16K, and Interleaved 2 of 5, can sometimes contain letters as well as numbers.

Woodland never got rich from bar codes, though he was awarded the 1992 National Medal of Technology by President Bush. But all those involved in the early days speak of the rewards of having brought a new way of doing business to the world. "This thing is a success story on the American way of doing things," Haberman says. "Our own initiative—take it on ourselves, inviting the world to join in. It has something to say about little guys with lots of vision." ★

Tony Seideman is a freelance writer who lives in New York City.

THE ANCIENT HISTORY OF SYSTEM/360

Developing System/360, in the early 1960s, meant spending five billion dollars to make every existing IBM computer obsolete. The gamble paid off—and reshaped the industry.

by James E. Strothman

Twenty-six years ago, on April 7, 1964, the International Business Machines Corporation changed the business world with one of the most momentous gambles ever made by a corporation. It introduced the System/360 family of computers.

Despite the staggering evolutionary leaps computers have made in the last quarter-century, fundamental technical concepts introduced with the 360 are still part of the backbone of the general-purpose computer industry. System/360 was the first product family that allowed business data-processing operations to grow from the smallest machine to the largest without the enormous expense of rewriting vital programs. Before then even IBM computers were a hodgepodge of incompatible machines. The few commercial computer users around faced major conversion problems and upheavals whenever their businesses grew too large for one machine and they were forced to switch to another—even from the same manufacturer. Small, medium, and large machines required their own armies of operators, even though they were being built to solve

similar business problems.

System/360 introduced upward and downward compatibility, allowing businesses for the first time to grow and prosper without being penalized. The system's popularity brought it high-volume sales, which in turn drove down manufacturing costs. This was a turning point in beginning the great drop in the cost of computing that has accompanied the exponential growth in computers' power.

Without technical concepts first embedded in System/360, the United States might still have not landed men on the moon. Automobiles would be less safe. Telephone systems might be much more complex and harder to use. Transportation and distribution networks for factory and farm products might be far less efficient.

As with any project of such magnitude, it was far from the work of one person. Facing stiff competition from companies like Remington Rand, General Electric, and Honeywell as the 1960s began, IBM's top management risked almost everything, investing five billion dollars on a new line of computers that would make all the existing ones obsolete. "We call this project

'you bet your company,'" one executive told *Fortune* magazine. But if there was one person most responsible for making the wager pay, for driving System/360 through the corporate technical and political bureaucracy from initial conception on, that person must be Bob O. Evans.

Born and reared in a small Nebraska town and trained in electrical engineering at Iowa State University, Evans joined IBM in 1951 as a junior engineer on one of the company's first computer projects, the Defense Calculator, later known as the 701. He helped run what he calls "sort of a nationwide emergency service" to keep the machines operating and customers happy. In 1955 he was noticed by Jerrier A. Haddad, an IBM executive in charge of new products. Haddad made Evans his administrative assistant, and Evans proved his worth when problems arose with a system built by IBM for the National Security Agency. Evans handpicked a group that worked seven days a week for nearly eight months to rebuild the NSA system and get it working.

An imposing, barrel-chested man, Evans was unyielding when he be-

lieved he was right. And because he usually was right, he earned top management's confidence and the power to pull strings within IBM to make things happen his way. He worked tirelessly, including on weekends. When making a point in a meeting, he might pound his fist on the table, but those who knew him best saw a gentle man behind the tough exterior—a man admired by those who worked for him and by top management too.

After fixing the National Security Agency's problem, Evans was promoted to run a top-secret IBM department serving the Navy. Later, in 1958, he was put in charge of all processing systems under development by the newly formed General Product Division (GPD), in Endicott, New York. GPD was one of two units within IBM that designed computers. The other—GPD's big rival—was the Data Systems Division (DSD), in Poughkeepsie, New York. GPD was responsible for lower-priced machines, DSD for bigger, higher-priced mainframes. And DSD had the task of planning the next generation of computers.

In January 1961 DSD was on the verge of unveiling a new line of computers, the 8000 series, that was to replace many of its existing computers. The 8000 was well received in presentations to corporate top management. However, as Frederick Brooks, who was in charge of the project, recalls, at one showing there was "one person who was extremely distressed by what he saw—and stood out like a dark cloud in the back of the auditorium." That person was T. Vincent Learson, the corporate executive in charge of both DSD and GPD and later the chairman of IBM.

As Learson noticed, the 8000 was falling short of expectations. Significant improvements had been planned in circuit technology, but pressure from the sales force to get the machine out fast had led to a decision to stick with older technology. And there were no plans to make machines within the 8000 series compatible with one another.

Some were to be organized using words, others with characters. Instruction sets would differ.

At the same time, other incompatible computers were continuing to be developed by GPD. Altogether seven noncompatible families of IBM computers had emerged in the preceding ten years. As Evans later recalled, "With so many types of architectures, IBM was spending most of its development resources propagating the wide variety of central processors. Little development effort was devoted to either peripherals or programming. A user could move from one processor in a family to one twice as fast, but only achieve 10 percent improvement in throughput [problem-solving ability], since the existing disk or tape peripheral devices and programming could not keep pace with the central processors."

Learson wanted to change this situation. Virtually overnight he thrust Evans into the DSD organizational hierarchy, below Charles DeCarlo, a DSD vice-president, but above Brooks, DSD's crack computer designer. Learson asked Evans to take a close look at whether the 8000 series should be announced at all. "His words were essentially, 'If it's right, build it, and if it's not right, do what's right,'" Evans says.

It was the first encounter between Evans and Brooks. Brooks, born and bred in North Carolina, had become enthralled as a teenager with the earliest computers. After graduating from Duke University as a physics major, Brooks went to Harvard to study under the computer pioneer Howard H. Aiken, and he eventually received a Ph.D. in computer science there.

From Harvard Brooks joined IBM in 1956 as an associate engineer and, like Evans, moved up fast in the technical ranks. He started out in a group designing a machine called Stretch that was supposed to stretch existing technologies. Stretch failed to meet its goals and caused IBM considerable embarrassment, but Brooks was given more key assignments. He helped design a

computer for a critical classified government project and then, in 1960, worked on an interdivisional task force developing what was known as the May Day Machine. After that Brooks was promoted to systems manager of an unannounced computer line being developed in Poughkeepsie. That was the 8000 series.

When Evans became his boss, he recalls, "one of Bob's first orders of business was that he and I go out to supper together. He tried to explain to me why the 8000 series was the wrong thing for the company to do. I did not find his arguments convincing." Brooks, like Evans, was persistent when he believed he was right. Unlike Evans, he was usually soft-spoken. For several months a fierce internal political battle raged over the fate of the 8000 project—with Brooks and his supporters on one side and Brooks's new boss, Evans, on the other.

In the January 1983 issue of *Annals of the History of Computing*, Brooks recalled both the war and the truce that ended it: "Bob and I fought bitterly with two separate armies against and for the 8000 series. He was arguing that we ought not to do a new product plan for the upper half of the business, but for the total business. I was arguing that that was a put-off, and it would mean delaying at least two years. The battle . . . went to the Corporate Management Committee twice. We won the first time, and they won the second time—and Bob was right."

As Evans bluntly remembers it, "I thought [the 8000 series] was poor, and I also thought the technology was a bum choice, and we could do a lot better."

By April Evans's superior at DSD, Charles DeCarlo, had been replaced by Evans's old boss Jerrier Haddad, who supported Evans's urgings for a better product line. Evans, winning the battle to kill the 8000 but realizing he had many wounded egos to heal, took all his adversaries, including Brooks, "away to the Gideon Putnam, a hotel in Saratoga Springs, to look at our belly button and decide how we were going to organize and what we were going to do." Evans allowed some Poughkeepsie favorite-son projects to continue, but his heart and mind were set on the New Product Line (NPL) concept of total system compatibility. He made a dramatic overture: "I so respected Brooks for his intellectual ability, I surprised him by offering him the senior job on what became System/360"—the job of systems manager. "He surprised me by taking it."

"To my utter amazement," Brooks recalls, "Bob asked me to take charge of that job after we had been fighting for months. I was dumbstruck at being asked to take charge of the juiciest part of his work."

Evans's victory in getting NPL started wasn't complete yet, and to cement it he would need the help of Donald T. Spaulding, a former boss who now led Learson's Group Staff—a half-dozen executives who could cut through organizational lines and strongly influence future product decisions. As Evans recalls, "Spaulding was very concerned about a key guy named John Haanstra."

Haanstra was with GPD, which was producing one of IBM's most popular and profitable machines, a small processor known as the 1401. The 1401 was threatened by a lower-priced competitor, the Honeywell 200, which came with a software tool that permitted it to run 1401 programs. The machine clearly worried Haanstra, and Evans feared he might bolt from supporting the New Product Line and muster all his division's energies behind a 1401 follow-on product. This would be a serious blow, since the low end of a typical computer product line has the highest volume of sales and actually produces the most profit. Therefore, the low end, for which in this case Haanstra's group would be responsible, would make the upper end feasible. Without GPD's support, System/360 would never see light.

This was especially true because System/360 was going to rely on new solid logic technology (SLT), a hybrid microminiature circuit design and packaging technology that would allow automated manufacturing on a mass production

"We call this project 'you bet your company,'" one IBM executive said.

line. Without the low end the volume of components being made would be too small to make economic sense.

Haanstra "was making sounds as if he would support the New Product Line, with [GPD] doing the low end," Evans says, but "Spaulding didn't really believe him, because the able John Haanstra had demonstrated some erraticism in the past." So in October 1961 Spaulding proposed an international top-secret task force to plan every detail of the New Product Line and make necessary compromises along the way. And in a stroke of political genius, he named as chairman of the group none other than John Haanstra. To no one's surprise, the vice-chairman was Bob Evans. In classic IBM obfuscation the task force of thirteen men—primarily top technical experts representing all the company's manufacturing and marketing divisions—was called the SPREAD (Systems Programming Research and Development) committee. Evans and other insiders preferred to say SPREAD meant "Spaulding's Plan to Reorganize Each and All Divisions."

Throughout November and December 1961 the thirteen met daily in strictest secrecy at the Sheraton New Englander Motel, in Greenwich, Connecticut. Their lengthy sessions were punctuated by heated technical arguments. When they concluded, on December 28, they had hammered out the framework for the System/360 product line, a detailed technical document dubbed the SPREAD report.

As Evans candidly recalled, "the stated purpose of the group was to develop a common plan. . . . But the real purpose was to get John Haanstra's name on the line, signed up in front of the corporation, to do the low end. The plan went a bit astray because, at the end of November [1961], Haanstra was promoted and went back to a bigger job. I took over as chairman. . . . Spaulding and I strategized, and we had Haanstra make the report to senior management in January 1962."

Joining Frederick Brooks as a chief designer of the system was another young computer architect, Dr. Gene M. Amdahl. Amdahl was from South Dakota, where electrification did not reach his parents' farm until he was in high school. Before that he had tried to make a cat's-whisker radio, but, he said, "there were no stations near enough to ever find out if it worked. You could get a little static, but that's all." He had earned his Ph.D. in theoretical physics at the University of Wisconsin. Evans saw to it that Amdahl played a key role in designing System/360's architecture. He explains: "Amdahl, in days before there were truly computer architects, was . . . a brilliant architect. I have yet to see his peer. He could visualize what happens internally in a computer during the computational process . . . and the flow of things during the solutions of problems. Amdahl kept the designs reasonably simple. He had a very good view of how data moved in a machine, and I thought that, in designing the data paths and designing the instruction repertoire of this family, Amdahl would be invaluable."

Amdahl, for his part, speaks of Evans as "a master at manipulating people. I liked him. I always got along well with him. But I always knew when he was manipulating me . . . and I would act in such a way as to make it come out the way I wanted it."

As Evans recalls, there was terrific feuding between Amdahl and Brooks while the two star designers worked on the 360 project together: "There was a time in 1963 when Brooks and Amdahl decided they couldn't work together anymore. They came to me, and I had to 'shoot' one or the other, so I concluded I had to shoot Brooks, as I believed the project couldn't afford to lose Amdahl. So I shot Brooks. He left the project."

Then the president of DSD, W. B. ("Bill") McWhirter, who "was out in Aspen at an executive conference, came running back and interceded with Brooks and pleaded with him to come back on the project," Evans says. "And he did. I accepted him back, and we went on."

It appears that while Evans was the chief proponent of upward compatibility, making the basic 360 machines compatible with the largest mainframe machines, Amdahl had much to do with extending compatibility downward to encompass the smallest computers.

Evans, when asked where the upward-downward compatibility notion originated, says, "I believe it started primarily with me," but adds, "the real seeds started years earlier when [IBM's] new San Jose laboratory had built a disk-based system called the 305," which was to be compatible with at least one other IBM processor. Amdahl, however, says downward compatibility was his idea: "I told them I wouldn't take the job unless I could do that." In a commentary in the April 1984 *Annals*, he wrote: "When I was being recruited by Bob Evans to head the architectural group, the task was to define a line of upward compatible processors. . . . I told Evans I'd do it, but insisted that the line of processors must be upward and downward compatible, or the same chaos would ensue."

Evans agrees that "the downward was really the trick. The issue was to have a machine that's skinny enough that you can profitably produce the low-cost, high-volume entry at the bottom of the line, and whether the constraints that are put on fulfilling the bottom of the line give enough performance at the high end. So that was the problem as we went to work."

In early 1962 Brooks held a competition among thirteen IBM engineering teams to come up with design ideas for the system. The winner was Gerrit A. ("Jerry") Blaauw, who, along with Amdahl, had the crucial idea of using base registers. A register is a storage device having a specified capacity, such as a bit (a single binary digit—the smallest unit of information), a byte (a sequence of bits), or a computer word. Blaauw and Amdahl's idea sped the processing by using abbreviated addressing, allowing data to be retrieved from storage by using shortened codes. Because shorter codes would require less memory, this would give greater power to small machines, and because of that, according to Brooks, it "was the key step that got us over the compatibility hump—and they had independently come up with that. It was not a totally new idea in the field, but it was new in the IBM company."

Brooks says the reason Blaauw edged out Amdahl in the competition was that "Jerry's machine was based on sizes that were powers of two and Gene's were based on sizes that were three times powers of two. So [Amdahl's] were twenty-four, forty-eight, ninety-six, with three index bits and everything that follows from that, and the six-bit byte. Jerry's were four, eight, sixteen, thirty-two, sixty-four, with an eight-bit byte. That led to a great 'six-eight' fight that took place in June." The eight-bit byte ultimately won because, having more permutations, it made possible a wider range of alphanumeric characters and symbols. Eight bits allowed 256 different combinations, meaning System/360 could be used for a wider range of business applications and also, eventually, in other countries around the world that had different alphabets and symbols. The eight-bit byte has been an almost universal computer standard ever since.

Despite the hidden motive behind the SPREAD meetings, the SPREAD report stood the test of time. During the next two and a half years, as IBM engineers and scientists labored in secrecy to build System/360, the SPREAD recommendations were followed without any significant deviation. The technology the report proposed not only became embodied in the bowels of System/360 but set many technical standards that are still followed by IBM and the rest of the industry today—and will probably continue to be well into the 1990s.

Evans listed seven basic points of the SPREAD report in an article in the January 1983 *Annals*. First, the central processing units were to be both versatile—handling scientific and business applications with equal ease—and totally compatible with one another. Second, they all were to accept the same peripheral devices, such as disks and printers. Third, although integrated circuits were being considered at the time, the processors were to rely on hybrid microminiaturization, chips that had discrete components wired on—a less advanced but also less risky technology. Fourth, uniform programming would be developed for the whole line. Fifth, a single high-level language that could serve both scientific and business needs would be designed. Sixth, the processors would have the power to address an unprecedented sixteen million characters, expandable to two billion characters. Seventh, the basic unit of information would be the eight-bit byte. In conclusion Evans wrote: "Perhaps most important, the SPREAD report permitted IBM to focus on an excellence not possible with multiple architectures. It resulted in powerful new peripherals, programming, terminals, high-volume applications, and complementary diversifications whose future can only be imagined."

Dr. Erich Bloch, who retired from IBM in 1984 to become director of the National Science Foundation, managed the development of the solid logic technology. By successfully unifying SLT circuit and package technology across the entire product line, he eased the way for broad standardization, which not only lowered manufacturing costs but also simplified training and reduced the number of parts needed at service centers. "Without [Bloch], we wouldn't have been in the game at all," Brooks has said.

Although System/360's hardware was in reasonably good shape by the time of the April 7, 1964, public announcement of the line, its operating system, known as OS/360, was not. An operating-system plan had been part of the project from the time of the SPREAD report. However, at the end of 1963 the programming group responsible for it went to management with a plan known as the Romans because it proposed four operating systems identified by the Roman numerals I, II, III, and IV.

"There was little compatibility

A fierce internal political battle raged over the fate of the 8000 project.

among the Romans," Brooks says. They were essentially four independent programming systems for different sizes of machines, completely defeating the compatibility goal. The Romans plan was killed, and a team of experts was sent off to a retreat in the woods in February 1964 to come up with a better idea. The group laid the groundwork for OS/360.

However, that system had problems too. It turned out to be the most complex operating system IBM had ever produced, a far more difficult design task than anyone had expected. As of the summer of 1964, several months after System/360 had been officially announced, the operating system was still full of bugs. At Evans's request, Brooks took over the matter. He hoped to get it cleared up by August, when, he told Evans, he planned to resign from IBM to head the computer science department at the University of North Carolina. Thomas Watson, Jr., the chair-

man of IBM, personally intervened and talked Brooks into working on the project one more year. In March 1965 the operating system successfully passed "Alpha test," which, Brooks said, "was the objective I was determined to see done when I stayed the extra year."

Those who succeeded Brooks wrestled with additional performance problems into yet another year, 1966, to the intense dismay of the IBM marketing people. There was one "big miss on 360," in Evans's words: its planners' failure to adopt a concept called dynamic address translation, which would have made time sharing much easier. Time sharing, which was very important in business computing until the personal-computer era began, permitted multiple remote users to use the same computer, via terminals, at the same time. Dynamic address translation, later also called virtual memory, automatically juggled users' data and programs, moving them in turn between main memory and disk storage.

The Massachusetts Institute of Technology was a major proponent of dy-

Brooks and Amdahl couldn't work together; Evans had to "shoot" one of them.

namic address translation. IBM's chairman Watson had instructed Evans to track what was going on at MIT. Evans sent experts, including Brooks and Amdahl, there, but the team concluded that changing the architecture to incorporate dynamic address translation would take too long and cost too much. A competitor, General Electric, listened to MIT, and one result was that the prestigious university purchased a GE system instead of one from IBM. Another leading-edge account, Bell Laboratories, shortly afterward did the same. But System/360 was so broadly successful elsewhere that it helped put GE out of the computer business entirely by 1970.

The first 360 computer released for sale—the 360-40—started being shipped in April 1965. Three other models soon followed. IBM's marketing staff breathed a huge collective sigh of relief. Control Data had already unveiled its 6600 computer, and an exasperated Watson had sent around a memo around IBM complaining that Control Data had managed to develop its machine faster in a research laboratory of only thirty-four people— "including the janitor."

But IBM had more orders waiting for the 360 than it could handle. In 1966 the company hired twenty-five thousand people worldwide and began building three million square feet of manufacturing space. By the end of that year a thousand 360s were being produced each month. The financial records speak for the smashing ultimate success of IBM's gamble. In the six years from 1966 through 1971, IBM's gross income more than doubled, from $3.6 billion to $8.3 billion. Net earnings after taxes did the same, rising from $477 million to $1.1 billion. In 1982 the direct descendants of System/360 were still accounting for more than half of all IBM's gross income and earnings.

IBM's primary computer architecture today is System/370—an evolutionary, not revolutionary, step beyond System/360, with many of 360's concepts embedded in it. System/360 and 370 architecture has been adopted by hundreds of companies, including many Japanese manufacturers—who make plug-compatible peripheral devices and processor—and thousands of software firms selling control and application programs. All this has helped prolong 360's mortality, as has the development of major operating systems using its architecture, many of which have themselves become industry standards: COBOL, the most widely used business data processing language; FORTRAN, a language used by scientists and engineers; and the Disk Operating System (DOS), the basis of the personal computer.

Most of the men responsible for making System/360 happen have thrived too. Bob O. Evans held a number of executive positions at IBM, retired in 1984, and is a general partner in a San Francisco-based investment firm. Frederick Brooks left IBM in 1965 to head the department of computer science at the University of North Carolina, where he remains active today. Gene M. Amdahl resigned from IBM in 1970 and founded an IBM archrival, the Amdahl Corporation, which produces a line of IBM-compatible processors. He has since left Amdahl and begun two other start-ups. T. Vincent Learson became chairman of the board of IBM when Watson retired in 1971 and is now retired himself.

Few of the System/360 computers themselves are still active. Most have been obsolete for years. But the dominance they gave IBM in the business computer design field is a legacy that has endured, however challenged, through many computer generations. ★

James E. Strothman is editor in chief of *Computer Pictures* magazine and was formerly editor in chief of *MIS Week*, a publication for information-systems managers. He is currently researching a historical book about the computer industry.

LESS WORK FOR MOTHER?

The modern convenience of the vacuum cleaner is serenely demonstrated in about 1910.

Modern technology enables the housewife to do much more in the house than ever before. That's good—and not so good.

by Ruth Schwartz Cowan

Things are never what they seem. Skimmed milk masquerades as cream. And laborsaving household appliances often do not save labor. This is the surprising conclusion reached by a small army of historians, sociologists, and home economists who have undertaken, in recent years, to study the one form of

What Maggie had once done with a broom, Mrs. Smith was now doing with a vacuum cleaner.

work that has turned out to be most resistant to inquiry and analysis—namely, housework.

During the first half of the twentieth century, the average American household was transformed by the introduction of a group of machines that profoundly altered the daily lives of housewives; the forty years between 1920 and 1960 witnessed what might be aptly called the "industrial revolution in the home." Where once there had been a wood- or coal-burning stove there now was a gas or electric range. Clothes that had once been scrubbed on a metal washboard were now tossed into a tub and cleansed by an electrically driven agitator. The dryer replaced the clothesline; the vacuum cleaner replaced the broom; the refrigerator replaced the icebox and the root cellar; an automatic pump, some piping, and a tap replaced the hand pump, the bucket, and the well. No one had to chop and haul wood any more. No one had to shovel out ashes or beat rugs or carry water; no one even had to toss egg whites with a fork for an hour to make an angel food cake.

And yet American housewives in 1960, 1970, and even 1980 continued to log about the same number of hours at their work as their grandmothers and mothers had in 1910, 1920, and 1930. The earliest time studies of housewives date from the very same period in which time studies of other workers were becoming popular—the first three decades of the twentieth century. The sample sizes of these studies were usually quite small, and they did not always define housework in precisely the same way (some counted an hour spent taking children to the playground as "work," while others called it "leisure"), but their results were more or less consistent: whether rural or urban, the average American housewife performed fifty to sixty hours of unpaid work in her home every week, and the only variable that significantly altered this was the number of small children.

A half century later not much had changed. Survey research had become much more sophisticated, and sample sizes had grown considerably, but the results of the time studies remained surprisingly consistent. The average American housewife, now armed with dozens of motors and thousands of electronic chips, still spends fifty to sixty hours a week doing housework. The only variable that significantly altered the size of that number was full time employment in the labor force; "working" housewives cut down the average number of hours that they spend cooking and cleaning, shopping and chauffeuring, to a not insignificant thirty-five—virtually the equivalent of another full-time job.

How can this be true? Surely even the most sophisticated advertising copywriter of all times could not fool almost the entire American population over the course of at least three generations. Laborsaving devices must be saving something, or Americans would not continue, year after year, to plunk down their hard-earned dollars for them.

And if laborsaving devices have not saved labor in the home, then what is it that has suddenly made it possible for more than 70 percent of the wives and mothers in the American population to enter the work force and stay there? A brief glance at the histories of some of the technologies that have transformed housework in the twentieth century will help us answer some of these questions.

The portable vacuum cleaner was one of the earliest electric appliances to make its appearance in American homes, and reasonably priced models appeared on the retail market as early as 1910. For decades prior to the turn of the century, inventors had been trying to create a carpet-cleaning system that would improve on the carpet sweeper with adjustable rotary brushes (patented by Melville Bissell in 1876), or the semiannual ritual of hauling rugs outside and beating them, or the practice of regularly sweeping the dirt out of a rug that had been covered with dampened, torn newspapers. Early efforts to solve the problem had focused on the use of large steam, gasoline, or electric motors attached to piston-type pumps and lots of hoses. Many of these "stationary" vacuum-cleaning systems were installed in apartment houses or hotels, but some were hauled around the streets in horse-drawn carriages by entrepreneurs hoping to establish themselves as "professional housecleaners."

In the first decade of the twentieth century, when fractional-horsepower electric motors became widely—and inexpensively—available, the portable vacuum cleaner intended for use in an individual household was born. One early model—invented by a woman, Corrine Dufour—consisted of a rotary brush, an electrically driven fan, and a wet sponge for absorbing the dust and dirt. Another, patented by David E. Kenney in 1907, had a twelve-inch nozzle, attached to a metal tube, attached to a flexible hose that led to a vacuum pump and separating devices. The Hoover, which was based on a brush, a fan, and a collecting bag, was on the market by 1908. The Electrolux, the first of the canister types of cleaner, which could vacuum something above the level of the floor, was brought over from Sweden in 1924 and met with immediate success.

These early vacuum cleaners were hardly a breeze to operate. All were heavy, and most were extremely cumbersome to boot. One early home economist mounted a basal metabolism machine on the back of one of her hapless students and proceeded to determine that more energy was expended in the effort to clean a sample carpet with a vacuum cleaner than when the same carpet was attacked with a hard broom. The difference, of course, was that the vacuum cleaner did a better job, at least on carpets, because a good deal of what the broom stirred up simply resettled a foot or two away from where it had first been lodged. Whatever the liabilities of the early vacuum

An automatic wringer supposedly makes life easier for a farm woman in Velmo, Missouri, in 1935. After the wash there will be plenty to iron.

cleaners may have been, Americans nonetheless appreciated their virtues; according to a market survey done in Zanesville, Ohio, in 1926, slightly more than half the households owned one. Eventually improvements in the design made these devices easier to operate. By 1960 vacuum cleaners could be found in 70 percent of the nation's homes.

When the vacuum cleaner is viewed in a historical context, however, it is easy to see why it did not save housewifely labor. Its introduction coincided almost precisely with the disappearance of the domestic servant. The number of persons engaged in household service dropped from 1,851,000 in 1910 to 1,411,000 in 1920, while the number of households enumerated in the census rose from 20.3 million to 24.4 million. Moreover, between 1900 and 1920 the number of household servants per

thousand persons dropped from 98.9 to 58.0, while during the 1920s the decline was even more precipitous as the restrictive immigration acts dried up what had once been the single most abundant source of domestic labor.

For the most economically comfortable segment of the population, this meant just one thing: the adult female head of the household was doing more housework than she had ever done before. What Maggie had once done with a broom, Mrs. Smith was now doing with a vacuum cleaner. Knowing that this was happening, several early copywriters for vacuum cleaner advertisements focused on its implications. The vacuum cleaner, General Electric announced in 1918, is better than a maid: it doesn't quit, get drunk, or demand higher wages. The switch from Maggie to Mrs. Smith shows up, in time-study statistics, as an increase in the

time that Mrs. Smith is spending at her work.

For those—and they were the vast majority of the population—who were not economically comfortable, the vacuum cleaner implied something else again: not an increase in the time spent in housework but an increase in the standard of living. In many households across the country, acquisition of a vacuum cleaner was connected to an expansion of living space, the move from a small apartment to a small house, the purchase of wall-to-wall carpeting. If this did not happen during the difficult 1930s, it became more possible during the expansive 1950s. As living quarters grew larger, standards for their upkeep increased; rugs had to be vacuumed every week, in some households every day, rather than semiannually, as had been customary. The net result, of course, was that when armed

161

with a vacuum cleaner, housewives whose parents had been poor could keep more space cleaner than their mothers and grandmothers would have ever believed possible. We might put this everyday phenomenon in language that economists can understand: The introduction of the vacuum cleaner led to improvements in productivity but not to any significant decrease in the amount of time expended by each worker.

The history of the washing machine illustrates a similar phenomenon. "Blue Monday" had traditionally been, as its name implies, the bane of a housewife's existence—especially when Monday turned out to be "Monday . . . and Tuesday to do the ironing." Thousands of patents for "new and improved" washers were issued during the nineteenth century in an effort to cash in on the housewife's despair.

Most of these early washing machines were wooden or metal tubs combined with some kind of hand-cranked mechanism that would rub or push or twirl laundry when the tub was filled with water and soap. At the end of the century, the Sears catalog offered four such washing machines, ranging in price from $2.50 to $4.25, all sold in combination with hand-cranked wringers.

These early machines may have saved time in the laundering process (four shirts could be washed at once instead of each having to be rubbed separately against a washboard), but they probably didn't save much energy. Lacking taps and drains, the tubs still had to be filled and emptied by hand, and each piece still had to bé run through a wringer and hung up to dry.

Not long after the appearance of fractional-horsepower motors, several enterprising manufacturers had the idea

of hooking them up to the crank mechanisms of washers and wringers—and the electric washer was born. By the 1920s, when mass production of such machines began, both the general structure of the machine (a central-shaft agitator rotating within a cylindrical tub, hooked up to the household water supply) and the general structure of the industry (oligopolistic—with a very few firms holding most of the patents and controlling most of the market) had achieved their final form. By 1926 just over a quarter of the families in Zanesville had an electric washer, but by 1941 fully 52 percent of all American households either owned or had interior access (which means that they could use coin-operated models installed in the basements of apartment houses) to such a machine. The automatic washer, which consisted of a vertically rotating washer cylinder that

Catching the 8:05 was the first chore of the suburban day in 1952. By 1974, women were spending eight hours a week making pickups and deliveries in

could also act as a centrifugal extractor, was introduced by the Bendix Home Appliance Corporation in 1938, but it remained expensive, and therefore inaccessible, until after World War II. This machine contained timing devices that allowed it to proceed through its various cycles automatically; by spinning the clothes around in the extractor phase of its cycle, it also eliminated the wringer. Although the Bendix subsequently disappeared from the retail market (versions of this sturdy machine may still be found in Laundromats), its design principles are replicated in the agitator washers that currently chug away in millions of American homes.

Both the early wringer washers and their more recent automatic cousins have released American women from the burden of drudgery. No one who has ever tried to launder a sheet by

their automobiles.

hand, and without the benefits of hot running water, would want to return to the days of the scrubboard and tub. But "labor" is composed of both "energy expenditure" and "time expenditure," and the history of laundry work demonstrates that the one may be conserved while the other is not.

The reason for this is, as with the vacuum cleaner, twofold. In the early decades of the century, many households employed laundresses to do their wash; this was true, surprisingly enough, even for some very poor households when wives and mothers were disabled or employed full-time in field or factory. Other households—rich and poor—used commercial laundry services. Large, mechanized "steam" laundries were first constructed in this country in the 1860s, and by the 1920s they could be found in virtually every urban neighborhood and many rural ones as well.

But the advent of the electric home washer spelled doom both for the laundress and for the commercial laundry; since the housewife's labor was unpaid, and since the washer took so much of the drudgery out of washday, the one-time expenditure for a machine seemed, in many families, a more sensible arrangement than continuous expenditure for domestic services. In the process, of course, the time spent on laundry work by the individual housewife, who had previously employed either a laundress or a service, was bound to increase.

For those who had not previously enjoyed the benefits of relief from washday drudgery, the electric washer meant something quite different but equally significant: an upgrading of household cleanliness. Men stopped wearing removable collars and cuffs, which meant that the whole of their shirts had to be washed and then ironed. Housewives began changing two sheets every week, instead of moving the top sheet to the bottom and adding only one that was fresh. Teenagers began changing their underwear every day instead of every weekend. In the early 1960s, when synthetic no-iron fabrics were introduced, the size of the household laundry load increased again; shirts and skirts, sheets and blouses that had once been sent out to the dry cleaner or the corner laundry

A new category was added to the housewife's traditional job description: chauffeur.

were now being tossed into the household wash basket. By the 1980s the average American housewife, armed now with an automatic washing machine and an automatic dryer, was processing roughly ten times (by weight) the amount of laundry that her mother had been accustomed to. Drudgery had disappeared, but the laundry hadn't. The average time spent on this chore in 1925 had been 5.8 hours per week; in 1964 it was 6.2.

And then there is the automobile. We do not usually think of our cars as household appliances, but that is precisely what they are since housework, as currently understood, could not possibly be performed without them. The average American housewife is today more likely to be found behind a steering wheel than in front of a stove. While writing this article I interrupted myself five times: once to take a child to field-hockey practice, then a second time, to bring her back when practice was finished; once to pick up some groceries at the supermarket; once to retrieve my husband, who was stranded at the train station; once for a trip to a doctor's office. Each time I was doing housework, and each time I had to use my car.

Like the washing machine and the vacuum cleaner, the automobile started to transform the nature of housework in the 1920s. Until the introduction of the Model T in 1908, automobiles had been playthings for the idle rich, and although many wealthy women learned to drive early in the century (and several participated in

Modern medicines altered not only the routines of housework but also the emotional commitment.

well-publicized auto races), they were hardly the women who were likely to be using their cars to haul groceries.

But by 1920, and certainly by 1930, all this had changed. Helen and Robert Lynd, who conducted an intensive study of Muncie, Indiana, between 1923 and 1925 (reported in their famous book *Middletown*), estimated that in Muncie in the 1890s only 125 families, all members of the "elite," owned a horse and buggy, but by 1923 there were 6,222 passenger cars in the city, "roughly one for every 7.1 persons, or two for every three families." By 1930, according to national statistics, there were roughly 30 million households in the United States—and 26 million registered automobiles.

What did the automobile mean for the housewife? Unlike public transportation systems, it was convenient. Located right at her doorstep, it could deposit her at the doorstep that she wanted or needed to visit. And unlike the bicycle or her own two feet, the automobile could carry bulky packages as well as several additional people. Acquisition of an automobile therefore meant that a housewife, once she had learned how to drive, could become her own door-to-door delivery service. And as more housewives acquired automobiles, more businessmen discovered the joys of dispensing with delivery services—particularly during the Depression.

To make a long story short, the iceman does not cometh anymore. Neither does the milkman, the bakery truck, the butcher, the grocer, the knife sharpener, the seamstress, or the doctor. Like many other businessmen, doctors discovered that their earnings increased when they stayed in their offices and transferred the responsibility for transportation to their ambulatory patients.

Thus a new category was added to the housewife's traditional job description: chauffeur. The suburban station wagon is now "Mom's Taxi." Children who once walked to school now have to be transported by their mothers; husbands who once walked home from work now have to be picked up by their wives; groceries that once were dispensed from pushcarts or horse-drawn wagons now have to be packed into paper bags and hauled home in family cars. "Contemporary women," one time-study expert reported in 1974, "spend about one full working day per week on the road and in stores compared with less than two hours per week for women in the 1920s." If everything we needed to maintain our homes and sustain our families were delivered right to our doorsteps—and every member of the family had independent means for getting where she or he wanted to go—the hours spent in housework by American housewives would decrease dramatically.

The histories of the vacuum cleaner, the washing machine, and the automobile illustrate the varied reasons why the time spent in housework has not markedly decreased in the United States during the last half century despite the introduction of so many ostensibly laborsaving appliances. But these histories do not help us understand what has made it possible for so many American wives and mothers to enter the labor force full-time during those same years. Until recently, one of the explanations most often offered for the startling increase in the participation of married women in the work force (up from 24.8 percent in 1950 to 50.1 percent in 1980) was household technology. What with microwave ovens and frozen foods, washer and dryer combinations and paper diapers, the reasoning goes, housework can now be done in no time at all, and women have so much time on their hands that they find they must go out and look for a job for fear of going stark, raving mad.

As every "working" housewife knows, this pattern of reasoning is itself stark, raving mad. Most adult women are in the work force today quite simply because they need the money. Indeed, most "working" housewives today hold down not one but two jobs; they put in what has come to be called a "double day." Secretaries, lab technicians, janitors, sewing machine operators, teachers, nurses, or physicians for eight (or nine or ten) hours, they race home to become chief cook and bottle washer for another five, leaving the cleaning and the marketing for Saturday and Sunday. Housework, as we have seen, still takes a lot of time, modern technology notwithstanding.

Yet household technologies have played a major role in facilitating (as opposed to causing) what some observers believe to be the most significant social revolution of our time. They do it in two ways, the first of which we have already noted. By relieving housework of the drudgery that it once entailed, washing machines, vacuum cleaners, dishwashers, and water pumps have made it feasible for a woman to put in a double day without destroying her health, to work full-time and still sustain herself and her family at a reasonably comfortable level.

The second relationship between household technology and the participation of married women in the work force is considerably more subtle. It involves the history of some technologies that we rarely think of as technologies at all—and certainly not as household appliances. Instead of being sheathed in stainless steel or porcelain, these devices appear in our kitchens in little brown bottles and bags of flour; instead of using switches and buttons to turn them on, we use hypodermic needles and sugar cubes. They are various forms of medication, the products not only of modern medicine but also of modern industrial chemistry: polio vaccines and vitamin pills; tetanus toxins and ampicillin; enriched breads and tuberculin tests.

Before any of these technologies had made their appearance, nursing may well have been the most time-consuming and most essential aspect of housework. During the eighteenth and nineteenth centuries and even during the first five decades of the twentieth century, it was the woman of the house who was expected (and who had been trained, usually by *her* mother) to sit up all night cooling and calming a feverish child, to change bandages on suppurating wounds, to clean bed linens stained with excrement, to prepare easily digestible broths, to cradle colicky infants on her lap for hours on end, to prepare bodies for burial. An attack of the measles might mean the care of a bedridden child for a month. Pneumonia might require six months of bed rest. A small knife cut could become infected and produce a fever that would rage for days. Every summer brought the fear of polio epidemics, and every polio epidemic left some group of mothers with the perpetual problem of tending to the needs of a handicapped child. Cholera, diphtheria, typhoid fever—if they weren't fatal—could mean weeks of sleepless nights and hard-pressed days. "Just as soon as the person is attacked," one experienced mother wrote to her worried daughter during a cholera epidemic in Oklahoma in 1885, "be it ever so slightly, he or she ought to go to bed immediately and stay there; put a mustard [plaster] over the bowels and if vomiting over the stomach. See that the feet are kept warm, either by warm iron or brick, or bottles of hot water. If the disease progresses the limbs will begin to cramp, which must be prevented by applying cloths wrung out of hot water and wrapping round them. When one is vomiting so terribly, of course, it is next to impossible to keep medicine down, but in cholera it must be done."

These were the routines to which American women were once accustomed, routines regarded as matters of life and death. To gain some sense of the way in which modern medicines have altered not only the routines of housework but also the emotional commitment that often accompanies such work, we need only read out a list of the diseases for which most American children are unlikely to succumb today, remembering how many of them once were fatal or terribly disabling: diphtheria, whooping cough, tetanus, pellagra, rickets, measles, mumps, tuberculosis, smallpox, cholera, malaria, and polio.

And many of today's ordinary childhood complaints, curable within a few days of the ingestion of antibiotics,

House-call days are over in this scene from 1955, the year the polio vaccine was developed.

once might have entailed weeks, or even months, of full-time attention: bronchitis; strep throat; scarlet fever; bacterial pneumonia; infections of the skin, or the eyes, or the ears, or the airways. In the days before the introduction of modern vaccines, antibiotics, and vitamin supplements, a mother who was employed full-time was a serious, sometimes life-endangering threat to the health of her family. This is part of the reason why life expectancy was always low and infant mortality high among the poorest segment of the population—those most likely to be dependent upon a mother's wages.

Thus modern technology, especially modern medical technology, has made it possible for married women to enter the work force by releasing housewives not just from drudgery but also from the dreaded emotional equation of female employment with poverty and disease. She may be exhausted at the end of her double day, but the modern "working" housewife can at least fall into bed knowing that her efforts have made it possible to sustain her family at a level of health and comfort that not so long ago was reserved only for those who were very rich. ∎

Ruth Schwartz Cowan is a professor of history and director of women's studies at the State University of New York at Stony Brook and author of *More Work for Mother: The Ironies of Household Technology from the Open Hearth to the Microwave* (Basic Books, 1983).

A GOOD CRYSTAL BALL IS HARD TO FIND

An inquiry into why predicting the impact of technology is such an uncertain—though not necessarily gloomy—science

by Nathan Rosenberg

Illustrated by Elwood H. Smith

Why do we consistently do such a poor job of anticipating the future effect of technological change? Why is our intellectual framework for thinking about the way technology transforms our lives so obviously inadequate? Such questions reasserted themselves to me when I encountered a piece of futurology given to President William McKinley in 1899 by Charles H. Duell. Duell was the commissioner of the Patent and Trademark Office at the time and, rather uncharacteristically for a public officeholder, was encouraging the President to close down his agency. His reason was startling in its simplicity: "Everything that can be invented has been invented."

Eighty-six years and approximately 3,800,000 patents later, we are properly disdainful of Duell's total bankruptcy of imagination. I resurrect him here only because he managed to express in extreme form, but with epigrammatic precision, a widely held view regarding the impact of technological change. In retrospect, it is apparent that we have persistently underestimated the effect of technological change on the growth of the economy. We especially have failed to anticipate the contribution that technological change would make to alleviate problems that earlier generations regarded as both serious and intractable.

Ever since the writings of Malthus and Ricardo at the beginning of the nineteenth century, economists have seemed to have a stranglehold on the expression of deeply pessimistic views of the future. Malthus, in particular, made clear in his classic essay on population, published in 1798, that he rejected naive Enlightenment views on the future prospects for improvement in the human condition. More recently, however, very pessimistic forecasts have emanated not from economists but from systems analysts, biologists, ecologists, and other natural scientists who have become concerned with social issues that transcend their narrowly defined professional spheres. Economists, in an interesting reversal of roles, now find themselves explaining why these pessimistic forecasts—in some cases, prophecies of doom—are unwarranted.

During the 1970s public discussion was preoccupied with visions of the imminent exhaustion of natural resources and pollution-induced ecological disasters that were bound to bring economic growth to an end. The dominant theme was struck in a collection of essays entitled *The Limits to Growth*, published in 1972. The book argued that inexorable constraints in natural resources placed a rigid upper limit on economic growth. Some futurologists believed that simple extrapolation of recent rates of utilization of key natural resources was sufficient to generate precise predictions of an apocalypse

awaiting humankind not too far down the road. The whole exercise was remarkably Malthusian. Indeed, it seemed to me as if Malthus had returned in the 1970s in the guise of a slightly off-the-rails computer programmer.

It is obviously true that nature imposes certain constraints upon resource supplies, but it is also true, and of fundamental importance, that many technological improvements, when they occur, vastly enlarge the resource base—that is, by making it possible to exploit resources that could not be exploited before, they add to our resources in economic, if not in geological, terms. So it should not be regarded as paradoxical to state that the United States has a far larger quantity of iron ore deposits within its borders today than it had fifty years ago. In the past few decades new processing techniques that prepare the ore for the blast furnace (pelletization and beneficiation) have made it possible to exploit immense deposits of hard, low-grade taconite ores that were ignored as long as the high-grade iron ores of the Mesabi Range were still abundant. The development of these new processing techniques has been equivalent to a gigantic expansion of resource supplies. In fact, pelletization and beneficiation have brought such great economies in transportation costs and blast-furnace efficiency that the energy cost of a finished ton of steel has declined substantially even though the iron content of the taconite ores is very low. Similar developments occurred in the nineteenth century. The introduction of the Gilchrist-Thomas basic steelmaking process in the late 1870s changed the course of European history by making possible, for the first time, the exploitation of the enormous deposits of high-phosphorus iron ore in Western Europe. Such "low-quality" deposits were simply not usable with earlier ironmaking technology.

The release of energy from the atom during the Second World War meant a vast expansion of energy supplies, although obviously there had been no changes in the natural environment or in the physical characteristics of uranium. The invention of the internal-combustion engine toward the end of the nineteenth century made possible the conversion of petroleum deposits into an energy source. Until then petroleum had served primarily as an illuminant, in the form of kerosene.

As recently as the 1930s natural gas was still seen as an unavoidable and dangerous nuisance that needed to be safely disposed of. Eventually the perfection of a technique for producing high-pressure pipelines transformed natural gas into our most attractive household fuel—one that now constitutes a large fraction of total energy supplies.

The points that have been systematically ignored, or systematically underappreciated, since the time of Malthus, are that natural resources possess economic significance only as a function of technological knowledge and that increases in such knowledge are fully equivalent to an expansion of the resource base of the economy. The best that can be said for the widespread intellectual parlor game of calculating how long it will take to exhaust the supply of a particular strategic raw material at current rates of utilization is that the long division is usually carried out correctly. Such calculations, however, are of very limited relevance to a technologically dynamic economy.

Technological innovation vastly expands the number and the quality of resources that are capable of being economically exploited. In this sense, technological innovation has been the most efficient of all adjustment mechanisms for dealing with the growing scarcity of natural resources.

There is another category of explanation to account for the difficulties we have in dealing with the future impact of technological change. Much of it is attributable to the high degree of specialization of technological knowledge that characterizes modern industrial societies. Since the time of Adam Smith, economists have emphasized the gains resulting from increasing specialization and division of labor. Such gains, from Smith's example of an eighteenth-century pin factory to the research activities of a modern university, have been immense. But while there are great benefits in specialization, there are also drawbacks. Experts of any kind tend to look at the world in terms of a very limited number of variables; indeed, that is a reasonable definition of what it means to be an expert. The old aphorism that an expert is someone who knows more and more about less and less conveys an important truth for the understanding of technological change ("When all you have is a hammer, everything looks like a nail").

A specialist is typically capable of extending and improving the methods of his expertness and applying them to new uses. However, the very nature of an expert's education and professional experience is likely to disqualify him for developing new technologies based on different principles or even for appreciating their potential significance.

The industrial history of the past century is replete with evidence for these assertions. Carriage makers played a negligible role in the development of the automobile (although Fisher Body did make the transition), and the makers of stagecoaches played no role in the development of the steam locomotive. The

makers of steam locomotives, in turn, made no contribution to, and showed no interest in, the new technology that displaced them, the diesel locomotive. This is hardly surprising. No amount of expertise in the operation and improvement of steam locomotives would equip an engineer with the capability to develop an engine based on such different principles. Similarly, many of the manufacturers of piston-driven aircraft engines could not negotiate their way into the jet age. The makers of vacuum tubes failed to transfer their dominance to the semiconductor market. Nor was nylon introduced by experts who knew a great deal about silkworms and mulberry leaves. And Western Union turned down the opportunity to purchase Alexander Graham Bell's telephone patent when it was offered for a mere hundred thousand dollars.

The failure of industrial firms to make the transition in these episodes of technological discontinuity is not due to some inherent failing or unavoidable human conservatism. Rather, it reflects the limitations of technical expertise. While experts in an existing field are obviously indispensable for generating improvements that draw upon their accumulated technical skills, those very skills may become barriers during periods of discontinuity. At such points those skills are no longer rele-

A new technology often has important but unanticipated applications.

vant for a technology based upon different skills or methodologies.

Although the technical skills employed in an industry may be of no use during such a drastic transition, technical skills in other industries may be very useful. For example, although the transition from propeller-driven aircraft engines to jet engines represented a genuine discontinuity for makers of propeller-driven engines, it meant much less of one for the manufacturers of steam turbines, who already possessed the designing and manufacturing skills necessary to exploit the new aircraft power plant. It is not surprising, then, that General Electric, America's largest manufacturer of steam turbines, entered the business of making aircraft engines when jet propulsion was introduced.

When drastically new technologies make their appearance, predicting their eventual impact is severely handicapped by the tendency to think about them in terms of the old

technology. It is difficult even to visualize the complete displacement of an old, long-dominant technology, let alone to apprehend a new technology as an entire system. Time and again new technologies have been thought of as little more than supplements to the limitations of the old. Thus, in the early years, railroads were considered feeders into the existing canal system, to be built where the terrain made canals impractical. In the same fashion the radio was thought by its originators to have potential applications mainly where wire communication was impractical: on ships at sea, for example.

The extent to which the old continues to dominate thinking about the new is nicely encapsulated in Thomas Edison's early practice of referring to his incandescent lamp as the "burner." More seriously, in Edison's work on an electric meter he attempted for a long time to develop a measure of electricity consumption in units of cubic feet! In the case of aircraft engines, the time intervals between overhauls of jet engines were originally based on the earlier practices with piston engines. As a result, for years a major benefit of jet engines—their much greater reliability and durability and, therefore, lower maintenance requirements—was nowhere near fully exploited.

If thinking about the future impact of new technologies is handicapped

by the force of conceptions based on the old, that form of thinking receives substantial reinforcement from the opposite direction. Inventions typically enter the world in very primitive form, and new technologies often appear distinctly unpromising at the outset. Their dominating characteristics are often high cost and poor performance, including an infuriating degree of unreliability ("Get a horse!"). The difficulty lies in predicting the sorts of improvements that will occur in the course of the new product's life. A disinterested observer who happened to be passing by Kitty Hawk on that fateful day in 1903 might surely be excused if he did not walk away with visions of 747s in his head.

Perhaps an even deeper issue is at stake here. Although existing technical expertise is not usually very useful in an encounter with genuine technical discontinuity, the case is rather different when technical *continuities* are involved. Technical experts are reasonably good at anticipating the kinds of performance improvements that can be teased out of a given technology once it has been established and its working principles are fairly well understood. Why, then, can't they deal the same way with new technologies?

The answer is largely that the impact of new or improved technologies is not just a matter of enhanced technical performance. It is, rather, a matter of translating such information into its potential economic and social significance. Doing this is extraordinarily difficult. Understanding the technical basis for wireless communication, as Marconi did, was a very different matter from understanding the possibilities for an entertainment broadcasting industry that would reach into every household, which Marconi could hardly have been expected to envisage.

Social change or economic impact is not something that can be extrapolated out of a piece of hardware. New technologies are, rather, building blocks. Their eventual importance will depend on what is subsequently designed and constructed with them. New technol-

Social effects cannot be extrapolated from a piece of hardware.

ogies are unrealized potentials that may take a very large number of eventual shapes. Moreover, most inventions have their origins in the attempt to solve very specific problems. Commonly, however, a solution, once found, has important applications in totally unintended contexts.

The steam engine, for example, was invented in the eighteenth century specifically as a device to pump water out of flooded mines. It was for a long time regarded exclusively as a pump. A succession of improvements later rendered it a feasible source of power for textile factories, iron mills, and an expanding array of industrial establishments. In the course of the early nineteenth century the steam engine became a general source of power and had major applications in transportation—railroads, steamships, and steamboats. In fact, in the United States before the Civil War, the main use of the steam engine was in transportation. Later in the nineteenth century the steam engine was used to produce a new source of power—electricity—which, in turn, satisfied innumerable final uses to which steam power itself was not applicable. Finally, the steam turbine displaced the steam engine in the generation of electric power, and the special features of electricity—its ease of transmission over long distances, the capacity for making power available in fractionalized units, and the far greater flexibility of electricity-powered equipment—spelled the eventual demise of the steam engine.

The life history of the steam engine, then, was shaped by forces that could hardly have been foreseen by inventors who were trying to remove water from coal mines. It was shaped by unanticipated applications to industry and transportation and even-

tually by the systematic exploitation of new technologies undreamed of at the time the steam engine itself was invented. The very existence of the steam engine served as a powerful stimulus to other inventions.

Such major innovations, once established, have the effect of inducing further innovation and investments over a wide frontier; indeed, this ability is a reasonably good definition of what constitutes a major innovation. But this definition also highlights the difficulties in foreseeing the eventual impact, since that depends on the size and the direction of these future innovations.

In the twentieth century another factor complicates the ability to foresee the eventual impact of technological change: the complex relationship between scientific research and technological innovation. This relationship is partially obscured by the prevailing linear model, which looks on innovation as originating in "blue-sky" basic research, which feeds downstream to applied research and, eventually, to new-product development. In fact, to an increasing degree it is the needs of the technological realm that shape scientific research, mobilizing it in specific directions. This is what the term *mission-oriented basic research* is all about. More to the point, this is what one of the most important institutional innovations of the twentieth century is all about: the industrial research laboratory. Industrial research labs have been specifically established to exploit scientific knowledge for industrial purposes. But nowadays the best of these labs generate much of the scientific knowledge that they exploit. At the same time, the problems encountered by sophisticated industrial technologies have served as powerful stimuli to scientific research even in the academic community. In these ways the responsiveness of scientific research to economic needs and opportunities has been powerfully reinforced.

For example, solid-state physics, presently the largest subdiscipline of physics, attracted only a few physicists half a century ago. In fact, the subject was not even taught at most universities. The situation was transformed, of course, by the invention of the transistor in 1948. The transistor demonstrated the potentially high payoff of solid-state research and led to a huge concentration of resources in that field, both in the university and in private industry. Thus transistor technology did not build upon a vast *earlier* research commitment; rather, the initial breakthrough of the transistor gave rise to a *subsequent* large-scale commitment of scientific resources.

Similarly, the advent of laser technology as a potentially important mode of voice transmission has served as a powerful device in determining the direction of scientific research. However, this research has generated a vast array of unanticipated applications, including optic surgery, precision measurement, navigational instruments, military applications in outer space, and the shaping or cutting of materials in manufacturing. At the same time, a high-payoff application of laser technology *was* clearly anticipated and successfully consummated. It was laser development that suggested the feasibility of using optical fibers for transmission purposes, which, in turn, pointed to the field of optics. As a result, optics in recent years has been converted from a relatively quiet intellectual backwater to a burgeoning field of research. It is likely that this scientific activity, in turn, will yield a new array of unanticipated applications.

The research system within modern industry thus affects technological predictability in two opposing ways. On the one hand, certain high-payoff applications (as in the case of laser technology) can be realized more rapidly and predictably through the applications of scientific research to technological breakthroughs. On the other hand, these very same scientific research activities have themselves generated a

large number of unanticipated applications. The overall impact of laser and fiber optics technologies is highly uncertain, even as the realization of *certain* applications appears to have become more predictable.

The concern that the primary impact of technological change will be increased levels of unemployment has deep intellectual roots going back to Marx and Ricardo. There was and there remains a widespread tendency to attribute the higher unemployment levels that emerged during the 1970s to the introduction of new technologies—especially electronic technologies—that purportedly had a strong laborsaving effect. Moreover, there is widespread apprehension that if we are now poised at one of those great discontinuities in history, the new technologies will generate a permanent pool of unemployed. This is because a number of the technologies—robotics, CAD/CAM (computer-aided design and computer-aided manufacturing), the growing capacity of the electronic chip, automation—are expected to have strong laborsaving effects.

It is, of course, always impossible to prove anything about the future by looking at the past. It is impossible to

prove that we are *not* poised at some genuine discontinuity in history. Moreover, it is painfully clear that the American economy has, in some important respects, been performing poorly for more than a decade. Productivity improvement has been particularly dismal, and the "natural" rate of unemployment seems to have been increasing.

Nevertheless, it is far from clear that high unemployment has been primarily due to the character of technological change, nor are there compelling reasons to believe that new technologies will have an unusual tendency to reduce jobs in the future. Some categories of employment will, of course, suffer. Technological change has increased unemployment in the past among such groups as farm workers, railroad workers, coal miners, and lumberjacks. The electric light bulb displaced the candle maker, the automobile put saddlers and whip makers out of business. The crucial question is whether technological change reduces *total* employment, not whether it eliminates specific jobs.

Although unemployment levels in the American economy were indeed high, by historical standards, during the 1970s, the number of employed people rose during that decade by a remarkable twenty million—from eighty million in mid-1970 to a hundred million in mid-1980. Whatever job-reducing forces may have been at work as a result of the new technologies, they were swamped by mechanisms working in the opposite direction.

It's worth pointing out, too, that laborsaving innovations are not the same as job-reducing innovations. The reductions in cost and price associated with laborsaving innovations may bring in their wake vast increases in specific kinds of employment and, in fact, have often done so. When Henry Ford introduced the progressive assembly line into the American automobile industry in 1913, the result was a huge reduction in the number of labor hours required to produce a car. But the resulting ability to sell a Model T Ford for only four hundred dollars was a revolutionary event that resulted in an immense increase in employment in the automobile industry. The demand for cars turned out to be highly elastic. On the other hand, when demand is inelastic, laborsaving innovations reduce the demand for labor in that sector but shift demand elsewhere. The final employment impact of technological change cannot be confined to the sector (or to the country) where it occurred; it is a problem in general equilibrium analysis, not partial equilibrium analysis. (Incidentally, new steps forward in automation may increase U.S. employment by repatriating activities that have moved offshore. Thus the automation of a variety of labor-intensive assembly-line work may well bring back to the United States jobs that have recently gone overseas, where labor is cheaper. Currently, in Silicon Valley, a number of industrial firms are confronting the choice between robotics and overseas assembly.)

Finally, as a more general matter, it seems to be much easier to anticipate the employment-displacing effects of technological change than the employment-expanding ones. The anticipation of the employment-expanding consequences of innovations seems to require a much greater exercise of the social imagination, an ability to foresee uses in entirely new social contexts. In the 1950s it was authoritatively predicted that fewer than a dozen computers could serve all of America's future computer needs. Even earlier Thomas J. Watson, Sr., president of IBM, wrote that a single computer built in 1948 "could solve all the important scientific problems in the world involving scientific calculations." He was reported to believe that computers had no commer-

It takes great imagination to foresee how a technology can create jobs.

cial possibilities. Even Thomas Edison is said by one of his biographers to have anticipated that the phonograph would be used primarily to record deathbed testaments. New innovations depend on cultural contexts, on how society chooses to mobilize and to exploit the potential of a piece of hardware. No one seems to have anticipated the astonishing amount of information processing that would take place in our society when the productivity of the calculating technology was increased by a couple of orders of magnitude.

There appears to be a systematic bias in perceptions about the future. It sharpens the awareness of possible job-reducing consequences of technological change but at the same time fails to identify the prospects for enlarged employment opportunities that flow from the ability to produce certain products more cheaply or to invent entirely new products with quite unanticipated uses and applications. A distinctive feature of Western capitalism seems to have been the ability to produce very cheap variants of products that, in an earlier age, were consumed only by a small elite: nylon stockings for silk ones, ball-point pens for Parker 51s, recorded stereophonic music for court musicians. In fact, we are still insufficiently aware of the extent to which sustained high rates of aggregate economic growth have depended on the continual introduction of new products to offset the retardation resulting from the slower rates of growth of older industries.

Equally important, discussions of the future impact of technological change that emphasize its net unemployment-generating effects have systematically ignored what has been perhaps the single most conspicuous feature of structural change

in the American economy for several decades: the expansion of the service sector. That sector is now far and away the largest in the economy, employing more workers than the entire commodity-producing sector. In 1982 service occupations accounted for at least two-thirds of all employment. Indeed, the growth in employment in the United States since the Second World War has been overwhelmingly a growth in the service sector, and there are now more musicians in the American labor force than coal miners, and several times as many real estate agents. Although certain aspects of the rise of the service sector have received a great deal of attention—for example, the apparently much slower growth of productivity—far less attention has been given to the connections between technological change and service employment. The story is a complicated one; indeed, it is a great many stories, since the service sector comprises so many very different kinds of activities.

There is no quick and easy way to summarize the changes that have occurred in the service sector in the past several decades, but if we are to come to grips with the impact of technological change, we need to examine its very diverse effect on the delivery of health care, education, recreation, retailing, insurance, finance, and government at all levels. It would be totally arbitrary to assume that the outcome of these experiences is likely to be declining future employment opportunities.

Put most simply, the reason we do so poorly at predicting the impact of technological change is that we are dealing with an extraordinarily complex and interdependent set of relationships. I would, however, insist that we should be able to do a somewhat better job of it in the future—if only by developing a better appreciation of why we have done so badly in the past. ∎

Nathan Rosenberg is Fairleigh S. Dickinson, Jr., professor of public policy at Stanford University. This article is adapted from a talk he gave there before a 1985 Symposium on Economics and Technology.

Machine Politics

Since the earliest days of democracy, as the world has sought the ideal form of government, it has also sought the ideal method of voting. The ancient Greeks decided public questions by clashing spears on shields. Colonial America at first favored the show of hands, or splitting into groups. Later the *viva voce* method, in which a voter would openly declare his preference (and then be thanked in florid fashion by the candidate), gained favor. New England pioneered the secret election, sometimes using grains of corn or beans to signify a yes or no and sometimes using written ballots. Down South, where fewer people could read, open voting persisted in some states until after the Civil War, when literacy requirements became politically useful.

By the mid-1800s paper ballots were widespread, and along with the advantage of secrecy came the greater possibility of fraud. Corrupt political operators stuffed ballot boxes and destroyed opposing votes. To combat such tactics, various inventors turned their attention to mechanical voting. As early as 1849 Jan Josef Baranowski of France described his *Scrutateur Mécanique*, and a decade later Werner von Siemens of Germany built a primitive *Abstimmungsapparate*.

Around 1870 at least four different models were used briefly in Great Britain, and more than a hundred American patents were issued for voting machines in the 1860s and 1870s. In most of these the voter pushed a button or inserted a key to drop a ball into a designated bin. Such devices promised to eliminate spoiled and ambiguous ballots, but the balls still had to be tallied, and the possibility of intentional or inadvertent miscounts remained. Few communities judged the machines worth the expense.

The modern voting machine was introduced in a local election in Lock-

An 1894 voter poses with the new machine.

port, New York, on April 12, 1892. It was designed by Jacob H. Myers of Rochester, a maker of theftproof bank safes, who saw his new invention as performing a similar function: fighting vote thieves. Its festive inauguration attracted the sort of turnout normally seen only for a presidential race, including "many aged men, also crippled men," according to a report by the town board. The New York *World* and Rochester *Herald* sent reporters.

Myers's wood-and-steel contraption was ten feet square, illuminated inside with an oil lamp. Except for size it was quite similar to today's machines. A voter entered, locked the door behind him, selected candidates from the Democratic, Republican, or Prohibition party by punching keys, and exited through another door, recording his choice by slamming it firmly. Votes were automatically totaled on numerical registers. No tedious counting was necessary, so the possibility of error or fraud was virtually eliminated. There were sixty candidates and two questions on the ballot, but the complete results were announced ten minutes

after the polls closed.

The innovation spread rapidly through upstate New York. Rochester used more than sixty-five voting machines in 1896, and by 1904 twenty cities and many more towns had made the switch. In 1920 more than half the state's population outside New York City voted by machine.

Progress elsewhere was less rapid. The prospect of honest elections did not always appeal to politicians, and the price of the machines—$600 at the turn of the century, $750 to $1,000 in the 1920s—was another obstacle. Proponents could point to the savings in printing, personnel, and litigation costs, but these all afforded ward heelers promising opportunities for dispensing favors and collecting graft.

In addition, there was the usual resistance to anything new. Voters worried that machines would not record their votes properly, though humans did a far less accurate job. As late as 1938 the Kentucky Supreme Court ruled that the state constitution required paper ballots. But as the twentieth century progressed, people became more comfortable with machines of all sorts. In the 1960 presidential election more than half the votes were recorded mechanically.

Today virtually all American elections are conducted by machines, but those of the Myers type are falling out of favor. Punch-card voting was introduced in Ohio in 1960, and optical scanners and video terminals have also recently become popular. As computers perform more and more of the work that used to be done by the mayor's son-in-law, fraud and incompetence are even less of a factor.

Mechanization can affect people's basic rights in various ways, some good and some not. But for a century now, one of the most fundamental rights of all—the right to vote—has been safeguarded by machines. ★

INDEX